ANTARCTIC RESEARCH SERIES

American Geophysical Union

ANTARCTIC
RESEARCH
SERIES

American Geophysical Union

Antarctic Soils and
Soil Forming Processes

Volume 8 ANTARCTIC
RESEARCH
SERIES

Antarctic Soils and
Soil Forming Processes

J. C. F. Tedrow, *Editor*

Published with the aid of a grant from the National Science Foundation

PUBLISHER
AMERICAN GEOPHYSICAL UNION
OF THE
National Academy of Sciences—National Research Council
Publication No. 1418
1966

Volume 8 | ANTARCTIC
RESEARCH
SERIES

ANTARCTIC SOILS AND SOIL FORMING PROCESSES

J. C. F. Tedrow, *Editor*

Library of Congress Catalogue Card No. 66-61849

List Price, $10.00

Printed by
The William Byrd Press, Inc.
Richmond, Virginia

THE ANTARCTIC RESEARCH SERIES

During the International Geophysical Year discussions were held among geophysicists, biologists, and geologists aimed at developing a medium for the publication of the papers resulting from the intensive research work being done in Antarctica. The Antarctic Research Series is designed to provide this medium, presenting authoritative work with uniformly high scientific and editorial standards from leading scientists engaged in antarctic research.

In a sense the series continues a tradition dating from the earliest days of geographic exploration and scientific expeditions—the tradition of the expeditionary volumes which set forth in rich detail everything that was seen and studied. But in much of the present antarctic work one expedition blends into the next, and it is no longer scientifically meaningful to separate them. However, antarctic research in all disciplines has a large degree of coherence and deserves the modern counterpart of the expeditionary volumes of past decades and centuries.

Papers appearing in the series represent original contributions too lengthy or otherwise unsuitable for publication in the standard scientific journals. The material published is directed not only to scientists actively engaged in the work but to graduate students and scientists in closely related fields as well. The series will serve as a source of information both for the specialist and for the layman versed in the biological and physical sciences. Many of the early volumes are cohesive collections of research papers grouped around a central theme. An editor for each book is drawn from the discipline it represents, as are the reviewers on whom each editor relies.

Early in 1963 the National Science Foundation made a grant to the American Geophysical Union to initiate the series, and a Board of Associate Editors was appointed to implement it. To represent the broad nature of the series, the members of the Board were chosen from all fields of antarctic research. They include Jarvis Hadley, representing geology and solid Earth geophysics; Harry W. Wells, aeronomy and geomagnetism; A. P. Crary, seismology and glaciology; George A. Llano, botany and zoology; Waldo L. Schmitt, marine biology and oceanography; and Morton J. Rubin, meteorolgy. AGU staff members responsible for the series are Judith S. McCombs, managing editor, and Marie L. Webner, style editor.

HARRY W. WELLS
Chairman, Board of Associate Editors
Antarctic Research Series

PREFACE

Are there, in fact, any soils in Antarctica? This is the question asked by laymen and professionals alike.

It is seventy years or more since man first set foot on the antarctic continent, and during this time explorers, naturalists, geologists, and others have given us considerable information on many ice-free areas and have photographed and mapped a considerable portion of the continent. Only within the last ten years, however, have the first systematic pedologic studies been undertaken. Although the observations of these preliminary studies are important and illuminating, knowledge of pedologic processes as a whole on the antarctic continent has not advanced much beyond a 'statement of the problem.'

One fascinating aspect of the problem of antarctic pedology is that in most of Antarctica's ice-free areas the processes are taking place in a system that lacks an effective organic component. Pedologists rightfully place a great deal of emphasis on the organic component of soil. When, late in the nineteenth century, pedology was recognized as an independent scientific discipline, it was generally agreed that the prime soil forming factors were: parent material, relief, climate, biotic elements, and time. In most climatic regions, except those frigid ones of the extreme southern latitudes, the importance of these factors has been clearly stated, and these statements have stood the test of time.

The question, then, seems to be: When there is virtually no organic matter present in the mineral substrata, can any of the surficial materials justifiably be called soils? To refer to certain virtually organic-free deposits as genetic soils is bending the spirit of the original definition of the term *soil*. On our willingness to do this will largely hinge the decision of whether or not we will recognize as genetic soils those materials in much of the ice-free areas of Antarctica that lack an effective organic component but otherwise appear to manifest some kind of a soil forming process.

Regardless of the eventual decision on definition, in Antarctica formidable and challenging tasks that should not be postponed or avoided simply because of a preponderance of ahumic conditions await the attention of the pedologist. Just as on the antarctic continent, geochemistry is being studied, the pursuit of investigations concerning chemical, physical, and mineral alteration and translocation within the surficial layers should continue.

That attempts at soil classification have traditionally failed to provide for conditions on the antarctic continent is of special interest. As a rule, global soil maps extend only to *circa* 60°S, which excludes, of course, all of Antarctica. This omission was understandable when, in earlier times, very little information about the continent was available, but in the light of contemporary knowledge it represents an omission that should be rectified.

To depict pedologic and related environmental conditions of the ice-free portions of Antarctica, it is logical to discuss the various facets of the environment as they affect the soil system. Accordingly, in the separate papers of this monograph the factors of soil formation are discussed by veteran polar investigators. These papers are not merely discussions of theory but reflect, primarily, actual field observations coupled with experience in pedology and cognate disciplines.

The contribution by R. L. Nichols on 'Geomorphology of Antarctica' not only summarizes much of the geomorphlogy of the continent but also takes into account surficial geology and glaciology. Nichols' report describes in some detail terrain features at various locations on the antarctic continent.

Among other subjects, W. S. Weyant, in 'The Antarctic Climate,' depicts various climatic conditions such as precipitation, humidity, ice inventory, radiation, and albedo of Antarctica. By request, Weyant also includes soil temperatures and related data, matters of interest to pedologists.

Under the title 'Preliminary Measurements of Growth and Nonsorted Polygons, Victoria Land, Antarctica,' T. E. Berg and R. F. Black present a comprehensive report on patterned ground and the cryodynamics of the ice-free areas of Antarctica. Berg and Black not only point out frost processes *per se* but also take into consideration patterned ground formation in connection with Quaternary history.

The biotic elements of the antarctic continent (excluding marine) are discussed in two reports, one by E. D. Rudolph, entitled 'Terrestrial Vegetation of Antarctica: Past and Present Studies,' and the other by W. L. Boyd, J. T. Staley, and J. W. Boyd, entitled 'Ecology of Soil Microorganisms of Antarctica.' The organic component of Antarctica is set forth in these two papers. Rudolph gives an account of plant life on the continent and its role in the soil system, and Boyd, Staley, and Boyd are concerned with the identification and functions of microorganisms within the soil.

These five papers constitute a report on the background for soil development. A sixth paper, 'Antarctic Soils,' by Tedrow and Ugolini, is concerned with the broad aspects of soil development on the continent.

The monograph is not intended to be a final report but rather, in its reflection of current knowledge of the subject, to place antarctic pedology in realistic perspective. It is hoped that the combined report will serve as a catalyst for future investigations.

The able assistance of Ruth M. Field, copy editor, who prepared the manuscripts for publication, is gratefully acknowledged.

J. C. F. TEDROW

CONTENTS

GEOMORPHOLOGY OF ANTARCTICA

Robert L. Nichols

Department of Geology, Tufts University, Medford, Massachusetts

Abstract. The Kukri Peneplain, located in part in south Victoria Land, is Lower Paleozoic or older and has been traced for over a thousand miles. Although a Permocarboniferous tillite containing striated fragments and resting on a glaciated pavement is found in the Horlick Mountains, there is no good evidence for Tertiary antarctic glaciation. The summit of the Antarctic Peninsula, a snow-covered plateau, is a differentially uplifted, dissected peneplain. The major features of the bedrock topography for much of Antarctica are the result of late Cenozoic block-faulting modified by glacial and fluvial erosion. Throughout Antarctica volcanic landforms are widespread and numerous. Glacial marine sediments completely surround the continent, covering not only the continental shelf but also the slope and adjacent ocean bottoms. The antarctic continental shelf, the deepest in the world, is characterized by both transverse depressions, due to glacial erosion, and longitudinal depressions, which may be due, in part, to glacial erosion. Multiple glaciation in the McMurdo Sound area has been demonstrated by several workers. Interglacial deposits have also been identified. Data from the first expedition to winter in the Antarctic, which were subsequently substantiated, prove that formerly the glaciers of Antarctica were more extensive. Elevated beaches, found on all sides of the continent, in general postdate the youngest glaciation. The highest are more than a hundred feet above sea level, their elevation being due to isostatic rebound following deglaciation. Some are pitted, owing to the melting of the ice on which they rest. Dry kettles and small saline lakes, surface and subsurface efflorescences of salts, calcite-veneered fragments, and undrained lakes that have very small areas in comparison to their basins, all prove that the deglaciated valleys and coastal areas around McMurdo Sound have been arid for thousands of years. Felsenmeers, nivation cirques, and solifluction deposits are found in the McMurdo Sound area, and frost-crack polygons are common and widely distributed. A careful study of a badly weathered fine-grained quartz diorite found at Marble Point, McMurdo Sound, showed that the breakup was due essentially to physical rather than chemical changes. Ice-cored moraines thousands of years old and covering scores of square miles are found in the McMurdo Sound area. Where the morainal topography is flat and the ice thus effectively and continuously covered with moraine, the ice-cored moraines will persist as long as present-day conditions continue, for the mean annual temperature is below 0°F. Fans, deltas, kames, valley trains, marginal channels, and nonpaired terraces, all formed by melt water, occur. Ventifacts are unusually well developed and numerous in the McMurdo Sound area. More than 1 foot of rock has commonly been removed from the larger ventifacts, and in a 3-foot-square area 53 ventifacts 1–5 inches long were counted. Since the mean annual air temperature at sea level in the McMurdo Sound area, as determined from bedrock, glacier, and air temperatures and from sea-ice thickness, is approximately −2°F, perennially frozen lakes are present.

KUKRI PENEPLAIN

The oldest antarctic erosion surface known to the writer is the Kukri Peneplain. It was first described by *Ferrar* [1907] from the Kukri Hills, McMurdo Sound, Victoria Land, was later studied by *Debenham* [1921*b*], and has more recently been investigated, described, and named by *Gunn and Warren* [1962]. Since this surface cuts the Precambrian or Cambrian basement rocks of south Victoria Land [*Goldich et al.*, 1958] and is overlain by the Beacon Sandstone, at least as old as the Devonian, the Kukri Peneplain is Early Paleozoic. It is a flat or gently undulating surface [*Zeller et al.*, 1961], was tilted during the Victoria Orogeny, and has been traced from the Horlick Mountains to Terra Nova Bay for over a thousand miles. A dolerite sill is commonly present between the peneplain and the

Fig. 1. Exhumed Kukri Peneplain cutting quartz monzonite at the base of Discovery Ridge, Horlick Mountains, Antarctica. The Devonian sedimentary rocks which were deposited on it have recently been removed. Photo by William E. Long.

overlying sandstone, and at Mount Suess, Mc-Murdo Sound, Victoria Land, several feet of the underlying granite is weathered.

The Kukri Peneplain has also been found in the Horlick Mountains at latitude 84°44.8'S, longitude 113°44'W [Long, 1961]. Here it has cut a quartz monzonite and is overlain by a Devonian basal conglomerate. It is an undulating surface. The upper part of the quartz monzonite was weathered before burial, and the surface in places has been exhumed and exposed (Figure 1).

Wood [1963], studying the geology of the Cape Hallett–Tucker Glacier district, Victoria Land, noticed a vague accordance of the summits of the interior mountains and suggested that these mountains may have been cut from a mature erosion surface, which he tentatively correlates with the pre-Devonian Kukri Peneplain.

Gunn and Walcott [1962], Grindley [1963], Ricker [1963], Skinner [1963], and Haskell et al. [1963] also have mentioned the Kukri Peneplain.

PALEOZOIC ANTARCTIC GLACIATION

The following criteria are useful in the identification of tillite: (1) polished, striated, and grooved pavements; (2) deposits with which tillites are commonly associated, such as varved lacustrine clays, eolian deposits, glaciofluvial beds, and marine tillites; (3) physical characteristics, such as lack of sorting and stratification, the presence of angular, striated, and soled fragments, and variations in thickness, plus the many other characteristics of tillite; (4) the presence of ventifacts, felsenmeers, and other periglacial features commonly associated with glacial deposits [Bryan, 1946]; (5) the presence of the surface textures that characterize the sand grains found in till [*Krinsley and Takahashi,* 1962*a, b*]; and (6) evidence of low temperatures, based on oxygen-isotope studies.

Long [1962], reporting recently on a Paleozoic tillite in the Horlick Mountains, writes: 'overlying the Horlick formation (Lower Devonian) is a unit about 800 feet thick composed of bluish-gray, silty, clayey matrix which includes pebbles, cobbles, and boulders of mixed lithology in an unsorted arrangement. The unit rests on a striated and grooved pavement that truncates the Horlick formation and parts of the basement rock. The lithology of included pebbles shows about 70 per cent sedimentary rocks, 23 per cent igneous rocks, and 7 per cent metamorphic rocks, all of uncertain source. More than 90 per cent of the pebbles counted are sub-rounded to angular with about 40 per cent subangular. About 10 per cent are striated. . . . Evidently these beds are of glacial origin and correspond to the well-documented Permocarboniferous tillites in Gondwana deposits of the southern hemisphere. Within the unit a boulder pavement shows crag-

and-tail features indicating glacial movement from west to east. The sandstone beds within the tillite are presumed to be deposited by water during ice retreats.' (Figure 2.) Since three of the four major categories of characteristics useful in the identification of tillites are accounted for here, this breccia can be identified as a tillite. As far as the writer knows, Long's account is the first authentic report of pre-Pleistocene glaciation in Antarctica [see also *Gunn and Warren,* 1962; *Grindley,* 1963].

TERTIARY ANTARCTIC GLACIATION

Since the antarctic ice cap has persisted long after the disappearance of the continental ice caps that covered North America, Europe, and other places, it might seem logical to assume that glaciation began in the Antarctic before it started elsewhere [*Nichols,* 1953, 1960]. That *Nordenskjöld* [1911], *Wright and Priestley* [1922], *Priestley* [1923], *Gould* [1939, 1940], and perhaps *Andersson* [1906] believe that glaciation started in the Antarctic in the Tertiary is, thus, not surprising, but their only

Fig. 2. Exhumed Permocarboniferous glaciated surface formed on an intercalated sandstone bed in the Buckeye Tillite, Horlick Mountains, Antarctica. Photo by William E. Long.

Fig. 3. The uplifted dissected Tertiary peneplain, Marguerite Bay, Antarctic Peninsula.

evidence for this is the presence of breccias. These breccias, however, are not resting on glaciated basements, nor are they found with the deposits and periglacial features with which till and tillite are commonly associated. The only criteria presented which suggest their glacial origin are: (1) clayey matrix, (2) angular and triangular fragments, (3) lack of stratification and sorting, and (4) a variety of lithologic types. These are features, however, that are characteristic not only of ice-laid deposits but also of mud flows, volcanic breccias, and fanglomerates.

This writer believes that as yet there is no good evidence for Tertiary antarctic glaciation. A study of the marine sediments surrounding the continent may, however, reveal proof of its existence.

TERTIARY PENEPLAIN

The summit of the Antarctic Peninsula is a snow-covered plateau. It is about two thousand feet high in the northern part of the peninsula; southward it gradually increases in altitude to reach a height of 6000 or more feet [*Nichols*, 1953, 1960]. The plateau is, therefore, hundreds of miles long; where greatly dissected it is only a few miles wide, and in other places it is scores of miles wide. Those who have sledged on it report it to be very flat with occasional domal mountains rising hundreds of feet above it (Figure 3).

In the northern part of the Antarctic Peninsula the plateau, according to *Andersson* [1906], cuts folded Jurassic graywacke, slate, volcanic tuff, gran-

ite, quartz diorite, and gabbro. It seems likely that in the Marguerite Bay area the plateau cuts schist, gneiss, argillite, a younger group of related intrusive bodies, including gabbro, diorite, and granite, and a still younger series of volcanic tuffs, breccias, and agglomerates, together with a red vuggy granite which intrudes them. Where it has been studied, and probably everywhere else, the plateau is, therefore, an erosion surface [*Howard*, 1950]. Evidence indicates that the plateau surface is middle or late Tertiary. The writer believes that the plateau is a differentially uplifted, dissected peneplain [*Holtedahl*, 1935] rather than an uplifted plain of marine denudation or a surface formed by cryoplanation [*Peltier*, 1950].

TERTIARY BLOCK-FAULT MOUNTAINS

It is generally agreed that the major features of the bedrock topography in much of Antarctica are the result of Tertiary block-faulting modified by glacial and fluvial erosion. This conclusion, however, is not based on careful geologic mapping but only on reconnaissance studies. Moreover, as the stratigraphy is not well known, precise structural measurements have not been made. The following criteria have been used to prove block-faulting: (1) Differential tilting and differences in altitude of the early Paleozoic Kukri Peneplain surface [*Gunn and Walcott*, 1962]. (2) Long, wide, deep, and straight valleys with different rock types on opposite sides [*Nichols*, 1953]. (3) Marked difference of rock types in adjacent areas [*Gunn and Warren*, 1962].

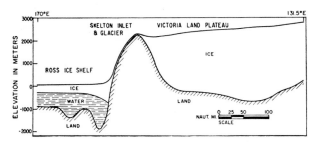

Fig. 4. A seismic profile from the Ross Ice Shelf westward up into the Victoria Land plateau, showing surface elevations, ice thickness, and bedrock topography. After A. P. Crary.

(4) Spurs and ridges terminating along a straight line [*Gunn and Warren*, 1962]. (5) Great dissected escarpments and a subrectangular plan of ranges [*Laird*, 1963]. (6) Presence of volcanoes in areas thought to be block-faulted. (7) Existence of the Beacon Sandstone below sea level and beneath Ross Island, as indicated by the inclusions of it in the lavas of Mount Erebus and by its presence thousands of feet above sea level on the west side of McMurdo Sound [*David and Priestley*, 1914; *David*, 1914]. (8) The seismic traverse from the Ross Ice Shelf westward on to the Victoria Land plateau, which shows that the bedrock west of the Royal Society Range is below sea level [*Crary*, 1959], tending to support the idea that the range is bounded by faults on both east and west and is, broadly speaking, a horst (Figure 4). (9) Massive block-faulting suggested by geophysical investigations [*Woollard*, 1962].

Ferrar [1907] was the first to recognize that the Royal Society Range is a fault-block mountain. Later, *David and Priestley* [1914] made further studies of this area and concluded that the range was a horst with faults on both the east and west sides [*Taylor*, 1930; *Ford*, 1964]. *Gould's* [1935] study of the Queen Maud Mountains convinced him that they were a horst and that the fault on the northeast side was essentially vertical with a displacement of not less than 6000–7000 feet. He was much impressed by the amount of erosion which had taken place since the faulting, as the fault-line scarp appeared to be between 10 and 20 miles from the fault.

More recent workers have shown that the mountain range (Antarctic Horst, Victoria Mountain System, Transantarctic Mountains), which extends sixteen hundred miles from near Cape Adare on the north at least to the Horlick Mountains on the southeast with individual peaks about fifteen thousand feet high, owes its origin to block-faulting in Late Tertiary and Quaternary times [*Gunn and Warren*, 1962; *Gunn*, 1963; *Gunn and Walcott*, 1962; *Skinner*, 1963; *Grindley*, 1963; *Long*, 1960].

The major topographic features in the Antarctic Peninsula may also be due to Tertiary block-faulting. George VI Sound has been assumed to be a tectonic valley [*Joerg*, 1937; *Stephenson*, 1940; *Fuchs*, 1951; *Nichols*, 1953]. *King* [1963] reports that Alexander Island is composed largely of fault blocks and that the island as a whole is tilted, the northern end being high and the southern end low; and *Gunn* [1963] has suggested that the Antarctic Peninsula may be due to block-faulting.

VOLCANIC LANDFORMS

Volcanic landforms are numerous and widespread in Antarctica. They are found in Victoria Land, Byrd Land, the subantarctic islands, and elsewhere. Shield and composite volcanoes, cinder cones, calderas, craters, nested craters, breached cones, plugs, somma ridges, aligned cones, and other features are present. They range in age from late Tertiary to historic.

Perhaps the most spectacular volcanic scenery is found in the McMurdo Sound region, south Victoria Land [*Ferrar*, 1907; *David and Priestley*, 1914]. Ross Island is found here. It is 50 miles long, entirely volcanic, and was formed by the coalescing of four volcanoes—Mounts Erebus, Terror, Bird, and Terra Nova [*Debenham*, 1923] (Figure 5). Mount Bird, approximately 5500 feet high, is probably a shield volcano. Mount Erebus, approximately 13,000 feet high, is an active volcano [*David and Priestley*, 1909b; *Murray*, 1909]. Mount Erebus has had a complex history. It appears to be a shield volcano [*Treves*, 1962] on top of which a composite cone has been built. Fang Ridge on the north side of the volcano at about ten thousand feet is a somma ridge. Three younger nested cones are found above it. Trachytes, kenytes, and basalt have been identified [*Smith*, 1954].

Hut Point Peninsula, a finger-like projection attached to the southwest side of Ross Island, is approximately 10 miles long, 1–2 miles wide, and

Fig. 5.   Ross Island, McMurdo Sound, Antarctica, is composed principally of coalescing shield volcanoes: Mt. Bird (*left*), Mt. Erebus (*center*), Mt. Terror (*right*), and Hut Point Peninsula (*foreground*). Photography flown by U. S. Navy for the U. S. Geological Survey.

has an average height of 800 feet (Figure 5). 'First Crater,' 'Middle Crater,' 'Breached Cone,' Crater Hill, 'Sulphur Cones,' and 'Half Moon Crater,' all located along the peninsula, attest to its volcanic origin. It owes its origin to a fissure, aligned southwest-northeast, which radiates from Mount Erebus.

Mount Discovery (9090 feet), Mount Morning (5780 feet), and numerous smaller cones, all extinct, are found on the adjacent mainland [*Debenham*, 1921a; *Taylor*, 1922; *Gunn and Warren*, 1962; *McCraw*, 1962; *Nichols*, 1962].

Byrd Land is largely volcanic [*Bentley and Ostenso*, 1961]. *Warner* [1945] has described cinder cones and basaltic flows aligned along the axis of the Fosdick Range. The Executive Committee Range consists of five isolated aligned peaks that rise about five thousand feet above the ice sheet that surrounds them. Mount Sidley, the most prominent of the five, is an extinct volcano whose crater has been breached by a cirque. Andesite, trachyte, basalt, lapilli tuff, and agglomerate have been

identified [*Doumani*, 1960, 1963]. The rest of the range is similar to Mount Sidley. The Crary Mountains and Toney Mountain are also volcanic. They contain stratiform volcanic cones that rise five thousand to seven thousand feet above the ice-plateau surface and show little erosional destruction. They are composed of basaltic flows and pyroclastics.

Doumani and Ehlers [1962] write: 'The morphology and physiographic distribution of the volcanoes of this part of West Antarctica as well as seismic profiles . . . suggest a form of archipelago, dotted with isolated volcanic islands rising separately from the floor of an ocean basin.'

Peter I Island [*Craddock and Hubbard*, 1961] in the Bellingshausen Sea and Gaussberg, Wilhelm II Coast, are also volcanic; and Recent volcanic activity in the South Shetland Islands [*Adie*, 1962; *Gunn*, 1963] and elsewhere [*Bellair*, 1963; *Bellair and Nougier*, 1963; *Stephenson*, 1963] has been described.

PRE-GLACIAL FLUVIAL CYCLE

Considerable thought has been given to the origin of the south Victoria Land valleys, which today are occupied by outlet glaciers. Three theories have been advanced: (1) The valleys are essentially tectonic but modified by glacial action [*Wright*, 1923; *Gould*, 1935]. (2) They were formed almost entirely by glacial erosion [*Taylor*, 1922]. (3) They are pre-glacial stream valleys modified by glacial action [*Priestley*, 1923].

In the first two theories the absence of a fluvial cycle immediately preceding glaciation is assumed. *Priestley* [1923] does not believe that a long period of fluvial erosion preceded glaciation in Victoria Land. He writes, 'It is quite likely that the finishing touch to the climatic environment necessary to bring about the Antarctic Ice Age was given by the tectonic movements which brought about the elevation of the horst. . . . In that case . . . the ice might have commenced work on virgin rock, comparatively untouched by any agent of denudation but subaerial weathering.' He further comments, 'There is nothing in the Robertson Bay district which lends its support to the hypothesis that the land was already deeply dissected when the ice-floods began to spread. There is, however, here and there, quite a suggestion of young modified river valleys.' He also notes, 'There is, indeed, little evidence of a pre-glacial stream topography in South Victoria Land generally.'

Gould [1939], on the other hand, impressed by the profound erosion in the Queen Maud Mountains horst where the present fault-line scarp is 15–20 miles from the fault, believes that there was a period of subaerial weathering and erosion prior to glaciation. He writes, 'To attribute such profound erosional results to cirque or cwm action seems incredible. It is rather more reasonable to believe that the faulting which produced the Queen Maud Mountains horst began in Tertiary time long before the inception of glacial conditions, and that the horst was being profoundly modified by the various processes of subaerial weathering and erosion even as it rose. . . . This being so, the horst zone throughout must have suffered modification by streams and other agencies before the culmination of glacial conditions.'

In a more recent report, *Gunn and Warren* [1962] write, 'The name Victoria Orogeny is given to the block-faulting movements, probably in Upper Tertiary and Quaternary times, that formed the present-day mountains of Victoria Land. . . . Probably the Victoria Mountains have always carried glaciers and no pre-glacial [fluvial] topography ever existed.'

Whatever the facts in Victoria Land, the presence of the uplifted peneplain in the Antarctic Peninsula makes it certain that in this area a long period of fluvial erosion preceded glaciation.

This important geomorphic problem merits further consideration. An analysis of hanging valleys, truncated spurs, transverse cross sections of valleys, distribution of rock units, and other features should be profitable. It may be found that glaciation was preceded in some areas by profound fluvial erosion, in others by only moderate fluvial erosion, and in still others by little or none. In many areas, no doubt, glacial erosion has removed all evidence of the pre-glacial topography.

GEOMORPHOLOGY OF CONTINENTAL SHELF

The average depth of the antarctic shelf edge is probably between 500 and 700 meters [*Nichols*, 1953, 1960; *Lebedev*, 1959; *Thiel*, 1962; *Lepley*, 1964]. The world average depth of the break in slope is 432 feet [*Shepard*, 1948]. *Shepard* [1948] believed that the antarctic shelf edge is the deep-

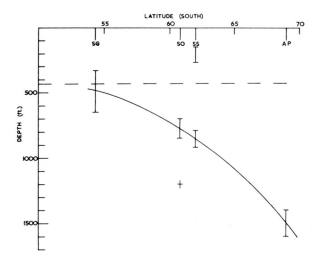

Fig. 6. Continental shelf depths in relation to latitude for the Scotia Ridge and Antarctic Peninsula: South Georgia (*SG*); South Orkney Islands (*SO*); South Shetland Islands (*SS*); and Antarctic Peninsula (*AP*). After R. J. Adie.

est in the world. *Arctowski* [1900a] was first to suggest that the great depth of the antarctic shelf might be due to submergence. *Priestley* [1923] believed that the submergence is due to the weight of the existing ice cap. *Fairbridge* [1952], however, believed that other factors were responsible.

Adie [1964], studying the depth of the continental shelves of Antarctica and some of the subantarctic islands, found the antarctic shelf to be the deepest, and the depths of the shelves of the subantarctic islands to decrease progressively with the decreasing latitude of the islands (Figure 6). He attributes this difference in depth to the fact that the northerly subantarctic islands have been more deglaciated than those farther south, and those farther south more deglaciated than continental Antarctica. Such a relationship strongly suggests that the great depth of the antarctic continental shelf is due to the weight of the existing ice sheet.

On this assumption, *Odell* [1952], *Nichols* [1960], and *Thiel* [1962] calculated the average thickness of the antarctic ice sheet. Their figures ranged from 1800 to 7660 feet.

As *Lisitzin* [1960, 1962] has pointed out, the unusual characteristics of the marine sediments that surround Antarctica are due to: (1) an almost complete absence of runoff; (2) a scarcity of chemical weathering; (3) the absence of significant wave erosion, because of the presence of the barrier, ice foot, fast ice, and the pack; (4) the low temperature of antarctic waters, which prevents precipitation of calcium carbonate; (5) the prolific growth of diatoms; (6) the importance of ice rafting; (7) the fact that wave motion is a negligible factor in the redistribution of bottom sediments, as the shelf is deep and the waves are dampened by floating ice; (8) the fact that glaciers and icebergs are the chief agents in the transport of material from land to ocean; and (9) Quaternary volcanism.

Glacial marine sediments completely surround the antarctic continent, covering not only the continental shelf but also the slope and adjacent ocean bottoms. The width of this zone of sediments ranges from 200 to 700 miles [*Hough*, 1950]. The minimum width is in the Indian Ocean sector between Enderby Land and Lars Christensen Coast where the inland ice does not reach the ocean. The width depends on the rate at which land ice reaches the ocean, the amount of morainal material carried by the bergs, the size of the bergs, and the speed with which the icebergs melt and drift northward [*Lisitzin,* 1960].

A zone of diatom oozes is found north of the glacial marine sediments, and still farther north are the foraminiferal oozes [*Lisitzin,* 1962]. The boundary between the glacial marine sediments and the diatom oozes, as shown by a study of cores, has migrated northward and southward for more than 1000 km. *Lisitzin* [1962] explains this migration as resulting from climatic changes that took place during the Pleistocene.

The glacial marine sediments are characterized by: (1) a lack of sorting; (2) mechanically disintegrated material; (3) material ranging in size from rock flour up to large angular fragments; and (4) a low organic content—mostly diatoms. Igneous, sedimentary, and metamorphic rock fragments, including schist, slate, graywacke, quartzite, scoria, pumice, volcanic glass, and granite, have been found in the glacial marine sediments. Quartz, feldspar, garnet, amphibole, zircon, epidote, and ore minerals have been identified, as well as spores and pollen of ferns, birch, alder, and Myrtaceae, dating from the Carboniferous, Permian, Triassic, Jurassic, and Tertiary [*Stetson and Upson,* 1937; *Hough,* 1950; *Lisitzin,* 1960, 1962; *Goodell et al.,* 1961; *Needham,* 1962; *Lepley,* 1964].

Taylor [1930] has suggested that the 'Davis Bank' off Queen Mary Coast, 'Mawson Bank' off Adélie Coast, and Pennell Bank in the Ross Sea may be vast terminal moraines [*Roos,* 1937; *Zhivago,* 1962]; and *Gould* [1940] has suggested that the Iselin Seamount may also be morainal. *Lepley* [1964] has described longitudinal and transverse ridges, which he believes may be end, lateral, or medial moraines, on the continental shelf of the eastern part of the Ross Sea off the Edward VII Peninsula.

Mawson [1935] has recorded terminal moraines 50–100 miles offshore that are hundreds of feet high. Although he suggests that: 'The height of the main offshore moraine is possibly to be reckoned at something of the order of 3000 feet,' it is most unlikely that moraines 3000 feet high could be formed on land or under water by either grounded or floating ice.

The continental shelf is characterized by both

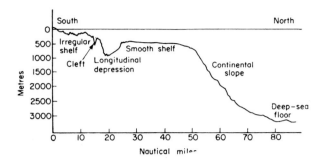

Fig. 7. A transverse cross section of a longitudinal depression on the antarctic continental shelf. The largest depression is 2000 miles long, about 10 miles wide, and between 1500 and 2000 feet deep. After A. P. Lisitzin and A. V. Zhivago.

transverse and longitudinal depressions. The transverse depressions, more or less perpendicular to the coast, are in some cases scores of miles wide and a thousand to two thousand feet below the inner shelf [*Crary*, 1959; *Crary et al.*, 1962; *Lepley*, 1964]. They are believed to result from glacial erosion.

The longitudinal depressions, roughly parallel to the coast, are much larger features. The largest of them extends more than two thousand miles from the Davis Sea nearly to Victoria Land. It is about 10 miles wide, between 1500 and 2500 feet deep, and is aligned along the middle of the shelf (Figure 7). In transverse cross section it is asymmetrical; the side toward the continent is steep whereas the offshore side is less steep. Long, narrow, secondary depressions are found along its floor [*Lisitzin and Zhivago*, 1960; *Zhivago*, 1962;

Lepley, 1964] and inshore from it are smaller and shorter longitudinal depressions. The asymmetry with the steep slope on the landward side suggests that it may be due in part to glacial erosion. For a discussion of its origin, see *Zhivago* [1962]; *Guilcher* [1963]; and *Lepley* [1964].

GLACIAL AND SUBGLACIAL TOPOGRAPHY

The oversnow traverses made on the antarctic continental ice sheet have yielded abundant data. The positions of the ice-surface topography and the subglacial bedrock topography are now known with a reasonable degree of accuracy for large areas of the continent. Contour maps showing ice-surface topography, bedrock topography, and ice thickness have been constructed [*Thiel*, 1962; *Bentley*, 1962].

The following topographic and geomorphic conclusions are based on these oversnow traverses: (1) In places, the surface of the continental ice sheet is over 4000 meters high [*Bentley*, 1962; *Thiel*, 1962]. (2) The greatest thickness of ice measured is 4270 meters [*Bentley and Ostenso*, 1961]. (3) The Ross Ice Shelf contains floating ice nearly 1000 meters thick [*Crary*, 1959], and the Ronne Ice Shelf contains floating ice over 1300 meters thick [*Thiel*, 1961]. (4) The combined Ronne and Filchner Ice Shelves are much larger than previously realized [*Bentley et al.*, 1960]. (5) The glacial surface of East Antarctica consists of a fairly simple dome-shaped structure [*Bentley*, 1962; *Bugayev and Tolstikov*, 1960], whereas that of West

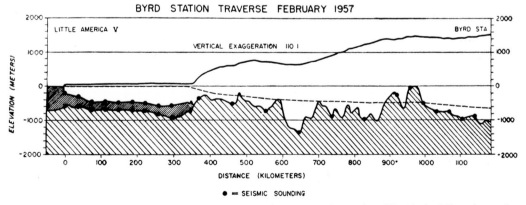

Fig. 8. A profile from Little America V to Byrd Station, West Antarctica. The dashed line shows the position of sea level relative to the rock surface (adjusted sea level) after removal of the ice and allowance for isostatic rebound. After C. R. Bentley and N. A. Ostenso.

Antarctica consists of two distinct high points with a saddle between them. (6) The present ice sheet in West Antarctica has grown from two smaller ice sheets that formed in the mountainous areas and later joined. (7) *Thiel* [1962] calculated that the average thickness of the antarctic ice sheet (grounded ice) is 1.97 km, that its area is 12.09 $\times$ 10^6 km², and that its volume is 23.8 $\times$ 10^6 km³. If all this ice were to melt suddenly without isostatic adjustment, the sea level would rise approximately 59 meters. (8) The area of the bedrock continent is not so large as a map of the ice sheet would suggest [*Ford*, 1964]. (9) The subglacial bedrock surface in East Antarctica, where known, is mostly near sea level [*Bentley*, 1962; *Ford*, 1964]. (10) The ice-rock interface beneath much of West Antarctica is well below sea level, and would still be below sea level after isostatic rebound following the removal of the ice (Figure 8) [*Thiel et al.*, 1959]. (11) The much-discussed major below-sea-level topographic connection between the Ross and Weddell seas does not exist. (12) A major channel, below sea level and beneath the ice of West Antarctica, probably exists between the Ross and Amundsen seas [*Bentley*, 1962; *Ford*, 1964]. This channel is deep enough to have existed before the land surface was depressed by the weight of the ice sheet. (13) Byrd Land would be an island after removal of the ice and isostatic rebound.

GLACIAL FEATURES

Glaciated outcrops, striations, polishing, roche moutonnée, glacially formed bedrock basins (Figure 9), cirques [*Taylor*, 1922; *Gould*, 1939, 1940; *Nichols*, 1953], horns, arêtes, truncated spurs [*Tay-*

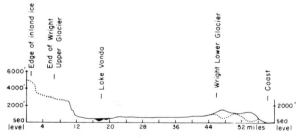

Fig. 9. A longitudinal profile of the Wright Valley, Victoria Land, showing Lake Vanda, which occupies an undrained bedrock basin resulting from glacial erosion. After Colin Bull.

Fig. 10. The ice-marginal channels, which are several hundred feet long and cut across an interglacial fan, Wright Valley, Victoria Land, Antarctica.

lor, 1922; *Nichols*, 1953], U-shaped valleys, hanging valleys, fjords, strandflats, and ice-marginal channels (Figure 10) [*Taylor*, 1922; *Calkin*, 1964a; *Nichols*, 1964b, 1965] have long been recognized.

The hanging valleys on the south side of the Wright Valley and elsewhere should be studied for possible fluviatile, glacial, and tectonic significance. A study of truncated spurs and hanging valleys may determine whether a fluviatile cycle preceded glaciation. Little attention has been paid to cirques. The conditions under which they were formed, the significance of some being below sea level, their age (especially when the area where they are found was once buried by ice from outside their basins), and whether cirques are as important as *Taylor* [1922] thought, should all be investigated.

Till and fossiliferous till [*David and Priestley*, 1909a, 1914; *Priestley and David*, 1912; *Speden*, 1962]; end, lateral, and ice-cored moraines; kame hillocks, terraces, plains, and moraines; valley trains; block terraces [*Nichols*, 1960; *Hoskins*, 1963]; mud-flow levees; and mirabilite [*Debenham*, 1919; *Rivard and Péwé*, 1962] are all found in the McMurdo Sound area.

MULTIPLE GLACIATION

If *Arctowski*'s [1900b, 1908] statement that the antarctic glaciers were formerly more extensive is the first important milestone in the study of antarctic glacial geology, then *Péwé*'s [1960a and 1960b] discovery of evidence for multiple glaciation in the McMurdo Sound area, Victoria Land, is the second.

Péwé recognized at least four major Quaternary glaciations. In summarizing his findings he writes [1960a]:

'Deposits of the earliest recognized glacial advance occur high on ridges and flat areas. The deposits are 2,000 feet above the valley floor, are badly weathered, and have little or no morainal form. Ice of this glaciation filled all the valleys and must have filled McMurdo Sound to an elevation of 2,000 feet.

'Deposits of the next two succeeding glaciations are distributed around the sound as well-preserved, but considerably subdued, moraines of both outlet and alpine glaciers. During the earlier of these two glaciations, alpine glaciers reached the expanded Koettlitz and Ferrar outlet glaciers. Outlet glaciers filled the southern part of McMurdo Sound to an elevation of about 1,000 feet. During the latter of these two advances many alpine glaciers did not reach the outlet glaciers.

'The latest major glaciation is represented by well-preserved ice-cored moraines. Number and position of deltas in drained glacier-ice–blocked lakes suggest the possibility of three stillstands or minor advances during this glaciation. Radiocarbon dating of algae in drained ponds indicates a minimum age of 6,000 years for this glaciation.'

Bull, McKelvey, and Webb [1962] found evidence for four glaciations in the Wright and Victoria valleys, south Victoria Land. They write: 'The earliest two glaciations were the most extensive; glaciers flowed eastwards from the ice plateau through the coastal ranges and cut broad valleys extending to McMurdo Sound and the Ross Sea. The moraines of these glaciations are thin and highly weathered. The third glaciation was less extensive, consisting of advances by smaller glaciers derived from the inland ice plateau, the Wilson Piedmont Glacier and névé fields in the dividing ranges. The surfaces of moraines of this glaciation are now partly covered by saline lakes, evaporite deposits and extensive areas of desert pavements strewn with ventifacts. The fourth and youngest glaciation comprised small advances by remnants of the plateau-fed valley glaciers. Thick boulder moraines of this glaciation overlie earlier deposits.'

Nichols [1961a] found evidence for four glaciations in the eastern end of the Wright Valley: 'The carving out of the bedrock basin of Lake Vanda by an outlet glacier which moved eastward down the Wright Valley represents the oldest glaciation recognized in the Wright Valley, McMurdo Sound, Antarctica. Three younger glaciations are marked by deposits from glaciers which moved from McMurdo Sound and the coastal mountains westward up the valley.

'The type deposit of the Pecten Glaciation, stratified gravels containing a high percentage of pecten shells, is on the floor of the Wright Valley approximately twenty-five miles from McMurdo Sound in a gully cut by a stream which came from Bull Pass. The shells were brought by glacial ice and meltwater streams from the floor of McMurdo Sound. Carbon-14 analysis proves that the shells are more than 35,000 years old. At the time the shells were being transported into the valley, there was approximately 3500 feet of ice in McMurdo Sound.

'The type deposit of the Loop Glaciation is approximately eight miles west of the Lower Wright Glacier. It is a prominent looped, steep-sided end moraine about 250 feet high which is younger than the pecten gravels. During the full-bodied stage of Loop Glaciation the Lower Wright Glacier extended more than nine miles farther up the Wright Valley than it does now. Deposits of the Loop Glaciation commonly show: (1) ventifacts from which more than one foot of rock has been removed by sandblasting; (2) odd-shaped boulders from which more than three feet of rock has weathered off; (3) a high proportion of boulders weathered down to ground level; (4) a pronounced yellow stain.

'Small discontinuous indistinct end moraines in the valley approximately five miles west of the Lower Wright Glacier can be traced into lateral moraines which on the north side of the valley near the Clark Valley are approximately 1000 feet above the floor. These were deposited during the oldest and most extensive stage of the Trilogy Glaciation, the youngest glaciation recognized in the Wright Valley. A prominent and extensive end moraine of Trilogy age on the floor of the Wright Valley near the mouth of the Clark Valley was deposited after the Lower Wright Glacier of

Trilogy time had retreated eastward approximately three miles from its most advanced position. Ice-cored moraines also of Trilogy age immediately in front of the Lower Wright Glacier and on the north side of the Wright Valley east of the melt-water stream of the Clark Glacier are even younger. All deposits of Trilogy age except those contaminated with weathered Loop material show: (1) a small amount of wind cutting; (2) an absence of odd-shaped weathered rocks and of boulders weathered down to ground level; (3) many upstanding boulders; (4) only minor staining.

'During the retreat of the Trilogy glaciers, the raised beaches which reach 67 feet above sea level around McMurdo Sound were built, and the level of Lake Vanda dropped approximately 185 feet. Carbon-14 analysis of the elephant seal buried in a raised beach at Marble Point indicates that the full-bodied stage of the Trilogy Glaciation probably occurred more than 7000 years ago.'

The glacial geology of the Victoria Valley system has been studied by Parker Calkin. He finds evidence of two major glaciations, the younger being subdivided into three episodes. He writes (personal communication, 1963), 'Two major glaciations are recorded in the Victoria Valley system but these may have been preceded by other glaciations. The first distinguishable glaciation, the Insel Glaciation, was an eastward flow of ice from the inland plateau, through the valleys to the coast. The Insel Drift includes: very silty till; erratic pebbles and cobbles on mesas 300 to 600 meters above the valley floors; and some lake silts. The till lacks morainal topography, and upstanding boulders are rare. During the recessional phase of the Insel Glaciation, deep meltwater channels were cut. Since the end of the glaciation, the shapes of the major valleys have not changed significantly.

'The second, or Victoria Glaciation, was marked by strong invasions from local ice fields and from the coast, and by weaker invasion from the inland ice plateau. This glaciation, which began more than 30,000 years B.P., is subdivided into three episodes.

'The Bull Drift episode included the most extensive glaciers of the Victoria Glaciation. At the maximum, the area was invaded by at least six glacier tongues which extended up to 20 km beyond their present positions, nearly filling the valley system. Till of the Bull Drift occupies about half of the valley floor area. Two large end moraines are well preserved, but most of the morainal topography is now subdued.

'During the following Vida Drift episode, the regimen became more vigorous. The retreat of the glaciers from their maximum of the Bull Drift episode stopped about 10 km from the present positions. Locally the glaciers readvanced. Large outwash fans and kames formed at the borders of glacial lakes. With continued retreat, thick ground and end moraines were deposited. These moraines are moderately well preserved and hummocky, standing several meters above adjacent deposits of the Bull Drift episode. Upstanding boulders are much more plentiful than on the older drifts, but are cavernously weathered. Vida till is very sandy.

'During the Packard Drift episode, which continues to the present, the glacier regimen has been less vigorous. Minor readvances occurred but most of the deposits represent a slow regular retreat of the glaciers to their present positions. The Packard Drift occurs largely as ground moraine, with areas of kame and kettle topography, and very bouldery ablation moraine still ice-cored. In most areas, there is no sharp break in weathering between the Packard and Vida deposits. However, the Packard till is more bouldery and the Packard deposits are sandier and fresher than the Vida deposits. Cavernous weathering and wind erosion is slight. Well-formed contraction polygons cover the Vida and Packard Drifts to within a few meters of the ice fronts.'

Calkin [1964b] has also demonstrated multiple glaciation in the Mount Gran area, southern Victoria Land. Additional field work will be needed to correlate these glacial deposits.

INTERGLACIAL FEATURES

An alluvial fan formed mainly in interglacial time is found on the north side of the Wright Valley approximately 8 miles west of the western terminus of the Wright Lower Glacier [*Nichols*, 1965] (Figures 10, 11). It is immediately beneath a hanging valley, adjacent to the prominent end moraine, which is the type deposit of the Loop glaciation [*Nichols*, 1961a]. The fan is several hundred feet high and is composed of alluvium that varies greatly in age and

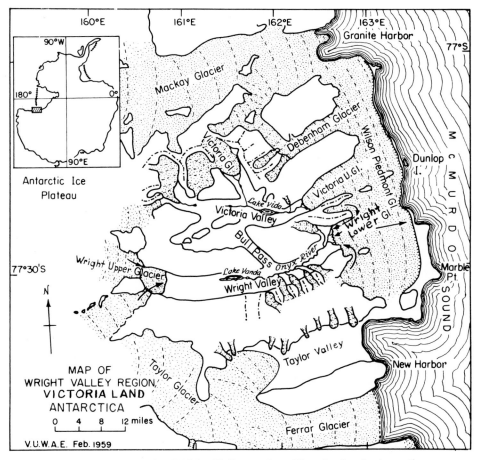

Fig. 11. Map of the Wright Valley region, Victoria Land, Antarctica.

coarseness. The main body of the fan is composed of subangular fragments up to 9 feet in diameter with a sandy, gravelly, brown-stained matrix. Most of the coarse-grained igneous and metamorphic fragments at the surface of the fan have been weathered and eroded down to ground level, probably by a combination of frost action [*Kelly and Zumberge,* 1961] and deflation. The main body of the fan appears to have been more profoundly weathered than the nearby Loop deposits. The basalt and dolerite fragments, which in general do not disintegrate, are considerably wind-cut.

A small patch of till, which, on the basis of its degree of weathering, is probably of Loop age, was deposited on the fan near its apex by a glacier that originated in the hanging valley above the fan.

The most striking feature of the fan is a series of channels that do not run up and down the fan but cut across it. They are not low places between lateral moraines deposited on the fan, but channels eroded into the fan. Some are several hundred feet long and up to 30 feet deep, and all slope downward up the valley. They terminate at the western or down-channel side of the fan, but in some cases do not start at the eastern or up-channel side of the fan (Figure 10). They were cut by melt-water streams marginal to the Wright Lower Glacier about the time it started to retreat from its most advanced position during the Loop glaciation. The fan was not completely destroyed by glacial erosion because it was frozen, the glacier was thin, and the fan was overridden by ice for only a short time. The presence of the marginal channels, the degree of weathering of the fan, and the occurrence of glacial deposits of Loop age superimposed upon the fan prove that the main body of the fan is pre-Loop in age.

The floor of one of the hanging valleys in the Wright Valley is approximately 2500 feet above the bottom of the valley. Some of this difference in elevation is undoubtedly due to differential glacial erosion, although some may be due to the pre-glacial history of the area. Truncated spurs are also found in the Wright Valley, and it seems likely that they have resulted from glacial erosion. The hanging valleys and truncated spurs were formed during the oldest glaciation(s), as some of them are found in those parts of the Wright Valley which were not overrun by the ice of the three younger glaciations. The fact that the floor of Lake Vanda is approximately 1000 feet lower than the valley floor at the western terminus of the Wright Lower Glacier, although it is more than 15 miles farther up the valley [*Bull*, 1960], is the best evidence of bedrock erosion by the eastward-moving ice of the oldest glaciation(s) (Figure 9). The magnitude of the bedrock erosion proves that the fan was formed after the oldest glaciation(s). The fact that the fan was deposited on a bedrock surface which slopes downward up-valley also proves that the fan postdates the oldest glaciation(s) and is in part of interglacial age.

Péwé [1960*a*] has described the interglacial lacustrine deposits in the Taylor Valley, Victoria Land. He writes, 'Many glacial lakes were formed when the "dry valleys" on the west side of McMurdo Sound were blocked by ice or moraines from the huge outlet glaciers during and immediately after the Taylor Glaciation. A large lake 1000 feet deep formed in Taylor Dry Valley when the glacial ice in the valley began to recede.

. . . Many dissected deltas and a thick deposit of laminated lake silt and clay are widespread in the valley bottom and attest the former presence of the lake. . . . The lake deposits were subsequently dissected and overridden by later glacier advances.'

Subsurface efflorescences occur in Loop deposits in the Wright Valley [*Nichols*, 1963*b*]. The active zone, at present, is less than 3 feet thick. If the salts were formed by upward-moving solutions, the climate almost certainly was warmer and the active zone consequently thicker when the salts accumulated. If, however, they were formed by downward-moving solutions, the salts were probably precipitated immediately above the permafrost. In any event, a Loop–Trilogy interglacial age for part of the layer is indicated by the fact that in the writer's experience (and confirmed by F. C. Ugolini, Ohio State University) it is, in general, thicker in Loop deposits than in Trilogy.

Some of the widespread scoria in the McMurdo Sound area, present in moraines, glaciofluvial deposits, beaches, and cinder cones, dates from interglacial time [*McCraw*, 1962; *Hamilton and Hayes*, 1960; *Angino, Turner, and Zeller*, 1960].

Speden [1962] has described the fossiliferous Quaternary marine deposits in the McMurdo Sound region, Antarctica. The Scallop Hill Formation is probably of an early Pleistocene interglacial age. The fossils in some of the south Victoria Land deposits that Speden has included in the Taylor Formation are probably Last Interglacial (Loop–Trilogy interglacial) in age.

Hough [1950] has identified glaciomarine sediments in cores from the Ross Sea sector. Age de-

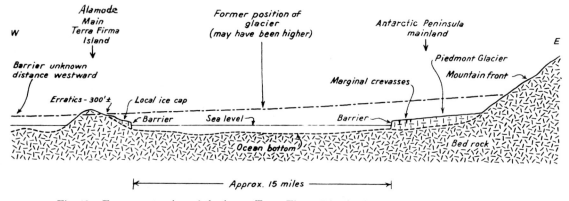

Fig. 12.   Former extension of the ice at Terra Firma Islands, Antarctic Peninsula, Antarctica.

Fig. 13. The Taylor Glacier (*left*) and Ferrar Glacier (*right*) are outlet glaciers fed by the continental icecap. Snowfields and alpine glaciers on the mountain between them. Victoria Land, Antarctica. U. S. Navy photograph.

terminations indicate that some of this material is interglacial.

DEGLACIATION

Gould [1939] has nicely summarized the data on antarctic deglaciation in the following statement: 'It is the testimony of all antarctic investigators, based upon information collected from all sides of the continent, that all the present glacial features, from the inland ice itself to the shelf ice masses about it, must be considered as shrunken remnants of a former, more intensive, and more extensive period of glaciation.' Members of the first expedition to winter in the Antarctic brought back data proving that the glaciers of the Antarctic were formerly more extensive [*Racovitza,* 1900; *Arctowski,* 1900*b,* 1908], and subsequent investigations have substantiated this [*Nichols,* 1953].

Proof for extensive deglaciation on the Antarctic Peninsula (Figure 12) is found at the Terra Firma Islands [*Nichols,* 1953]. Alamode Island, the largest of these islands, is in Marguerite Bay (approximately 68°45′S and 67°31′W) about 15 miles west of the tidewater terminus of the piedmont glacier on the mainland. A relatively flat area of several acres about 300 feet above sea level, the country rock of which is a dark-gray pyroclastic felsitic breccia, is found on the island. Numerous pink granite glacial erratics are found on the flat. Similar pink granite occurs on the mainland, and probably below sea level between the mainland and the island. During a more extensive stage of glaciation the mainland ice extended out to and beyond the Terra Firma Islands. Fragments of pink granite and other rock types were plucked from outcrops on the mainland and from submarine ledges between the mainland and the islands and were deposited on the flat. At this time the piedmont glacier on the mainland was probably more than 2000 feet thick at its present terminus and extended more than 20 miles farther out into Marguerite Bay.

Extensive deglaciation in the McMurdo Sound area, Victoria Land, is proved by a layer of gravel, about a foot thick and 20 feet long, approximately 25 miles from McMurdo Sound in the Wright Valley. The gravel is a glaciofluvial deposit and contains many pecten shells [*Nichols*, 1961*a*]. The shells were initially transported by glacial ice from the bottom of McMurdo Sound up into the Wright Valley and were later picked up and redeposited by melt-water streams. At this time there was more than 3000 feet of glacial ice in McMurdo Sound, and much of the now-deglaciated area around McMurdo Sound was buried by thousands of feet of glacial ice.

ORIGIN OF THE 'DRY VALLEYS'

Several bedrock valleys more than 30 miles long, completely or incompletely filled with outlet and piedmont glaciers, extend from the continental ice

sheet on the west down to McMurdo Sound on the east. They are, from north to south, the Mackay, Victoria, Wright, Taylor, and Ferrar valleys; and there are others (Figure 11). The Ferrar and Mackay valleys are occupied by outlet glaciers that more or less completely fill them and reach McMurdo Sound. Although the upper part of the Taylor Valley is occupied by an outlet glacier, the lower 20 miles are essentially ice-free (Figure 13). Glacial deposits prove that the valley was once occupied by an outlet glacier that reached McMurdo Sound [*Péwé*, 1960*a*]. The ice-free condition of the lower part of the Taylor Valley is due, therefore, to deglaciation rather than to non-glaciation. The lower part of the Wright Valley is occupied by the Wright Lower Glacier, a channel glacier that is a part of the Wilson Piedmont Glacier; and the upper part of the valley is occupied by the Wright Upper Glacier, an outlet glacier. The 30-odd miles between these two glaciers are

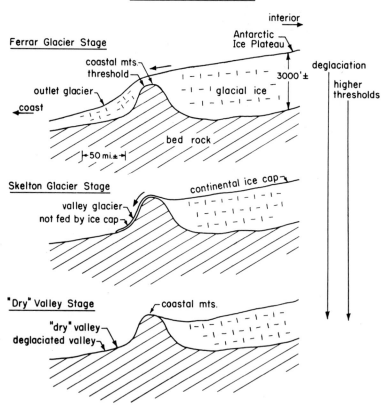

Fig. 14. Diagrams showing how the cols act as obstructions or thresholds and control the size of the outlet glaciers.

Fig. 15. Crevassed piedmont glacier, icebergs caught in sea ice, and barrier coastline, Alexander Island, Antarctic Peninsula. Photo by Ronne Antarctic Research Expedition.

essentially ice-free; and here, too, glacial features prove that the valley was once completely occupied by an outlet glacier that reached McMurdo Sound [*Nichols*, 1961a]. The situation in the Victoria Valley is similar to that in the Wright Valley. These deglaciated valleys are called, locally, 'dry valleys.'

The presence of valleys filled with outlet glaciers adjacent to deglaciated ice-free valleys requires explanation. The ice-filled and ice-free valleys are all close to one another, oriented in the same direction, about the same size, at about the same altitude, and they all have the same relation to the

antarctic ice sheet and McMurdo Sound. Climate, therefore, is not the explanation for the difference.

A seismic survey by *Crary* [1959] showed that the bedrock topography, which is immediately inland from the coastal mountains and buried by the continental ice sheet, is lower than the ice-filled and ice-free valleys, and that, in places, it is even below sea level (Figure 4). This survey, and the distribution of the mountain peaks, showed that the heads of these valleys are separated from the low interior basin by ice-buried cols between mountain peaks. Whether these cols are due to block-faulting, pre-glacial fluviatile erosion, headward growth of cirques before the full-bodied stage of the ice sheet, or to a combination of these processes, is not known.

Bull, McKelvey, and Webb [1962] and *Gunn and Warren* [1962] correctly concluded that the outlet glaciers in the valleys vary in size and are almost absent in the Wright and Victoria valleys because the cols vary in height. Where the cols at the heads of the valleys are high relative to the surface of the ice sheet, they restrict the flow of ice from the continental ice sheet into the valleys; where they are low, they facilitate it.

Figure 14 shows how the cols act as obstructions and control the size of the outlet glaciers in the valleys, and how a small decrease in the elevation of the surface of the ice sheet can cause a disproportionate reduction in the size of the outlet glaciers. With the continued lowering and final disappearance of the outlet glaciers during deglaciation, the katabatic winds which blew from

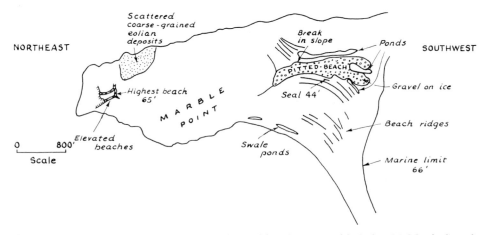

Fig. 16. Map showing distribution of the elevated beaches at Marble Point, McMurdo Sound, Antarctica.

Fig. 17. The elevated pitted beach (*enclosed by white lines*) and the elevated beaches with ridge and swale topography at Marble Point. The marine limit is 66 feet above sea level. Photograph by U. S. Navy.

the plateau down the valleys became progressively warmer and drier; and it is these winds which are probably responsible for there being less snow in the 'dry' valleys than in the coastal areas.

The lengths of the outlet glaciers indicate that the Ferrar col is lower relative to the ice sheet than the Taylor col, and still lower than the cols in the Wright and Victoria valleys. That this relationship between cols has existed from early in the glacial history of the area is suggested by the following. It is now generally accepted, because

Fig. 18. Pitted elevated beach approximately 45 feet above sea level at Marble Point. In general the pits are 10 to 50 feet in diameter and as much as 6 feet deep.

of *Péwé*'s [1960*a*] pioneering work, that the McMurdo Sound area has been glaciated four or more times and that each successive glaciation was less extensive than the one that preceded it. The Ferrar Valley, therefore, has been occupied four or more times by outlet glaciers that reached McMurdo Sound. *Péwé* [1960*b*] has shown that outlet glaciers in the Taylor Valley reached McMurdo Sound only twice. *Nichols* [1961*a*] and *Calkin* [1964*a*] have found definite evidence in the Wright and Victoria valleys for only one invasion by outlet glaciers that reached McMurdo Sound [see, however, *Bull, McKelvey, and Webb*, 1962, 1964; *McGregor*, 1963].

ELEVATED BEACHES

The following types of coasts are found along McMurdo Sound between Cape Chocolate and Granite Harbor: bedrock (11 miles), mantle-rock (30 miles), ice-cliff (48 miles), and ice-cored moraine (9 miles) [*Nichols*, 1963*a*]. Ice-cliff coasts are much more common in the Antarctic as a whole than in the McMurdo Sound area, where large deglaciated areas are present (Figure 15). Till, outwash, raised beaches, talus, deltas, and block terraces are found along the mantle-rock coasts of the continent.

The antarctic elevated beaches, owing to low temperatures, absence of vegetation, and presence of permafrost and land and sea ice, have certain characteristics not found on beaches formed in temperate climates [*Nichols*, 1961*b*]. They commonly show one or more of the following features: (1) They rest on ice. (2) They are pitted because of the melting of buried ice (Figures 16, 17, 18). (3) They have ridges and mounds formed because of ice-push and/or deposition from stranded ice. (4)

TABLE 1. Elevated Beaches of Marguerite Bay, Antarctic Peninsula, Antarctica

Location	Maximum Altitude	Area Dimensions	Special Features	Remarks
Mushroom Island	Approximately 20 feet	Small	—	Being buried by talus
Moraine Cove	Approximately 20 feet	Small	—	Beach roundstones intermingled with morainal fragments
Black Thumb	25 feet	Many acres	—	Upper part several hundred feet from strand line. Upper part being buried by talus
Small unnamed island between Black Thumb and Red Rock Ridge. Bearing to center Safety Col N. 25°E. Bearing to Black Thumb N. 127°E.	12 feet	—	—	Elevated?
Small unnamed island near Black Thumb	Above sea level	Small; in a chasm	—	Elevated?
Small unnamed island between Black Thumb and Red Rock Ridge	27 feet	200 feet long, 600 feet wide	Pocket beach	Beach ridges. Beach roundstones up to 46 feet. Other slightly elevated beaches
Red Rock Ridge (north side)	110 feet	—	Coarse boulder beach	Highest beach in the Marguerite Bay area
Red Rock Ridge (south side)	Somewhat more than 30 feet	2000 feet long	—	—
Neny Island (east side)	Nearly 50 feet	Extensive	Well-developed beach ridges	—
Neny Island (north side)	90 feet	Extensive	On strand flat in places	Buried by talus and alluvial-fan deposits in places; pitted beach ridges
Roman Four Promontory	Slightly elevated	—	—	At least three small beaches
Safety Col (east corner)	Approximately 30 feet	—	—	—
Little Thumb	More than 20 feet	Extensive	On strand flat	—
Pyrox Island	Approximately 50 feet	Extensive	At northwest side, beach cliffed at strand line	In part elevated tombolos. Many areas
Islands 50 miles west of Stonington Island	Above sea level	—	—	Two small beaches—elevated?
Two islands 10–15 miles southwest of Adelaide Island	Above sea level	—	—	Two small beaches—elevated?
Stonington Island	70 feet	Cover large part of island	Crescentic scars. Pitted roundstones	—

TABLE 2.   Antarctic Elevated Beaches, Marine Caves, Marine Terraces

Location	Altitude	Remarks	Observer or Authority
Cockburn Island, Graham Land	13 feet	Beds of sand and gravel	Andersson [1906, pp. 57–58]
Hope Bay, Graham Land	10 feet above sea level, perhaps higher	Numerous rounded pebbles not now reached by waves	Andersson [1906, pp. 57]
Sidney Herbert Sound, Graham Land	About 13 feet	Marine stratified bouldery fossiliferous clay. Marine till. Deposited below sea level	Andersson [1906, pp. 58–59]
West Antarctica	32–49 feet	—	Nordenskjöld [1913, p. 14]
Jenny Island, Marguerite Bay, Graham Land	26 feet	Elevated beach, 1300–1600 feet long; 160–330 feet wide. Whalebone	Bongrain [1914, p. 49]
South of Adelaide Island, Graham Land	80 feet	Many beaches	Fleming [1940, pp. 94, 97]

They have beach ridges that terminate abruptly because ice was present when they were formed. (5) Ice-rafted fragments are found on them. (6) They have poorly rounded beach stones. (7) Frost cracks and solifluction deposits are found on them. (8) The beach ridges may have short erosional gaps that were formed by melt-water streams. (9) They contain cold-water fossils. (10) Ventifacts are present.

The elevated beaches on the Antarctic Peninsula have been described by *Andersson* [1906], *Nordenskjöld* [1913], *Bongrain* [1914], *Fleming* [1940], and the writer [*Nichols*, 1953, 1960] (Tables 1 and 2). The highest is 110 feet above sea level. The roundstones on the oldest of these beaches are commonly split and shattered by frost action, roughened by exfoliation and surrounded by accumulations of spalled fragments, and covered with numerous well-developed pits. Ground moraine is the most impor-

tant source for these beaches, talus a much less important source. In places the beaches are being progressively buried by talus, alluvium, snowdrift ice slabs, and fringing glaciers.

Raised beaches, wave-cut platforms, sea caves, and sea stacks are common along the coasts of the islands of the Scotia Ridge (South Georgia, the South Sandwich, South Orkney, and South Shetland islands) and the Antarctic Peninsula [*Adie*, 1963]. *Adie* [1963], after an analysis of field observations and air photographs of this region, writes: 'The oldest known raised beaches and wave-cut platforms are probably of late Pliocene age, whereas the youngest ones are of a late Recent age.'

Løken (1959) has reported on higher sea levels in the Windmill Islands, Knox Coast, and *Meguro et al.* [1963] have found raised beaches about a hundred feet above sea level along the Prince Olav Coast in Queen Maud Land.

The elevated beaches in Victoria Land have been described by *Taylor* [1922], *Priestley* [1923], *David and Priestley* [1909a], and the writer [*Nichols*, 1953, 1960, 1961c, 1963a] (Figures 19, 20, 21 and Table 3). These beaches were derived mainly from till and outwash and have been buried locally by solifluction, by eolian, outwash, and landslide deposits, and by talus and snowdrift-ice slabs. A radiocarbon measurement of an elephant seal (L 594, Lamont) buried in an elevated beach about 44 feet above sea level at Marble Point indicates that this beach is 4600 ± 200 years old. The pits on some of the highest beach ridges, the several feet of ice beneath beaches 45–55 feet above

Fig. 19. The elevated beaches just north of Marble Point, McMurdo Sound, Antarctica. Photograph by U. S. Navy.

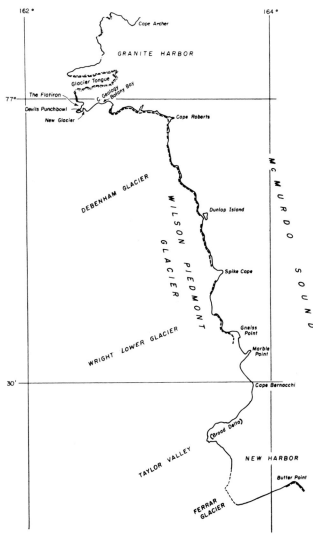

Fig. 20. Map showing localities in McMurdo Sound, Antarctica.

Marble Point, is about 40 feet above sea level. Well-developed elevated beaches disappear less than 2 miles south of Cape Bernacchi, perhaps because cyclic, shelf, or glacial ice persisted in New Harbor, whereas farther north the coast was open at times, permitting the formation of the beaches. These beaches postdate the youngest glaciation recognized in the Wright Lower Valley, and the highest are probably about seven thousand years old [Nichols, 1963a].

There is as yet no good agreement concerning the changes of sea level during the past five thousand years. However, the latest carbon-14 dates of organisms and plants that lived close to sea level in relatively stable areas indicate that 4600 ± 200 years ago, when the elephant seal at Marble Point was buried with beach gravels by wave action, sea level the world around was approximately 15 feet lower than at present [Shepard, 1963]. This indicates that the Marble Point area has risen isostatically about 59 feet during the last 4600 ± 200 years.

ELEVATED WAVE-WASHED SURFACES

Elevated wave-washed bedrock surfaces in the Mc-Murdo Sound area are found at Marble Point, Cape Roberts, Spike Cape, and elsewhere, but are best developed at Gneiss Point (Figures 21, 22, 23). Here, the wave-washed surface, which extends from the marine limit down to the present sea level and for a few thousand feet along the coast, contrasts sharply with the area above it (Figures 22, 23). An indistinct elevated beach is commonly found immediately above the wave-washed surface. Bedrock surfaces, till, and kame and solifluction deposits are found still higher up. An occasional elevated pocket beach, and thin eolian deposits and residual sand and gravel formed by the weathering of the bedrock after the formation of the wave-washed surface, are found in the wave-washed area. Small solifluction lobes and sheets cover some of the uppermost part of the area. Also present is fluviatile material deposited by streamlets formed by the melting of snowdrifts. The fluviatile material occurs in thin layers and in fans 3 or 4 feet long and several inches thick. Small amounts of silt and sand of eolian and fluviatile origin are commonly found interbedded in and veneering snowdrifts. Snowdrift morainal deposits form when the snow melts and this material is let down. These

sea level, the buried elephant seal in an elevated beach 44 feet above sea level, and the gravel ridges on slightly elevated beaches deposited by stranded gravel-veneered pieces of ice that broke off from an ice foot, indicate that all the beaches were formed in a climate like that now found in the McMurdo Sound area. The highest beach studied by the writer is at Dunlop Island and is 67 feet above sea level [Nichols, 1961c]. The highest beaches at Marble Point and Cape Roberts, approximately 30 miles apart, are about 66 feet above sea level. The marine limit between these two points is, therefore, essentially horizontal. The highest beach at Cape Bernacchi, about 3 miles south of

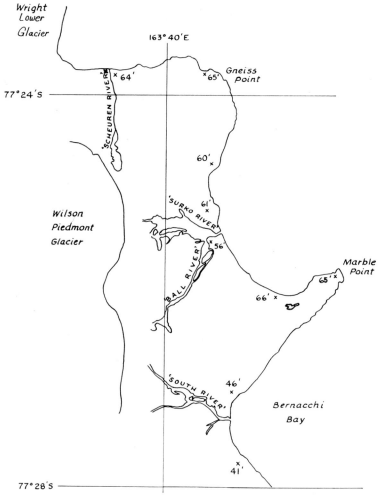

Fig. 21. Map showing the location of the elevated beaches near Marble
Point (numbers indicate elevations of marine limit).

deposits with their micromorainal topography are easily identified and are common in the wave-washed area. In general, only fine-grained mantle rock is found in the wave-washed area, whereas above it both fine and coarse mantle rock are found. Figures 22 and 23 show chasms with diverse orientation. Most, if not all, of the chasms have been formed by glacial erosion along zones of weakness. The upper limit of the wave-washed surface is probably between 60 and 70 feet above sea level.

ELEVATED MARINE-BOULDER PAVEMENTS

An elevated marine-boulder pavement (wave-washed till) on a small promontory between the Wright Lower Glacier and Gneiss Point (Figures 21,

24) is flanked on two sides by snowdrift-ice slabs; inland it terminates against till and thin kame-hillock deposits; on the seaward side it is bordered by bedrock which extends downward to sea level. It is found on a flattish area a few hundred feet long and somewhat less in width very close to the marine limit. The boulders have been slightly rounded and cover more than three times as much area as does the matrix. This pavement was undoubtedly derived from a bouldery till. Elevated beach gravels close by are at about the same elevation. The pavement was in a very exposed position when it was being acted upon by waves, as the snowdrift-ice slabs that flank it today did not then exist.

This boulder pavement can be differentiated from

TABLE 3. Elevated beaches of McMurdo Sound, South Victoria Land, Antarctica

Location	Maximum Altitude (feet)	Remarks	Location	Maximum Altitude (feet)	Remarks
The Flatiron, Granite Harbor*	47	Poorly developed	Immediately west of mouth of 'Scheuren R.'	64	—
Botany Bay, Granite Harbor	56	Individual marine round-stones found 10 feet higher	Immediately east of mouth of 'Scheuren R.'	64	—
Devils Punchbowl, Granite Harbor	30	Undoubtedly goes higher; snow prevented measurement	Immediately north of 'Gneiss Point'	65	U. S. Navy Survey
Cape Geology, Granite Harbor	63	Well-developed wave-washed bedrock surface	Immediately south of Gneiss Point	60	U. S. Navy Survey
¼–½ mile S.W. Cape Geology	56; 47	Described by *Taylor* [1922, pp. 22–23]	Immediately north of 'Surko River'	61	U. S. Navy Survey
Cape Roberts†	66	Elevated beach ridges terminating against glacier and perpendicular to it; elevated wave-washed bedrock and marine boulder pavements	Immediately south of 'Surko River'	56	U. S. Navy Survey
			Marble Point near pitted beach	66	U. S. Navy Survey
Dunlop Island‡	67	Elevated wave-washed bedrock also present	Eastern tip of Marble Point	65	—
			Immediately north of 'South River'	46	—
Spike Cape and adjacent mainland§	55	Elevated wave-washed bedrock; highest beach pitted in places; glacial deposits above beaches badly weathered	Immediately south of 'South River'	41	—
			Cape Bernacchi	39–40	Pile of boulders surrounded by solifluction deposits; probably an elevated beach
Immediately north of Wright Lower Glacier	56	Highest beach pitted	South of Ferrar Glacier	No elevated beaches	—

* Dimensions of area are small.
† Tied islands and elevated tombolos.
‡ 1 mile long; ½ mile wide; excellently developed beach ridges.
§ Well-developed beach ridges terminating against glacier and nearly perpendicular to it.

bouldery till and from felsenmeers only with difficulty. The slight rounding of the boulders and their great concentration, the exposed position of the pavement with respect to the ocean, the gentle seaward slope of the pavement and its relationship to the marine limit, together with the presence of nearby elevated-beach deposits at about the same elevation, prove the marine origin of the pavement.

Another marine-boulder pavement associated with elevated-beach gravels is at a slightly lower elevation on the peninsula immediately east of this pavement.

PERIGLACIAL FEATURES

Aridity

Although little is yet known about precipitation in Antarctica, all measurements and calculations indi-cate that the continent as a whole receives only a small amount of precipitation.

Mellor [1959] calculated the mean annual precipitation on 14 million sq km of Antarctica to be 14 grams per cm². *Lister and Pratt* [1959] calculated the annual net accumulation over the whole continent to be 13 grams per cm². As the mean annual precipitation for Antarctica as a whole is approximately equal to the mean annual snow accumulation, the calculations of Mellor and of Lister and Pratt are in substantial agreement [*Meinardus*, 1938; *Loewe*, 1957; *Cameron and Goldthwait*, 1961]. The most arid region of the United States (southeastern California, southwestern Arizona, and western Nevada) receives approximately 12 cm of rainfall per year [*Visher*, 1954].

In view of glaciological and meteorological evi-

Fig. 22. Elevated wave-washed surfaces and glacial grooves in bedrock, Gneiss Point, McMurdo Sound, Antarctica. Photograph by U. S. Navy.

Fig. 24. An elevated marine-boulder pavement (wave-washed till) between Gneiss Point and the Wright Lower Glacier, McMurdo Sound, Antarctica.

dence for aridity in Antarctica as a whole, it is not surprising that geological features indicate long-continued aridity in the area around McMurdo Sound [*Gunn and Warren,* 1962; *Nichols,* 1963*b*].

Dry kettles and small saline lakes (Figure 25) [*Ball and Nichols,* 1960; *Barghoorn and Nichols,* 1961; *Gibson,* 1962; *Tedrow, Ugolini, and Janetschek,* 1963], surface and subsurface efflorescences of salts (Figures 26, 27), calcite veneers on the subsurface portions of fragments, and undrained lakes are found in the deglaciated valleys and coastal areas around McMurdo Sound. Undrained and salty lakes, surface efflorescences, desert varnish, and a

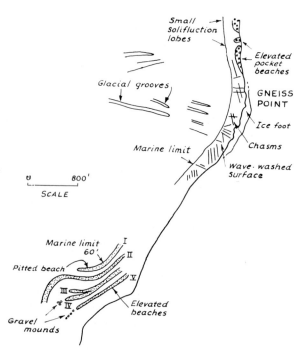

Fig. 23. Map showing the wave-washed surfaces and the elevated beaches, Gneiss Point, Antarctica.

Fig. 25. Saline pond in the upper end of the Wright Valley. Soluble white salts veneer the area immediately surrounding the pond. Photograph by U. S. Navy.

Fig. 26. A surface efflorescence at Dunlop Island, McMurdo Sound, Antarctica, formed by the evaporation of water which moved upward because of capillarity. There is snow to the left of the ice axe.

Fig. 28. A felsenmeer developed on a porphyry dike, near Lake Vanda, Wright Valley, Victoria Land.

low relative humidity are found in Bunger Hills, Knox Coast [*Shumskiy,* 1957]. All these features characterize arid areas and are found in Antarctica partly because of its periglacial climate.

The saline ponds occur in the Wright Valley and elsewhere (Figure 25). The salt concentration in one pond is approximately four times that of sea water. The principal dissolved salt is NaCl. $MgCl_2$, $CaSO_4$, and $CaCO_3$ are also present. Immediately above the pond the ground is covered with a thin veneer of very soluble white salts.

Lake Vanda, an undrained lake, occupies a bedrock basin in the Wright Valley. Undrained lakes are found only in arid regions where evaporation exceeds precipitation. Generally the areas of these

lakes are small compared with their basins. In 1940 Great Salt Lake occupied about 1500 square miles and the basin about 54,000 square miles; the ratio was about 1:36. The Dead Sea is approximately 340 square miles in area, and its basin approximately 10,000 square miles; the ratio is approximately 1:29. The ratio for Lake Vanda is considerably smaller than that of either Great Salt Lake or the Dead Sea [*Nichols,* 1963b]. Such a low ratio indicates that the present-day precipitation yields no significant runoff and that the area is very arid. An analysis of the above features also indicates that in this part of Antarctica something like the present degree of aridity has existed for several thousand years.

Fig. 27. A subsurface efflorescence of salts in the Wright Valley, McMurdo Sound, Antarctica. The great solubility of the salts proves that the area has been arid since their formation.

Fig. 29. A felsenmeer composed of Ferrar dolerite found near Gneiss Point, McMurdo Sound. Adjacent fragments can commonly be fitted together.

Felsenmeers

In the McMurdo Sound area felsenmeers are developed on both bedrock and blocky till, but they are not common. Excellent examples are found immediately east and south of Lake Vanda, Wright Valley. Here porphyry dikes are completely buried by slabs removed from them by frost-shattering (Figure 28). The slabs are commonly less than a foot long and are essentially unweathered, as they ring when struck with a hammer.

The dikes stand 10 feet and more above the country rock. This relation is due, in part at least, to post-glacial erosion. The dikes have been intruded into coarse-grained igneous rocks [McKelvey and Webb, 1962] which, on disintegration, break up into grains. The grains are removed by the strong winds in the valley, and the country rock is lowered. Because the dikes frost-shatter into slabs too large to be removed by the wind, the country rock is eroded much more rapidly and, with the passage of time, the dikes have come to stand above the country rock.

The Ferrar dolerite [Harrington, 1958] crops out inland from Gneiss Point, McMurdo Sound. Here the till contains an abundance of large dolerite fragments. Frost-shattering of both fragments and bedrock has formed small felsenmeers (Figure 29), which can be easily differentiated from rocky till as follows: (1) The fragments in the felsenmeers are more angular than those in the till. (2) Adjacent fragments in the felsenmeers, which have similar lithology, can commonly be fitted together. (3) There are more fragments and less matrix in the felsenmeers than in the till. Frost-shattering has been active in this area for some time, as evidenced by different degrees of weathering on the faces of the frost-shattered blocks. Some faces are fresh and unweathered, proving that frost-shattering is also a current process. Felsenmeers are found in the Sør-Rondane Mountains, Queen Maud Land [Autenboer, 1963], in the Dufek Massif [Aughenbaugh, 1961], and in the Antarctic Peninsula [Nordenskjöld, 1911].

The air temperature at Marble Point, about a mile from the dolerite felsenmeers, crossed 32°F a minimum of 78 times from 1 November 1958 to 1 November 1959. During the same time interval the soil temperature 1 inch below the surface crossed 32°F at least 104 times [Nichols and Bull, 1964a].

Frost-shattering should, therefore, take place at the present time in the McMurdo Sound area, wherever the rocks have the necessary structural weaknesses and there is sufficient moisture.

Ice-Cored Moraines

Ice-cored moraines covering scores of square miles are found in the McMurdo Sound area at the following localities: (1) between Butter Point and the Blue Glacier, (2) Cape Chocolate, (3) between the Hobbs and the Blue glaciers, (4) Ross Island, (5) northwest side of Koettlitz Glacier, (6) Wright and Victoria valleys, and (7) Mount Gran area [Ferrar, 1907; David and Priestley, 1914; Taylor, 1922; Wright and Priestley, 1922; Péwé, 1960a; Calkin, 1964a, b]. The core may be floating, grounded, or inland ice. Commonly the ice is so well concealed by the moraine that the only evidence of its existence is the presence of excessive melt water, ice close by, or a tidal crack.

Under the prevailing conditions some of these ice-cored moraines are permanent features, whereas others are only temporary. Ablation moraine will form on those parts of a glacier that contain englacial and/or superglacial material and are below the firn-line. As the moraine increases in thickness it becomes more effective as an insulator and wastage proceeds at a slower and slower rate. Where the mean annual temperature is above 32°F, ablation will continue, if conditions remain constant, until no more ice is left. On the other hand, where the mean annual temperature is below 32°F the ablation moraine increases in thickness only until it is as thick as the active zone is deep. When this happens no further ablation takes place, as the glacial ice is in the permafrost zone and its temperature at all times is everywhere at or below 32°F. Under these conditions the ice-cored moraine is a permanent feature unless the morainal topography is so steep that falling, sliding, and flowing of the moraine continually exposes ice. Ice-cored moraines in the McMurdo Sound area, where the mean annual temperature is about 0°F, are thousands of years old; and those on topography so flat that the moraine cannot slide will persist as long as the present conditions continue.

Ice-cored morainal topography is commonly characterized by knobs and mounds that may be as much as a hundred feet high, and by valleys and kettles. Ponds up to two hundred yards long, in which algae grow, are commonly found in the kettles. Streams may run from pond to pond. The topography is controlled by distribution of ice, as the moraine is only a few feet thick. Ice crops out here and there, but in most places the moraine completely conceals it. Talus, fans, flowtill, and lake deposits are found in the kettles. Mirabilite is found on those ice-cored moraines that border McMurdo Sound. Wind-polished and wind-cut stones are present, sand-wedge polygons are abundant, and the moraine is stained but only slightly weathered. *Péwé* [1960a] associates all the ice-cored moraines that he studied with the Koettlitz glaciation. Dead algae found in the ice-cored moraine in front of the Hobbs Glacier are reported to be 5900 ± 140 years old on the basis of carbon-14 measurements.

Where ice-cored morainal topography is characterized by steep cones and kettles, it constantly changes. The moraine veneering the ice of a steep cone may slide or flow down into the adjacent kettle. The ice in the cone, now not so well insulated, will ablate more rapidly and decrease progressively in height. The ice in the kettle, now better insulated, will, however, ablate more slowly. In time, the topography may become inverted, with the cone becoming a kettle and the kettle a cone.

Numerous examples show that inversion of topography takes place. A layer of algal peat about an inch thick and covering hundreds of square feet was seen by *Taylor* [1922] on a low mound in the ice-cored moraines south of the Blue Glacier. The peat must have grown in a pond at the bottom of a kettle. Its presence on a low mound proves an inversion of topography. The pond has been drained and its bottom dissected and the ice in the higher ice-cored moraine which once surrounded it has been ablated; as a result the former moraine is now lower than what was once the bottom of the pond.

A stratigraphic section found in a wave-eroded slope located approximately half a mile south of the Blue Glacier included, top to bottom: 1 foot of topset beds composed of sand and gravel; 5 feet of foreset beds composed of sand and gravel; 1 foot of flowtill containing silt, pebbles, and peat fragments; 1 foot of fluviatile peaty granule gravel; 2 feet of ablation moraine; and 22 feet of glacial ice extending down to and undoubtedly below sea level.

Fig. 30. Ice-cored moraine, Wright Valley, Victoria Land, Antarctica. The moraine covers hundreds of acres and is commonly only 1–2 feet thick.

The topset beds were found at the surface of a slightly sloping area that covered about 5 acres next to the strand line. This surface was in general 15–20 feet higher than the area around it. At one time, however, it was a depression in which fluviatile gravel, flowtill, and deltaic deposits accumulated. These features prove that an inversion of topography has taken place, and they give an idea of the processes active in ice-cored moraines.

An ice-cored moraine covering hundreds of acres is found on the north side of the eastern end of the Wright Valley about a mile southeast of the Clark Glacier and immediately below the easternmost cirque glacier. The surface is generally flat, the average relief being less than 5 feet. In detail it is characterized by hillocks, kettles, and frost furrows. The hillocks are commonly less than 5 feet high and 40 feet across; the kettles are up to 4 feet deep and 30 feet across; and the moraine is covered by more frost furrows than any other deposit that the writer has studied in the Antarctic (Figure 30). The great abundance of frost furrows is due to the fact that there is more ice in this deposit than in other antarctic surficial deposits. Large rocks, some 10 feet long, are abundant. Stratified sand and gravel are found at the surface, and in places large rocks derived from adjacent hillocks rest on the sand and gravel. At no time during the two field seasons when the writer studied this deposit was there enough melt water to have deposited the sand and gravel. Ice does not crop out at the surface, although digging showed that it is present beneath 1–2 feet of moraine (Figure 31), and

Fig. 31. Ice-cored moraine, Wright Valley, Victoria Land. The ice does not crop out at the surface, although digging showed that it is present beneath 1–2 feet of moraine (shovel and ice axe indicate scale).

Fig. 33. The active ice-cored kame moraine at the terminus of the Wright Lower Glacier, Wright Valley, Victoria Land.

its widespread distribution, cleanness, and vertical extent prove that it is glacial rather than ice-wedge ice or the ice found in lenses at the top of the permafrost. The small amount of melt water, the scarcity of wet moraine, and the absence of ice at the surface suggest that most of the ice is in the permafrost zone and perfecly insulated. A ravine 15–20 feet deep has been cut into the ice-cored moraine, and in places it terminates in a steep slope more than 50 feet high. The ravine and slope suggest that 50 feet of ice is still present in places beneath the moraine. Several kames are found near the margin

Fig. 32. An ice-cored alluvial cone at the terminus of the Wright Lower Glacier, Wright Valley, Victoria Land. A small fosse and an ice-contact slope are found next to the glacier.

of the ice-cored moraine; two are more than 50 feet high. Their height and the absence of significant relief on the ice-cored moraine suggest that they are not perforated kames and were therefore formed in front of the glacier from which the ice-cored moraine was derived. Considerably more than 50 feet of ice has apparently been lost by ablation.

The yellow color of the surface of the moraine, the veneer of travertine on the bottom of fragments, the small amount of wind polishing and cutting, and the crumbly weathered surfaces of some fragments all suggest that the deposit has some antiquity. Although probably thousands of years old, it is the youngest deposit in the Wright Valley [*Nichols*, 1961a], just as ice-cored moraines are the youngest deposits around McMurdo Sound [*Péwé*, 1960a].

An active ice-cored kame moraine is located adjacent to the north side of the Wright Lower Glacier at the eastern end of the Wright Valley. In places it is being built out into 'Wright Lake'; elsewhere it is bounded by a marginal melt-water stream that runs into the lake. It extends for more than half a mile along the terminus of the glacier. In places, where the melt-water streams that build it are small and overloaded, the kame moraine is a series of steep alluvial cones (Figure 32). Where the streams are larger and not so heavily loaded, it is an alluvial apron composed of coalescing fans (Figure 33). The stratified, cross-bedded sand of which it is composed rests on ice. In one place the sand is more than 8 feet thick. Since the active

Fig. 34. The kame moraine at the terminus of the Wright Lower Glacier, Wright Valley. It consists of coalescing fans and cones, is composed of cross-bedded sand, and rests on ice; its surface is dotted with rocks that fell from the glacier or rolled off knobs of ice; and small ridges and valleys, which resulted from the thrust of the glacier, are present.

zone in this area is less than 3 feet thick and the melt water very close to 32°F, the ice core is probably in the permafrost; if so, it is permanently preserved as long as the present conditions persist. The ice core is thin and must be stagnant. A small fosse and an ice-contact slope are present where the ice front has recently retreated a short distance. Where ice is surrounded by outwash, pinnacled ice is formed by radiation.

Rocks fall onto the outwash from the glacier, and also roll off small detached knobs of ice, protected by ablation moraine, onto the outwash that surrounds them (Figure 34). Channels up to 6 feet deep, eroded into unfrozen sand, frozen sand, and ice, are common. Swiftly moving streams flow in the channels at the height of the melt season. Kettle holes up to 30 feet in diameter are present. At one place immediately adjacent to the glacier, a layer of frozen sand was tilted up by a minor glacial re-advance, so that it dipped at an angle of 50 degrees toward the glacier. A series of ridges and valleys essentially parallel to the ice front could be traced for scores of feet. The ridges were only a few feet apart and the valleys only a few feet deep. This topography resulted from the thrust of the glacier into frozen outwash sand.

The sand in the kame moraine is very well rounded, and was formed by the mechanical breakup of an eolian facies of the Beacon Sandstone that crops out in the upper part of the Wright Valley [McKelvey and Webb, 1962]. The winter winds, which blow eastward, carry the sand down the valley and up onto the Wright Lower Glacier. The kame moraine was formed during the summer season, when this sand was washed off the glacier by melt-water streams.

Nivation Cirques

Small nivation cirques formed in both bedrock and unconsolidated deposits are found in the coastal areas around McMurdo Sound (Figure 35). The snowbanks incise themselves into bedrock because the melt water derived from them increases frost-shattering, and into unconsolidated deposits because the melt water forms alluvial cones and fans, soli-fluction lobes and sheets, and sand flows [Nichols, 1963c]. Nivation, however, is only a minor process

Fig. 35. A snow slab in a miniature nivation cirque cut in unconsolidated uplifted marine deposits near Marble Point, McMurdo Sound.

in the McMurdo Sound area. Much more geologic work is being done by eolian, fluviatile, marine, and glacial processes, and by mass-wasting not related to nivation.

It is the writer's impression, as a result of both field work and reading, that nivation cirques are much more common in northwest Greenland and perhaps also in Iceland and Spitzbergen [*Lewis*, 1939; *McCabe*, 1939] than in the McMurdo Sound area of Antarctica. If so, less snowfall and lower temperatures in Antarctica may be responsible. These factors would increase the wastage of snow by sublimation and decrease it by melting.

Patterned Ground

Frost-crack polygons are very common and widely distributed in the coastal areas around McMurdo Sound. They are commonly 10–40 feet in diameter and are outlined by intersecting furrows and by trenches with marginal levees. They are found in till, in glaciofluvial, lake, and deltaic sediments, and in eolian and beach deposits. Wedges of ice that pinch out at depth commonly fill the contraction cracks.

Péwé [1959], however, has shown that sand wedges may also fill the cracks. Where these are found there is a scarcity of moisture due to the aridity of the area, and sand blown into the furrows trickles down into the contraction cracks [*Black and Berg*, 1963a, b].

Sand wedges are being formed at the present time in the Wright Valley. Small inverted cones a few inches in diameter have been seen forming in the eolian sand in the furrows. The trickling of the sand down into open contraction cracks is responsible for the formation of cones at the surface.

In the writer's experience, sorted polygons are not common. Their rarity in the McMurdo Sound area is probably due in part to a lack of soil moisture. *Aughenbaugh* found them, however, in the Dufek Massif on both flat and sloping areas. He writes [1961], 'The typical polygon has fines in the elevated center with cobble and boulder rings, and a diameter of 1½ to 3 meters. Polygons become elongated on hillsides, and, at the steepest slopes found, form a series of long parallel trenches.' *Nichols* [1953] reports their presence on the Terra Firma Islands, Marguerite Bay, Antarctic Peninsula, but in only one locality. Stone polygons are found in Bunger Hills [*Shumskiy*, 1957] and excellently developed stone stripes are found in the Snow Hill Island area, Antarctic Peninsula [*Nordenskjöld*, 1911].

Depth to Permafrost

Based on thermocouple data, the maximum depth of thaw in till for the 1958–1959 season at Marble Point, McMurdo Sound, was 40.6 cm (Figure 36). As determined from six test pits the depth of thaw ranged from 42.7 to 67.1 cm with an average of 54.9 cm. During the 1957–1958 season the maximum depth of thaw in till averaged 67.1 cm. A comparison of weather data shows that the 1957–1958

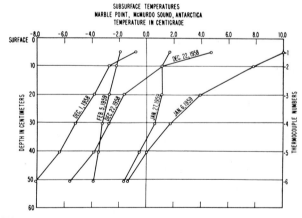

Fig. 36. The depth of thaw in till for the 1958–1959 season at Marble Point, McMurdo Sound, Antarctica.

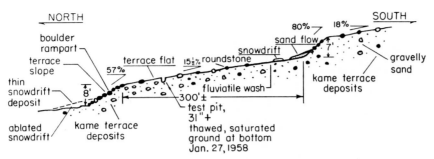

Fig. 37. Transverse cross section of solifluction lobes on the north-facing slope of the eastern shoulder of Hogback Hill, McMurdo Sound, Antarctica.

season was considerably warmer than the 1958–1959 season. Depth of thaw will vary with thickness of snow cover, moisture content and albedo of the ground, changing weather from season to season, and other factors. The depth to permafrost (maximum depth of thaw) in this area is, therefore, greater than 67.1 cm [*Nichols and Ball*, 1964a]. Little is known about the thickness of the permafrost, its temperature, or other characteristics. Geophysical studies are in order.

Solifluction

In the writer's experience, solifluction features are most abundant and best developed on the north-facing slope of the eastern shoulder of Hogback Hill, McMurdo Sound. Here most of the details of the topography are due to solifluction. The solifluction lobes and sheets range in area from several hundred square feet to many acres, the terrace flats commonly have gradients of about 16 per cent, and the terminal clifflets range in height from less than 1 foot to more than 12 feet (Figure 37). The very soft, mobile, water-saturated material found here in the 1957–1958 field season proves that solifluction is a current process. The buried portions of many fragments around McMurdo Sound have a thin, smooth veneer of calcite. Overturned calcite-veneered fragments are common on the solifluction lobes and sheets. Calcite is not found, however, on the newly buried surfaces. This proves that the fragments were only recently overturned and substantiates the conclusion that solifluction is a current process in this area.

In the McMurdo Sound area solifluction occurs only where enough snow accumulates for melt water to be formed. In this dry region, where it never rains and where the normal snow cover commonly

sublimates, the ground can become water-saturated only downslope from glaciers or from the larger snowdrifts. In the vicinity of Hogback Hill and Marble Point the prevailing winds are from the south during the winter months when most of the snowfall occurs. Solifluction, therefore, tends to be better developed on north-facing slopes, as at Hogback Hill, where insolation is greatest and snowdrifts more abundant. At Hogback Hill, moreover, the terminal clifflets of the solifluction lobes and sheets generally face toward the north. Snow accumulates in the lee of these clifflets, and melt water derived from this accumulation increases the mobility of the ground immediately downslope. In this area, therefore, the solifluction process developed a topography that favored its continued existence.

A smoothly graded solifluction slope, which extends from three nivation cirques down to the raised beaches, is found near Marble Point. Scores of small solifluction lobes, many 1–2 feet thick and covering only a few hundred square feet, are located near the cirques. The presence in the cirques of snowdrifts that linger long into the summer has undoubtedly been an important factor in the formation of this solifluction area.

Solifluction deposits are better developed in the coastal areas around McMurdo Sound than in the 'dry valleys.' The greater aridity in the valleys does not favor solifluction.

Weathering

Many of the fragments on the older glacial deposits in the Wright Valley and elsewhere, which are composed of salic coarse-grained igneous and metamorphic rocks, have been weathered into odd shapes. They are pitted, honeycombed, and cavern-

Fig. 38. A pitted cavernous fragment with soft, crumbly, weathered surfaces, Wright Valley, Victoria Land, Antarctica.

ous (Figure 38). They are characterized by soft, flaky, and crumbly surfaces, in sharp contrast to the hard, polished surfaces of the ventifacts. More than 3 feet of rock has been removed from some of the fragments. Commonly more than a quarter of an inch of material can easily be removed by scratching with an ice axe. The older bedrock surfaces have been similarly weathered and eroded.

Cailleux and Calkin [1963] made an interesting study of the orientation of the hollows in the cavernously weathered granite and granitic gneiss boulders in the Victoria Valley, Victoria Land. They found that there was no preferred orientation of weathered hollows in the boulders. As the summer winds in the valley are northeast and the winter winds southwest, they concluded that wind is not the most important factor in the formation of the hollows.

Many fragments on the older deposits in the Wright Valley, especially those composed of coarse-grained salic igneous and metamorphic rocks, have been weathered and eroded down to ground level (Figure 39). Some are more than 6 feet in diameter, and in places more than a score can be found in an area of several thousand square feet.

It has generally been assumed that weathering in polar regions is primarily a physical process. *Kelly and Zumberge* [1961] have made a careful study of a badly weathered fine-grained quartz diorite at Marble Point, McMurdo Sound, Antarc-

tica, which substantiates this assumption. Although the study was undertaken because these workers felt that a strong case for chemical weathering in Antarctica might be demonstrated, chemical and thermal analyses and petrographic studies showed that, with the exception of changes involving the minor constituents, the mineral and chemical composition of the rock as a whole was not changed by the weathering. There was no significant change in combined silica, Al_2O_3, Na_2O, CaO, or K_2O, and no clay minerals were formed. The only appreciable chemical change was the oxidation of the ferrous iron in the pyrrhotite and biotite, which resulted in the formation of limonite. The study showed that the breakup of the quartz diorite was due essentially to physical rather than to chemical changes and that frost action and the crystallization of halite were responsible. It seems likely, therefore, that the weathering and erosion of the fragments found on the older deposits in the Wright Valley resulted primarily from frost action and deflation.

Nichols [1961a], *Calkin and Cailleux* [1962], and others have used degree of cavernous weathering of boulders to date glacial deposits. Discrimination must be used, however, as cavernous fragments may have fallen from cliffs onto glaciers, or may have been picked up and redeposited by thin glacial ice with only minor changes in shape. Indeed, in places in the Wright Valley the writer found it difficult, at first, to determine whether certain

Fig. 39. Fragments weathered and eroded down to ground level owing primarily to frost action and deflation, Wright Valley, Antarctica.

glacial deposits were Loop or Trilogy in age [Nichols, 1961a] because the younger Trilogy ice had picked up and redeposited cavernous boulders from older Loop deposits.

WORK OF RUNNING WATER

Antarctic Peninsula

Alluvial fan. An alluvial fan is found on the north side of Neny Island, Marguerite Bay, Antarctic Peninsula. It is about 200 feet wide where it terminates along the strand line, and its apex is about 110 feet above sea level. It rests on bedrock, talus, and elevated and modern beach deposits. Gullies margined by poorly developed levees are found on it. Surface irregularities suggest that some deposition took place on an irregular snow cover [Nichols, 1937]. The fan owes its existence to a col located above it and between the two principal peaks of Neny Island. Since the bottom of the col slopes northward, the melt water formed in it is funneled downward toward the fan. This fan was the only significant deposit of alluvium seen by the writer. During the winter there is no channeled running water in this part of the Antarctic and during the summer only a very small amount [Nichols, 1953, 1960]; hence channeled water performs an insignificant amount of geologic work and is much less important as a geologic process than ice, waves and shore currents, and talus-forming processes.

McMurdo Sound area. During the 1957–1958 field season two streams at Marble Point, McMurdo Sound, were gaged. In one the peak flow in January was approximately 30 cubic feet per second, in the other 50 cubic feet per second (personal communication, John R. Davis). With this volume of runoff, both here and presumably elsewhere, it is not surprising that landforms resulting from both erosional and depositional activity of running water are common in the McMurdo Sound area. As no rain has ever been reported, these features are all formed by melt water; and many are formed on, adjacent to, or close to ice. The Onyx River in the Wright Valley, 15 or more miles long, is the largest river known to the writer; in places its width, depth, and velocity make it very difficult to cross.

The following features result from the depositional activity of running water.

Marine deltas: Marine deltas are found at the mouth of the unnamed river that reaches McMurdo Sound immediately south of Marble Point [Nichols, 1961c]; at the mouth of Taylor Valley; and at Cape Chocolate [Speden, 1960].

Lacustrine deltas: Lacustrine deltas are common. They are described under 'Ice-Cored Moraines' and 'Lakes.'

Fans: In addition to the large fan described above under 'Interglacial Features,' several other large fans are found on both the south and north sides of the Wright Valley and east of Lake Vanda. The elevated beaches and lacustrine clifflets above Lake Vanda cross the fans on the north side of the lake. *Calkin* [1964a] has studied the fans at the southeast end of Bull Pass and the fan on the north side of the Wright Valley just below Bull Pass. Small fans are ubiquitous.

Kames: A prominent and extensive kame moraine of Trilogy age [Nichols, 1961a] is located in the Wright Valley about a mile west of the Wright Lower Glacier. It is characterized by valleys, ridges, knobs, and a few kettle holes. It has a maximum relief of more than 60 feet and extends across the valley for about a mile. It is very bouldery. In general, less than an inch of material has been removed from the boulders by weathering. Digging shows that it is composed of stratified pebbly and cobbly sand. A kame moraine, described above, which is being formed at the present time, is found adjacent to the Wright Lower Glacier. Excellently formed and preserved kame terraces are located in the Clark Valley, and kame hillocks and ridges are found near Marble Point.

Valley train: A valley train approximately 3 miles long extends westward from the kame moraine a mile west of the Wright Lower Glacier. It is characterized by large kettle holes several hundred yards long, by topography so irregular that recognition is at first difficult, and by large fragments that dot its surface. Dissection by the Onyx River reveals the stratified material of which it is composed. It was deposited on stagnant ice, and large fragments fell onto the outwash from those ice blocks that were not completely buried.

Torrential boulder deposits: Torrential fluviatile bouldery deposits, containing boulders more than 3 feet in diameter, are found in the Wright Valley. The fan at the northwestern end of Lake

Vanda contains boulders up to 3 feet in diameter; the fan 8 miles west of the Wright Lower Glacier contains fragments still larger. Thin bouldery deposits are found at the southern end of Bull Pass and on the south side of the Wright Valley just west of the Meserve Glacier. The melt-water streams seen during the 1959–1961 field seasons were depositing much finer material. *Calkin* [1964a] noted that the older fans near Lake Vida in Victoria Valley are coarser than those being formed now. It is not known whether these coarse deposits were formed: (1) by the periodic drainage of ice-dammed lakes; (2) during a climate warmer than that at present when water was more abundant than now; (3) by larger melt-water streams derived from more extensive and larger glaciers; (4) by melt-water streams formed by volcanic heat; or whether, which seems most unlikely, the 1959–1961 field seasons were unusually cold.

The following features resulting from the erosional activity of running water are present.

Thaw channels in ice: Valleys, meander scars, and cutoffs cut by melt-water streams in the Koettlitz Glacier have been described by *Taylor* [1922]. Sizable melt-water channels are located near the terminus of the Taylor and Wright Lower glaciers. A ravine 15–20 feet deep has been cut in the ice-cored moraine at the eastern end of Wright Valley.

Marginal channels: The most striking feature of the fan that is 8 miles west of the Wright Lower Glacier is the series of channels which do not run up and down the fan but cut across it. The channels were cut by melt-water streams marginal to the Wright Lower Glacier about the time it started to retreat from its most advanced position during Loop glaciation [*Nichols,* 1961a]. *Calkin* [1964a] has made an interesting study of marginal channels cut in both bedrock and moraine, and *Taylor* [1922] has described what he calls 'contour gullies,' which may be marginal melt-water channels.

Fluvial boulder pavements: Fluvial boulder pavements, formed when the fine-grained material in till is removed by streams, are common near Marble Point.

Valleys cut in surficial deposits: A melt-water stream from the Commonwealth Glacier, Taylor Valley, has cut a V-shaped ravine approximately 50 feet deep through the moraine at the mouth of the

Taylor Valley, and a somewhat smaller V-shaped ravine has been cut in glaciofluvial deposits at the southern end of Bull Pass.

Perhaps the most impressive example of fluviatile erosion is found at Cape Chocolate. Here, along the Salmon Stream, a series of six non-paired terraces have been cut as much as 35 feet into till, outwash, and glacio-lacustrine deposits [*Speden,* 1960]. Non-paired terraces are also found along the Hobbs Stream about 1500 feet to the north. Similar terraces are found at the mouth of the Taylor Valley, a short distance south of the terminus of the Blue Glacier, on the north side of New Harbor, and along the Onyx River in the Wright Valley.

It is the impression of the writer, based only on reconnaissance field work, that, among the exogenous forces, glacial ice is responsible for more topography in the McMurdo Sound area than any other process, and that waves and shore currents and wind, for less than any other process. Solifluction and running water are intermediate in importance.

WORK OF WIND

Eolian Deposits

Although in the Antarctic eolian deposits are not of importance, small deposits are found in the McMurdo Sound area. One, located south of Marble Point, is more than half a mile long and, in most places, only a few feet thick. The deposit is found on both gentle and steep slopes, and in the southern part of the area small climbing dunes are found. The deposit was probably formed in early winter, when the snow cover is not extensive but when the winds are strong and the deposits from which the sand was derived are dry. The fact that it is found near the strand line suggests that both the modern and elevated beaches nearby are the principal sources for it.

A smaller eolian deposit, on the south side of Marble Point near its eastern terminus, buries elevated beaches. A mechanical analysis of this deposit showed that it contains 13 per cent of the granule sizes and is, therefore, much coarser than the average eolian deposit [*Twenhofel,* 1932; *Nichols,* 1961c]. The analysis proves that the winds at times are exceptionally strong.

Fig. 40. A ventifact, Wright Valley, Victoria Land, Antarctica.

Eolian sand sheets are found at several places in the Wright Valley. Most of them cover several acres but only thinly veneer the underlying glacial deposits. The sand was derived from the glacio-fluvial deposits widely distributed in the valley.

Eolian sand sheets and dunes are found at the southern end of Bull Pass. Here dunes have dammed up a ravine cut in outwash deposits, and a small perennially frozen pond has been formed.

The largest eolian deposit in the McMurdo Sound area is just east of Lake Vida in the Victoria Valley. It is more than 4 miles long and 1 mile wide, and barchans 50 feet high and 300 feet long are present [*Webb and McKelvey*, 1959; *Calkin*, 1964a].

Ventifacts

Ventifacts are found near Marble Point, in the Taylor and Wright valleys, and elsewhere in the McMurdo Sound area [*Péwé*, 1960b; *Webb and McKelvey*, 1959; *Nichols*, 1961b]. They are unusually well developed and numerous on the older glacial deposits in the Wright Valley [*Nichols*, 1961a] (Figure 40). Commonly more than a foot of rock has been removed from the larger ventifacts. In a 3-foot-square area, 53 ventifacts 1–5 inches long were counted. In many places in the area thousands of shining ventifacts can be seen between the sun and the observer. The larger ventifacts have a hard, shiny, wind-cut, and polished surface on their western sides, and a soft, flaky, crumbly, weathered surface on their eastern sides (Figure 41). During the two summer field seasons (1959–1960, 1960–

1961) the writer spent in the Wright Valley, the winds were not strong enough either to polish or to cut rock. Strong winds moving from the ice plateau eastward down the valley during the winter months were, therefore, responsible for this unusual development of ventifacts (Figure 42). That wind-cutting has taken place as much as 3–4 feet above ground level indicates that the winds were very strong. The ventifacts are found only near the bottom of the valley. It is not known whether this is due to a lack of sand in the upper part of the valley or whether the winds are katabatic and have, therefore, no great vertical extent.

The following factors favored the unusual development of ventifacts in the Wright Valley: (1) The area is devoid of vegetation. (2) The deposits on which the ventifacts are found are old. (3) The snowfall is light. (4) The winds are strong. (5) There is enough sand to do the cutting but not enough to bury the ventifacts.

Wind Direction

Although in the Wright Valley the prevailing winter winds are from the west, at Marble Point they are from the south. This is shown by the following: (1) Ventifacts are cut and polished only on their south sides. (2) The sand shadows which form in the lee of obstacles occur on the north sides. (3)

Fig. 41. A large ventifact, Wright Valley, Antarctica. Hard, shiny, wind-cut surface on the right; soft, flaky, crumbly, weathered surface on the left; wind moved from right to left (field notebook gives scale).

Fig. 42. A ventifact pavement, Wright Valley, Antarctica. The larger fragments have had a foot of rock removed by wind-cutting.

Most of the grains and flakes blown from blocks of marble and other rapidly weathering rocks are on the north sides of the blocks. (4) The largest snowdrifts, when seen early in the spring, are on the north sides of obstacles. (5) The snowdrift-ice slabs are without exception on north-facing slopes [*Nichols*, 1964*a*]. (6) The lee bedding in the snow barchans on the sea ice invariably slopes northward, and the horns of the barchans also point northward. (7) The sastrugi on the sea ice are commonly undercut on the south side. In the Wright Valley the winter winds are topographically controlled, whereas at Marble Point they are not so controlled.

LAKES

Classification

Since all the exogenous forces are active in various parts of Antarctica and since Recent volcanic activity has taken place in the McMurdo Sound area and elsewhere, it is not surprising to find that lake basins have been formed in many different ways. These ways may be divided into the ten following classifications.

I. Lakes on ice. The bay ice in Neny Fjord, Marguerite Bay, Antarctic Peninsula, has been folded by the thrust of the Neny Glacier into a series of open synclinal troughs and anticlinal ridges. These troughs cover hundreds of acres and are roughly parallel to the edge of the glacier. When they were formed the bay ice was several feet thick. The distance from ridge to ridge is fifty or more feet; from crest to trough it is several feet. Ponds more than 900 feet long, 20–30 feet wide,

and several feet deep occupy the synclinal troughs during the summer months before the breakup of the sea ice [*Nichols*, 1960]. Some ponds are connected with the sea water by cracks or thaw holes; those not connected contain only fresh water. Those connected have fresh water only at the surface; apparently the warm, fresh water floats on the heavier sea water. Where the ice shelf has been folded, larger lakes may form.

Ice-cored moraines, as has been indicated, are common in the McMurdo Sound area. They are commonly characterized by knob and kettle topography. Some of the kettles contain superglacial pools, ponds, and lakes. 'Alph Lake' in the ice-cored moraine on the northwest side of the Koettlitz Glacier is the largest of these. When studied by *Taylor* [1922] it was about ¾ mile long and ½ mile wide.

II. Ice-dammed lakes. Ice-dammed lakes are common. Lakes Bonney, Chad, and Fryxell in the Taylor Valley and the lake adjacent to the western terminus of the Wright Lower Glacier in the Wright Valley, all more than 1 mile long, are among the largest. Glacial ice forms the larger ice-dammed lakes, snowdrift ice slabs the smaller. They are commonly dammed not only by ice but also by talus, bedrock, or till [*Taylor*, 1922]. Ice-dammed lakes now drained, which were formed when the glaciers were more extensive, have also been recognized [*Péwé*, 1960*a*]. One of these, located in the Taylor Valley, was 1000 feet deep. Small ice-dammed lakes are common in the depressions between glaciers and valley walls.

III. Glacial rock basin lakes. Lake Vanda in the Wright Valley and Lake Vida in the Victoria Valley are excellent examples of lakes occupying bedrock basins formed by glacial erosion. Both are undrained. Lake Vanda is approximately 4 miles long, averages less than a mile wide, and is more than 217 feet deep. Outlet glaciers that moved from the Antarctic Ice Plateau eastward down the Wright Valley carved out the basin. The Onyx River, a melt-water stream that flows approximately 15 miles up the Wright Valley, originates at the western terminus of the Wright Lower Glacier and is the only river that empties into Lake Vanda. This unusual reversal of drainage results from a great deal of glacial bedrock erosion in the vicinity of Lake Vanda, and from glacial deposition and a smaller amount of glacial bedrock erosion near the terminus of the Wright Lower Glacier [Nichols, 1962]. Lake Vida, also about 4 miles long, has an area of about 8 square miles [Webb and McKelvey, 1959; Calkin, 1964a].

IV. *Moraine-dammed lakes.* Numerous small moraine-dammed lakes are located in the Wright Valley at Marble Point and elsewhere. Two larger examples are found in the Miers and Ward valleys [Gunn and Warren, 1962].

V. *Kettle lakes in outwash.* A valley train is located at the eastern end of the Wright Valley immediately west of the prominent end-moraine on the floor of the valley near the mouth of the Clark Valley. It was deposited on stagnant ice and is, therefore, characterized by numerous kettle holes. Those kettles, which are flooded by the Onyx River during the melt season, contain small ponds; the other kettles are dry.

VI. *Kettles in beaches.* Some of the elevated beaches in the McMurdo Sound area rest on ice. At Marble Point these beaches are thinner than the thickness of the active zone. Melting of the underlying ice, therefore, has taken place and small kettles have been formed [Nichols, 1961b]. Small ponds are found in some of the kettles.

VII. *Beach ridge and swale ponds.* An excellent series of beach ridges and swales has been formed at Marble Point, McMurdo Sound, and Ridley Beach, Cape Adare. Small, narrow, elongated ponds are found in the swales [Ferrar, 1907; Wright and Priestley, 1922; Priestley, 1923].

VIII. *Dune-dammed lakes.* A ravine cut in outwash deposits at the southern end of Bull Pass, Wright Valley, has been dammed by dunes, and a small pond has been formed. In a pitted valley train at the eastern end of the Wright Valley, a meander scar is 15–20 feet high and 300 feet across was cut by the Onyx River. At the foot of the scar drifted snow, covering an area 200 feet long and 50 feet wide, collected. Later, wind-blown sand was deposited on the snow. When the area was visited on 30 December 1959, scores of kettles up to 15 feet long and 3 feet deep had formed in the sand because of the melting of the snow. Many of the kettles contained small pools.

IX. *Lakes of volcanic origin.* A small round lake approximately an eighth of a mile in diameter is located near the southern tip of Hut Point Peninsula, Ross Island, a half mile west of Crater Hill [Debenham, 1923]. It lies in a depression between cinder cones. A small frozen pond in the crater of a cinder cone less than a mile northeast of McMurdo Station has been described by Cailleux [1962].

Many small lakes are found near Cape Royds and Cape Barne, Ross Island [Debenham, 1923]. David and Priestley [1914] thought these lakes occupied rock basins excavated by ice. Debenham thought that they occupied basins between lava flows. He also made the very interesting suggestion that 'Deep Lake' and 'Sunk Lake' near Cape Barne occupy basins formed by faulting of lava flows extruded onto ice [Debenham, 1923].

X. *Relict lakes.* Numerous lakes are found in the Vestfold Hills, Ingrid Christensen Coast. Some are saline and below sea level. Molluscan remains of a species still living on the coast are found around them. The valley in which the lakes occur was originally an arm of the sea, which, subsequently, was isolated by a relative lowering of sea level with respect to land. Still later the sea water was lowered and concentrated by evaporation [McLeod, 1963].

Perennially Frozen Lakes

In the McMurdo Sound area, more ice can form on lakes during the cold season than can be ablated in the warm season. Those lakes which are deeper than the thickness of ice that can be ablated during the summer months, therefore, are perennially frozen.

Among the larger perennially frozen lakes are Lake Vida in the Victoria Valley, Lake Vanda and the lake immediately west of Wright Lower Glacier in the Wright Valley, and Lakes Fryxell and Bonney in the Taylor Valley. There are many smaller perennially frozen lakes.

Corings on Lake Bonney showed 13.8 feet of ice; corings on Lake Vanda indicate that the ice is 11–12 feet thick [*Angino and Armitage*, 1963; *Wilson*, 1964]. Borings on the ice-dammed lake immediately west of the Wright Lower Glacier showed 12.3 feet of ice, and a trench dug in 'Blue Lake,' Ross Island, went through 20 feet of ice [*David and Priestley*, 1914]. A narrow moat of water borders these lakes during the warm season.

Any ponds not perennially frozen are shallow, excessively saline, or fed with melt water above 32°F.

Ice Mounds

The surface of the ice on many small frozen ponds is convex upward. These ice mounds are cut by vertical crevasses which are wide at the top, pinch out to nothing at depth, and have a maximum width and depth at the top of the mound. If the pond is completely frozen, the ice is a biconvex lens. In some instances the crevasses penetrated the whole thickness of the ice, and water filled the lower part of the cracks and froze [*David and Priestley*, 1914; *Taylor*, 1922]. One of these mounds was 40–50 feet in diameter and 1½ feet high; the crevasses were 25–30 feet long, about 15 feet apart, and 6 inches wide at the top [*Cailleux*, 1962]. The expansion resulting from freezing is responsible for the ice mounds and their crevasses, although contraction of ice due to a lowering of temperature may be partly responsible for the crevasses [*Autenboer*, 1962]. Commonly the ice of the mounds is cut by tight cracks, suggesting that it has been subjected to stress.

Lacustrine Deposits

Varved silts. Varved silts containing large ice-rafted boulders are found on the north side of Salmon Stream, Cape Chocolate [*Speden*, 1960]. An excellent section of varved silts dissected by the

Hobbs Stream and capped by glaciofluvial deposits is located less than a mile away at the terminus of the Hobbs Glacier. These sediments probably accumulated in late Koettlitz time in a lake dammed by the Koettlitz Glacier [*Péwé*, 1960*a*]. Laminated lake silt and clay are widespread on the bottom of Taylor Valley [*Péwé*, 1960*a*].

Pyritic sediments. Black pyritic sands and silts occur in saline ponds in the Wright Valley [*Barghoorn and Nichols*, 1961], in the deposits of 'Green Lake,' Cape Royds, Ross Island [*David and Priestley*, 1914], in a small pond in the elevated marine beaches at Marble Point, and elsewhere in the McMurdo Sound area. The upper surface of the sediments at the bottom of these ponds is light brown. Immediately below the surface and extending down, however, the sediments are black. The sediment smells strongly of H_2S. The black color is due to the presence of iron sulfide, probably of the type described as hydrotroilite ($FeS-nH_2O$), an amorphous, hydrous monosulfide of iron [*Twenhofel*, 1950]. The iron sulfide is precipitated by sulfate reduction induced by *Desulfovibrio* in the bottom muds. An energy source for the sulfate-reducing bacteria is available from decaying algae, diatoms, and other microplankton that occur in these waters. The presence of H_2S in Lake Vanda [*Angino and Armitage*, 1963] indicates the existence of pyritic sediments at the bottom of the lake.

Evaporites. Saline ponds and lakes are found in the coastal areas of Antarctica, and chemical pre-

Fig. 43. Algal peat found near Gneiss Point, McMurdo Sound, Antarctica. In places it is 2–3 feet thick and covers a few acres.

Fig. 44. The perennially frozen Lake Vanda, Wright Valley, McMurdo Sound, Antarctica. The elevated beaches, deltas, and lacustrine cliffs extend 185 feet above it. Photograph by U. S. Navy.

cipitates due to evaporation have been formed. Areas veneered with very soluble white salts commonly surround the ponds, and as much as 29 inches of evaporites have been formed by complete desiccation of ponds. Gypsum, calcite, mirabilite, calcium chloride, sodium iodate, and sodium nitrate have been identified, [*Péwé*, 1960a; *Gibson*, 1962; *Nichols*, 1963b].

Peat. Surprisingly large quantities of algal peat are found in the McMurdo Sound area at the bottom of ponds and lakes and in areas once occupied by them (Figure 43) [*David and Priestley*, 1914; *Taylor*, 1922]. It is not a true peat, however, as little decomposition of the algal material has taken place. Near 'Terrace Lake,' Ross Island, it is 2–3 feet thick. None of these accumulations are more than a few acres in extent. It seems likely that the skua gulls, which frequent these coastal lakes, have been partly responsible for the abundance of this material [*Goldman*, 1963]. *Péwé* [1960a] reports that carbon-14 measurements indicate that some of this material is several thousand years old.

Deltas. Deltas associated with both present and former lakes occur in a number of places [*Webb and McKelvey*, 1959; *Péwé*, 1960a; *Speden*, 1960; *Gunn and Warren*, 1962; *Nichols*, 1962]. Four level oval areas about a thousand yards long and half that in width are located immediately east of Lake Bonney, Taylor Valley. They were formed

by the complete filling of four lakes by deltas. *Taylor* [1922] calls them silt lakes.

Lake Vanda

Lake Vanda is one of the most interesting lakes in Antarctica. Elevated beaches, silty offshore lacustrine deposits, deltas, and lacustrine cliffs prove that it was once approximately 185 feet higher (Figure 44) [*Nichols*, 1962]. Although the mean annual temperature of the area around Lake Vanda is probably not far from 0°F, temperatures in excess of 75°F have been reported from the bottom of the lake [*Armitage and House*, 1962; *Wilson and Wellman*, 1962; *Angino and Armitage*, 1963]. This high temperature has been attributed by *Nichols* [1962] to volcanic heating, by *Wilson and Wellman* [1962] to the trapping and storing of solar energy in a nonconvective saline layer at the bottom of the lake, and by *Ragotzkie and Likens* [1964] to solar radiation and conduction from the bottom. The lacustrine cliffs immediately above Lake Vanda, some of which are 14 feet high, could not have been formed in a moat of water only 20 feet wide and a few feet deep such as now exists on the margin of the lake during the summer months. The size and excellent development of the cliffs require for their formation more open water than exists at present. If solar energy alone is responsible for the high temperatures of Lake Vanda, the elevated lacustrine cliffs must have been formed when the climate was warmer than now.

The upper 180 feet of Lake Vanda is essentially potable with less than 1000 ppm of dissolved salts, whereas that part below 200 feet is more than three times as saline as sea water with more than 100,000 ppm of dissolved salts [*Armitage and House*, 1962; *Wilson and Wellman*, 1962; *Angino and Armitage*, 1963].

It is not known for certain how these dissolved salts originated. Six possibilities suggest themselves: (1) The salts may have been originally interbedded in the Beacon group, which crops out in the Wright Valley [*McKelvey and Webb*, 1961]. (2) The salts may be related to the volcanic activity [*Palache et al.*, 1951]. (3) The salts may have been concentrated by the freezing of salt water trapped in some way by the glacier that moved from McMurdo Sound up the Wright Valley [*Nichols*, 1961a] and transported from the ocean up the Wright Valley [*De-*

benham, 1919]. (4) An arm of the sea may have extended from McMurdo Sound up the Wright Valley during interglacial or interstadial time or both. This seems unlikely, however, as the elevated beaches in the McMurdo Sound area, all of which are related to the most recent glaciation, are less than 70 feet above sea level [Nichols, 1961c], and the bedrock threshold at the eastern end of the Wright Valley may be a thousand feet above sea level (Colin Bull, personal communication). (5) The salt may have been transported from McMurdo Sound up the Wright Valley, as finely divided salt spray or salty snow or both, by onshore winds [Jackson, 1905]. (6) The sulfates may have been formed by the interaction of H_2SO_4 resulting from the oxidation of pyrite with minerals containing sodium, calcium, and magnesium.

Using the data of Angino and Armitage [1963], the writer has concluded that this chemical stratification in Lake Vanda was formed as follows [Nichols, 1963d].

It seems certain that evaporation resulting from the aridity of the area was one of the factors responsible for concentrating the salts in the bottom layer of the lake. During the full-bodied stage of Loop glaciation (third oldest glaciation recognized in the eastern end of the Wright Valley by the writer [Nichols, 1961a]), Lake Vanda was saline, salts having been carried onto it from its inception [Nichols, 1962]. During Late Loop time, due to an increase in temperature [Schell, 1961], more melt water began to reach the lake, causing the lake to rise progressively and attain its highest level. Meanwhile, the Wright Lower and Upper glaciers and the local alpine glaciers progressively retreated and decreased in area. Still later, in Late Loop time, evaporation and sublimation from the lake increased, owing to its greater area and perhaps owing to still higher air temperatures. At the same time, progressively less melt water was furnished from the reduced area of the glaciers. Because of the new equilibrium between in-flowing water and evaporation, Lake Vanda began to shrink and to increase in salinity. During Loop–Trilogy (youngest glaciation recognized in the eastern end of the Wright Valley [Nichols, 1961a]) interglacial time, the lake became still smaller and more saline. Finally, during the Trilogy glaciation, because the increased coldness further decreased the quantity

of melt water reaching the lake, it was reduced to a still smaller saline pond, the waters of which are now near the bottom of the present Lake Vanda.

During late Trilogy time, because of a rise in temperature, more and more melt water reached Lake Vanda, which progressively rose as the glaciers progressively retreated. The presence of elevated beaches, deltas, and silty offshore lacustrine deposits, weathered about as much as the Trilogy deposits at the eastern end of the valley, proves that Lake Vanda finally rose 185 feet above its present level and was then more than 400 feet deep.

The melt water flowed into the saline pond with little mixing because: (1) the saline water had a specific gravity of approximately 1.08 [Wilson and Wellman, 1962]; (2) the velocity of the melt water that first reached the saline pond was low because its volume was small; (3) wind-driven turbulence in the lake waters was almost nonexistent, if the lake was perennially frozen; (4) the melt water may initially have flowed out on top of ice and not on top of the saline waters; and (5) the freshwater layer, as it grew deeper, inhibited mixing.

The temperature may have continued to rise still later in late Trilogy and post-Trilogy time, but finally, because the valley was arid and because the amount of melt water reaching the lake continued to decrease as the glaciers progressively retreated and the area of glacial ice supplying melt water progressively diminished, the lake level began to drop and continued until it reached its present position. The salts in the upper, potable part of the lake have accumulated in late Trilogy and post Trilogy time. They were carried into the upper part of the lake by the Onyx River and perhaps by other melt-water streams, and were probably also derived from the lower saline waters by mixing and diffusion. The layer between 140 and 160 feet is more saline than any other layer above 180 feet. This may be due to the mixing of younger fresh melt water with the older saline water, or perhaps to the complexities of Trilogy glaciation.

Wilson [1964] has concluded that the chemical stratification is due essentially to the same mechanism. He does not, however, like the writer, explain the presence of salts above the saline layer as due to a combination of mixing, diffusion, and transportation into the lake by the Onyx River, but rather as resulting solely from diffusion from the

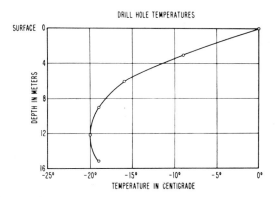

Fig. 45. Curve showing the distribution of temperature in the drill hole at Marble Point, McMurdo Sound, Antarctica.

saline layer. Using data collected by *Wilson and Wellman* [1962], *Wilson* [1964] calculated that the existing concentration profile could be formed in 1200 years. He concluded, therefore, that the arrival of the fresh water which flowed over the saline layer was due to a climatic change 1200 years ago.

A beach at Marble Point, McMurdo Sound, approximately 44 feet above sea level, is about 4600 ± 200 years old as determined by a carbon-14 analysis (L-594, personal communication, W. S. Broecker) [*Nichols*, 1963a]. The highest beaches at Marble Point (approximately 66 feet above sea level) are therefore perhaps 7000 years old. On the basis of their degree of weathering, the beaches roughly correlate with the deposits laid down in the eastern end of the Wright Valley during the Trilogy glaciation, the youngest glaciation recognized in the valley [*Nichols*, 1961a]. During the full-bodied stage of Trilogy glaciation, the Wright Lower Glacier extended approximately five miles farther up the Wright Valley than at present and was about a thousand feet thick at its present terminus.

The greater extent of the Wright Lower Glacier in the Wright Valley during Trilogy time, considered together with the present proximity of the highest elevated beaches and the terminal positions of the glaciers around McMurdo Sound, makes it certain that at many places these glaciers must have advanced out into McMurdo Sound beyond the positions of the highest elevated beaches during the most extensive stage of Trilogy time. The highest beaches around McMurdo Sound were not formed, therefore, until the Trilogy glaciers had retreated considerably from their most advanced positions out in McMurdo Sound. Thus the full-

bodied stage of Trilogy glaciation occurred more than seven thousand years ago. It would seem from this analysis that the fresh water first began to flow out over the saline layer in Lake Vanda not 1200 but several thousand years ago.

It is difficult to reconcile the two points of view. However, if the surface of the saline layer was frozen when the fresh water first flowed out over it, and, more important, if over a period of many years only a small quantity of water reached the lake each summer, all this fresh water might have frozen solid during the succeeding winters. If a thick layer of ice was formed in this way, diffusion from the saline layer would have been greatly reduced or perhaps even prevented as long as the layer of ice existed.

GEOLOGIC EVIDENCE OF LOW TEMPERATURES

The mean annual air temperature at sea level in the McMurdo Sound area, Antarctica, as determined from bedrock, glacier, and air temperatures and from sea-ice thickness, is approximately −2°F [*Nichols and Ball*, 1964b].

A hole was drilled in bedrock close to sea level near Marble Point, McMurdo Sound, early in February 1958. The temperature at a depth of 40 feet was −4°F. As the annual temperature wave is small at this depth, the mean annual air temperature is probably within a few degrees of −4°F (Figure 45).

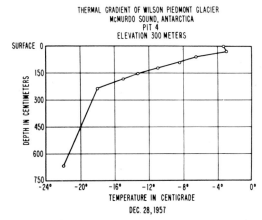

Fig. 46. Thermal gradient near the surface of the Wilson Piedmont Glacier, McMurdo Sound, Antarctica, elevation 1000 feet, 28 December 1957.

During the 1957–1958 field season, a temperature of −7.6°F was found at a depth of 22 feet at the bottom of two holes drilled in the Wilson Piedmont Glacier, at an altitude of approximately 1000 feet and 3 miles inland from its terminus near Marble Point. Since the temperature was decreasing slowly with increasing depth near the bottom of these holes, −7.6°F is not far from the mean annual air temperature for this area. When corrected for altitude, the glacial data give a sea-level mean annual air temperature of approximately −4°F (Figure 46).

The thickness of the sea ice in McMurdo Sound close to Marble Point was measured during the 1958–1959 field season. The average of 318 measurements was 8 feet. Calculation shows (personal communication, Francis Birch) that a mean annual temperature of approximately +1.4°F is necessary to form this thickness of ice.

The mean annual air temperature at Ross Island, McMurdo Sound, for the 5-year interval 1902, 1903, 1908–1909, 1911, and 1912 was +0.7°F; the mean annual temperature for the 7-year interval 1957–1963 was +0.1°F (personal communication, William S. Weyant).

Acknowledgments. Joseph H. Hartshorn and Charles E. Stearns read parts of the manuscript and made numerous valuable suggestions. The Antarctic Program of the National Science Foundation supported the work. The Commanding Officer, U. S. Navy Construction Battalion Reconnaissance Unit, and the U. S. Weather Bureau provided some of the data.

REFERENCES

Adie, R. J., The geology of Antarctica, *Antarctic Research, Geophysical Monograph 7*, pp. 26–39, American Geophysical Union, Washington, D. C., 1962.

Adie, R. J., Sea-level changes in the Scotia Arc and Graham Land, Polar Record, *11*(75), 252–253, 1963.

Adie, R. J., Sea-level changes in the Scotia Arc and Graham Land, in *Antarctic Geology*, edited by R. J. Adie, pp. 27–32, North-Holland Publishing Co., Amsterdam, 1964.

Andersson, J. G., On the geology of Graham Land, *Bull. Geol. Inst. Univ. Upsala, 7* (1904–1905), 19–71, 1906.

Angino, E. E., and K. B. Armitage, A geochemical study of Lakes Bonney and Vanda, Victoria Land, Antarctica, *J. Geol., 71*(1) 89–95, 1963.

Angino, E. E., M. D. Turner, and E. J. Zeller, Reconnaissance geology of the Mt. Nussbaum Area, Taylor Dry Valley, Victoria Land, Antarctica, *Bull. Geol. Soc. Am., 71* (12, pt. 2), 1816, 1960.

Arctowski, H., The bathymetrical conditions of the antarctic regions, in *Through the First Antarctic Night* by F. A. Cook, pp. 436–443, Doubleday & McClure Co., New York 1900*a*.

Arctowski, H., Sur l'ancienne extension des glaciers dans la région des terres découvertes par l'expédition antarctique Belge, *Compt. Rend. Acad. Sci., Paris, 131*, 479–481, 1900*b*.

Arctowski, H., Géologie, les glaciers, glaciers actuels et vestiges de leur ancienne extension, Expédition Antarctique Belge, Voyage du S. Y. Belgica, 1897–1899, *Rapports Scientifiques*, pp. 59–64, 1908.

Armitage, K. B., and H. B. House, A limnological reconnaissance in the area of McMurdo Sound, Antarctica, *Limnology and Oceanography, 7*, 36–41, 1962.

Aughenbaugh, N. B., Preliminary report on the geology of the Dufek Massif, *IGY Glaciol. Rept., 4*, 155–193, 1961.

Autenboer, T. Van, Ice mounds and melt phenomena in the Sør-Rondane, Antarctica, *J. Glaciol., 4*(33), 349–354, 1962.

Autenboer, T. Van, Geomorphology and glacial geology of the Sør-Rondane Mountains, Dronning Maud Land, *Polar Record, 11*(75), 752, 1963.

Ball, D. G., and R. L. Nichols, Saline lakes and drill-hole brines, McMurdo Sound, Antarctica, *Bull. Geol. Soc. Am., 71*, 1703–1708, 1960.

Barghoorn, E. S., and R. L. Nichols, Sulfate-reducing bacteria and pyritic sediments in Antarctica, *Science, 134* (3473), 190, 1961.

Bellair, P., Recent data on the geology of Iles Crozet, *Polar Record, 11*(75), 747, 1963.

Bellair, P., and J. Nougier, The volcanism of Presqu'île Rallier du Baty (Iles de Kergulen), *Polar Record, 11*(75), 747–748, 1963.

Bentley, C. R., Glacial and subglacial geography of Antarctica, in *Antarctic Research, Geophysical Monograph 7*, pp. 11–25, American Geophysical Union, Washington, D.C., 1962.

Bentley, C. R., and N. A. Ostenso, Glacial and subglacial topography of West Antarctica, *J. Glaciol., 3*(29), 882–911, 1961.

Bentley, C. R., A. P. Crary, N. A. Ostenso, and E. C. Thiel, Structure of West Antarctica—The results of U. S. IGY oversnow traverses reveal the nature of a large portion of ice-covered Antarctica, *Science, 131*(3394), 131–136, 1960.

Black, R. F., and T. E. Berg, Hydrothermal regimen of patterned ground, Victoria Land, Antarctica, extract of *Publication No. 61 of the I. A. S. N. Commission of Snow and Ice*, pp. 121–127, 1963*a*.

Black, R. F., and T. E. Berg, Dating with patterned ground, Victoria Land, Antarctica, *Trans. Am. Geophys. Union, 44*, 48, 1963*b*.

Bongrain, M., *Description des côtes et banquises, Instructions Nautiques, Deuxième Expédition Antarctique Française, 1908–1910*, 59 pp., Masson et Cie, Paris, 1914.

Bryan, K., Cryopedology—the study of frozen ground and intensive frost-action with suggestions on nomenclature, *Am. J. Sci., 244*, 622–642, 1946.

Bugayev, V. A., and E. I. Tolstikov, Principal features of the relief of East Antarctica, *Inform. Bull. Soviet Antarctic Expedition, 16,* 11–15, 1960.

Bull, C., Gravity observations in the Wright Valley area, Victoria Land, Antarctica, *New Zealand J. Geol. Geophys., 3*(4), 543–552, 1960.

Bull, C., B. C. McKelvey, and P. N. Webb, Quaternary glaciations in southern Victoria Land, Antarctica, *J. Glaciol., 4*(31), 63–78, 1962.

Bull, C., B. C. McKelvey, and P. N. Webb, Glacial benches in South Victoria Land, *J. Glaciol., 5*(37), 131–134, 1964.

Cailleux, A., Ice mounds on frozen lakes in McMurdo Sound, Antarctica, *J. Glaciol., 4*(31), 131–133, 1962.

Cailleux, A., and P. Calkin, Orientation of hollows in cavernously weathered boulders in Antarctica, *Biul. Peryglacjalny, 12,* 147–150, 1963.

Calkin, P. E., Geomorphology and glacial geology of the Victoria Valley system, southern Victoria Land, Antarctica, *Ohio State Univ. Inst. Polar Studies Rept. 10,* 66 pp., 1964a.

Calkin, P. E., Glacial geology of the Mount Gran area, southern Victoria Land, Antarctica, *Bull. Geol. Soc. Am., 75*(10), 1031–1036, 1964b.

Calkin, P., and A. Cailleux, A quantitative study of cavernous weathering (taffonis) and its application to glacial chronology in Victoria Valley, Antarctica, *Z. Geomorphol., N. F., 6,* 317–324, 1962.

Cameron, R. L., and R. P. Goldthwait, The US-IGY contribution to antarctic glaciology, Symposium on Antarctic Glaciology, Helinski, *Intern. Assoc. Sci. Hydrol. Publ., 55,* 7–13, 1961.

Craddock, C., and H. A. Hubbard, Preliminary geologic report on an United States expedition to Bellingshousen Sea, Antarctica, *Science, 133,* 886–887, 1961.

Crary, A. P., Oversnow traverses from IGY Little America Station, *Natl. Acad. Sci. IGY Bull., 27,* 11–15, 1959.

Crary, A. P., E. S. Robinson, H. F. Bennett, and W. W. Boyd, Jr., Glaciological regimen of the Ross Ice Shelf, *J. Geophys. Res., 67*(7), 2791–2807, 1962.

David, T. W. E., Antarctica and some of its problems, *Geograph. J., 43*(6), 605–630, 1914.

David, T. W. E., and R. E. Priestley, Geological observations in Antarctica by the British Antarctic Expedition, 1907–1909, in *The Heart of the Antarctic,* by E. H. Shackleton, vol. 2, pp. 276–331, J. B. Lippincott and Co., Philadelphia, 1909a.

David, T. W. E., and R. E. Priestley, Notes in regard to Mount Erebus, in *The Heart of the Antarctic,* by E. H. Shackleton, vol. 2, pp. 324–327, J. B. Lippincott and Co., Philadelphia, 1909b.

David, T. W. E., and R. E. Priestley, *Reports on the Scientific Investigations, Glaciology, Physiography, Stratigraphy, and Tectonic Geology of South Victoria Land, British Antarctic Expedition, 1907–1909,* vol. 1, 319 pp., Heinemann, London, 1914.

Debenham, F., A new mode of transportation by ice: the raised marine muds of South Victoria Land (Antarctica), *Quart. J. Geol. Soc. London, 75,* 51–76, 1919.

Debenham, F., Recent and local deposits of McMurdo Sound region, Natural History Reports, British Antarctic (Terra Nova) Expedition, 1910, *Geol. 1* (3), 63–100, 1921a.

Debenham, F., The sandstone etc. of the McMurdo Sound, Terra Nova Bay, and Beardmore Glacier regions, Natural History Reports, British Antarctic (Terra Nova) Expedition, 1910, *Geol., 1*(4a), 103–119, 1921-b.

Debenham, F., *The Physiography of the Ross Archipelago, British Antarctic (Terra Nova) Expedition, 1910–1913,* 39 pp., Harrison and Sons, Ltd., London, 1923.

Doumani, G. A., Geological observations in West Antarctica during recent oversnow traverses, *Natl. Acad. Sci. IGY Bull., 41,* 6–10, 1960.

Doumani, G. A., Volcanoes of the Executive Committee Range, Marie Byrd Land, *Polar Record, 11*(75), 787, 1963.

Doumani, G. A., and E. G. Ehlers, Petrography of rocks from mountains in Marie Byrd Land, West Antarctica, *Bull. Geol. Soc. Am., 73,* part 2, 877–882, 1962.

Fairbridge, R. W., The geology of the Antarctic, in *The Antarctic Today,* by F. A. Simpson, pp. 56–101, New Zealand Antarctic Society and A. H. and A. W. Reed, Wellington, N.Z., 1952.

Ferrar, H. T., Report on the field-geology of the region explored during the 'Discovery' Antarctic Expedition, 1901–1904, National Antarctic Expedition, 1901–1904, Natural History Reports, *Geol., 1,* 100 pp., 1907.

Fleming, W. L. S., Relic glacial forms on the western seaboard of Graham Land, *Geograph. J., 96,* 93–100, 1940.

Ford, A. B., Review of antarctic geology, *Natl. Acad. Sci. IG Bull., 82,* 1–19, 1964.

Fuchs, V. E., Exploration in British Antarctica, *Geograph. J., 117*(4), 399–421, 1951.

Gibson, G. W., Geological investigations in southern Victoria Land, Antarctica, part 8, evaporite salts in the Victoria Valley region, *New Zealand J. Geol. Geophys., 5,* 361–374, 1962.

Goldich, S. S., A. O. Nier, and A. L. Washburn, A^{40}/K^{40} age of gneiss from McMurdo Sound, Antarctica, *Trans. Am. Geophys. Union, 39*(5), 956–958, 1958.

Goldman, C. R., Primary productivity studies on Antarctic ponds and lakes, *Polar Record, 11*(73), 503, 1963.

Goodell, H. G., W. M. McKnight, J. K. Osmond, and A. S. Govsline, Sedimentology of antarctic bottom sediments taken during Deep Freeze Four, a progress report, Dept. of Geology, Florida State Univ. (unpublished), 52 pp., 1961.

Gould, L. M., Structure of the Queen Maud Mountains, Antarctica, *Bull. Geol. Soc. Am., 46,* 973–984, 1935.

Gould, L. M., The glacial geology of the Pacific Antarctic, *Proc. 6th Pacific Sci. Congr., 2,* 723–740, 1939.

Gould, L. M., Glaciers of Antarctica, *Proc. Am. Phil. Soc., 82,* 835–877, 1940.

Grindley, G. W., The geology of the Queen Alexandra Range, Beardmore Glacier, Ross Dependency, Antarctica; with notes on the correlation of Gondwana sequences, *New Zealand J. Geol. Geophys., 6*(3), 307–347, 1963.

Guilcher, A., Continental shelf and slope (continental margin), in *The Sea,* edited by M. N. Hill, vol. III, pp. 281–311, John Wiley & Sons, New York, London, 1963.

Gunn, B. M., Geological structure and stratigraphic correlation in Antarctica, *New Zealand J. Geol. Geophys., 6*(3), 423–443, 1963.

Gunn, B. M., and R. I. Walcott, The geology of the Mt. Markham region, Ross Dependency, Antarctica, *New Zealand J. Geol. Geophys., 5*(3), 407–426, 1962.

Gunn, B. M., and G. Warren, Geology of Victoria Land between the Mawson and Mulock glaciers, Antarctica, *New Zealand Geol. Survey Bull., 71*(n.s.), 157 pp., 1962.

Hamilton, W., and P. T. Hayes, Geology of Taylor Glacier—Taylor Dry Valley region, South Victoria Land, Antarctica, *Geol. Survey Profess. Paper, 400-B,* pp. 376–378, 1960.

Harrington, H. J., Nomenclature of rock units in the Ross Sea region, Antarctica, *Nature, 182*(4631), 290, 1958.

Haskell, T. R., J. P. Kennett, and W. M. Prebble, Basement and sedimentary geology of the Darwin Glacier area, *Polar Record, 11*(75), 765–766, 1963.

Holtedahl, O., On the geology and physiography of some Antarctic and sub-Antarctic islands, with notes on the character and origin of fjords and strandflats of some northern lands, Oslo, Jacob Dybwad, *Scientific Results of the Norwegian Antarctic Expeditions, 1927-1928,* vol. 1, 172 pp., 1935.

Hoskins, A. K., Block terraces in the Neny Fjord area, Marguerite Bay, Graham Land, *Brit. Antarctic Survey Bull., 1,* 45–49, 1963.

Hough, J. L., Pleistocene lithology of antarctic ocean-bottom sediments, *J. Geol., 58,* 254–260, 1950.

Howard, A. D., Geomorphology of Antarctica: a summation, *Bull. Geol. Soc. Am., 61,* 1472–1473, 1950.

Jackson, D. D., The normal distribution of chlorine in the natural waters of New York and New England, *U. S. Geological Survey Water-Supply and Irrigation Paper 144,* 31 pp., 1905.

Joerg, W. L. G., The cartographical results of Ellsworth's trans-Antarctic flight of 1935, *Geograph. Rev., 27,* 430–444, 1937.

Kelly, W. C., and J. H. Zumberge, Weathering of a quartz diorite at Marble Point, McMurdo Sound, Antarctica, *J. Geol., 69*(4), 433–446, 1961.

King, L. C., Pre-glacial geomorphology of Alexander Island, *Polar Record, 11*(75), 750, 1963.

Krinsley, D., and T. Takahashi, Applications of electron microscopy to geology, *Trans. New York Acad. Sci., 2* (25), 3–22, 1962a.

Krinsley, D., and T. Takahashi, Surface textures of sand grains—an application of electron microscopy: glaciation, *Science, 138,* 1262–1264, 1962b.

Laird, M. G., Geomorphology and stratigraphy of the Nimrod Glacier–Beaumont Bay region, southern Victoria Land, Antarctica, *New Zealand J. Geol. Geophys., 6*(3), 465–484, 1963.

Lebedev, V., *Antarctica,* Foreign Languages Publishing House, Moscow, 259 pp., 1959.

Lepley, L. K., Submarine geomorphology of eastern Ross and Sulzberger Bay, Antarctica, M.S. thesis, Texas A&M University, 1964.

Lewis, W. V., Snow-patch erosion in Iceland, *Geograph. J., 94*(2), 153–161, 1939.

Lisitzin, A. P., Bottom sediments of the eastern Antarctic and the southern Indian Ocean, *Deep-Sea Research, 7*(2), 89–99, 1960.

Lisitzin, A. P., Bottom sediments of the Antarctic, in *Antarctic Research, Geophysical Monograph 7,* pp. 81–88, American Geophysical Union, Washington, D. C., 1962.

Lisitzin, A. P., and A. V. Zhivago, Marine geological work of the Soviet Antarctic Expedition, 1955–1957, *Deep-Sea Research, 6*(2), 77–87, 1960.

Lister, H., and G. Pratt, Geophysical investigations of the Commonwealth Trans-Antarctic Expedition, *Geograph. J., 125*(3-4), 343–356, 1959.

Loewe, F., Precipitation and evaporation in the Antarctic, in *Meteorology of the Antarctic,* edited by M. P. van Rooy, pp. 71–90, Weather Bureau, Department of Transport, Pretoria, South Africa, 1957.

Løken, O., Evidences of higher sea levels in the Windmill Islands, *Ohio State Univ. Res. Found., Rept. 825-1,* pt. III, pp. 28–33, 1959.

Long, W. E., Geologic investigation of the Central Horlick Mountains, Antarctica, *Natl. Acad. Sci. IGY Bull., 37,* pp. 10–15, 1960.

Long, William E., Preliminary report of the geology of the Central Range of the Horlick Mountains, Antarctica, Reports of Antarctica Geological Observations 1956–1960, *IGY Glaciological Rept. 4,* pp. 123–142, 1961.

Long, W. E., Sedimentary rocks of the Buckeye Range, Horlick Mountains, Antarctica, *Science, 136*(3513), 319–321, 1962.

Mawson, D., The unveiling of Antarctica, *Australian and New Zealand Association for the Advancement of Science, Rept. of the 22nd Meeting,* 1–37, 1935.

McCabe, L. H., Nivation and corrie erosion in West Spitsbergen, *Geograph. J., 94*(6), 447–465, 1939.

McCraw, J. D., Volcanic detritus in Taylor Valley, Victoria Land, Antarctica, *New Zealand J. Geol. Geophys., 5*(5), 740–745, 1962.

McGregor, V. R., Structural or glacial benches?, *J. Glaciol., 4*(34), 494–495, 1963.

McKelvey, B. C., and P. N. Webb, Geological reconnaissance in Victoria Land, Antarctica, *Nature, 189,* 545–547, 1961.

McKelvey, B. C., and P. N. Webb, Geological investigations in southern Victoria Land, Antarctica—Geology of Wright Valley, *New Zealand J. Geol. Geophys., 5*(1), 143–162, 1962.

McLeod, I. R., The saline lakes of the Vestfold Hills, Princess Elizabeth Land, *Polar Record, 11*(75), 750, 1963.

Meguro, H., *et al.,* Quaternary marine sediments and their geological dates with reference to the geomorphology of Kronprins Olav Kyst, *Polar Record, 11*(75), 254–255, 1963.

Meinardus, W., Klimakunde der Antarktis, in *Handbuch der Klimatologie,* edited by W. Köppen and R. Geiger, Band IV, Teil U, Ul-U133, Gebrüder Borntraeger, Berlin, 1938.

Mellor, M., Mass balance studies in Antarctica, *J. Glaciol.*, *3*, 522–533, 1959.

Murray, J., Additional notes on eruptions, in *The Heart of the Antarctic*, edited by E. H. Shackleton, vol. 2, pp. 327–331, J. B. Lippincott Co., Philadelphia, 1909.

Needham, H. D., Ice-rafted rocks from the Atlantic Ocean off the coast of the Cape of Good Hope, *Deep-Sea Research, 9*, 475–486, 1962.

Nichols, R. L., New mechanism for the formation of kettleholes and eskers, *Proc. Geol. Soc. Am. (1936)*, pp. 403–404, 1937.

Nichols, R. L., Geomorphology of Marguerite Bay, Palmer Peninsula, Antarctica, *Office of Naval Research Tech. Rept. No. 12,* Ronne Antarctic Expedition, 151 pp., 1953.

Nichols, R. L., Geomorphology of Marguerite Bay area, Palmer Peninsula, Antarctica, *Bull. Geol. Soc. Am., 71,* 1421–1450, 1960.

Nichols, R. L., Multiple glaciation in the Wright Valley, McMurdo Sound, Antarctica (abstract), p. 317 in *Tenth Pacific Science Congress of the Pacific Science Association, 487* pp., 1961a.

Nichols, R. L., Characteristics of beaches formed in polar climates, *Am. J. Sci., 259,* 694–708, 1961b.

Nichols, R. L., Coastal geomorphology, McMurdo Sound, Antarctica, preliminary report, *Reports of Antarctica Geological Observations 1956–1960, IGY Glaciol. Rept. 4,* 51–101, 1961c.

Nichols, R. L., Geology of Lake Vanda, Wright Valley, South Victoria Land, Antarctica, *Antarctic Research, Geophysical Monograph 7,* pp. 47–52, American Geophysical Union, Washington, D. C., 1962.

Nichols, R. L., Geomorphology of the McMurdo Sound coast, South Victoria Land, Antarctica, Abstracts for 1962, *Geological Society of America, Special Paper No. 73,* p. 211, 1963a.

Nichols, R. L., Geologic features demonstrating aridity of McMurdo Sound area, Antarctica, *Am. J. Sci., 261,* 20–31, 1963b.

Nichols, R. L., Miniature nivation cirques near Marble Point, McMurdo Sound, Antarctica, *J. Glaciol., 4*(34), 477–479, 1963c.

Nichols, R. L., Origin of chemical stratification in Lake Vanda, South Victoria Land, *Polar Record, 11*(75), 751–752, 1963d.

Nichols, R. L., Snowdrift-ice slabs and historic antarctic climatic warming, *J. Glaciol., 5*(39), 345–351, 1964a.

Nichols, R. L., Present status of antarctic glacial geology, in *Antarctic Geology,* edited by R. J. Adie, pp. 123–137, North-Holland Publishing Co., Amsterdam, 1964b.

Nichols, R. L., Antarctic interglacial features, *J. Glaciol., 5*(40), 433–449, 1965.

Nichols, R. L., and D. G. Ball, Soil temperatures, Marble Point, McMurdo Sound, Antarctica, *J. Glaciol., 5*(39), 357–359, 1964a.

Nichols, R. L., and D. G. Ball, Four-fold check on mean annual temperature, McMurdo Sound, Antarctica, *J. Glaciol., 5*(39), 353–355, 1964b.

Nordenskjöld, O., *Die Schwedische Südpolar-Expedition und ihre geographische Tätigkeit, Wissenschaftliche Ergeb-* *nisse der Schwedischen Südpolar-Expedition, 1901–1903,* 232 pp., Lithographisches Institut des Generalstabs, Stockholm, 1911.

Nordenskjöld, O., Antarktis, in *Handbuch der Regionalen Geologie,* edited by G. Steinmann and O. Wilckens, Heidelberg, 29 pp., 1913.

Odell, N. E., Antarctic glaciers and glaciology, in *The Antarctic Today,* edited by F. A. Simpson, pp. 25–55, A. H. and A. W. Reed in conjunction with the New Zealand Antarctic Society, Wellington, N. Z., 1952.

Palache, C., H. Berman, and C. Frondel, *The System of Mineralogy of James Dwight Dana and Edward Salisbury Dana,* 7th ed., vol. 2, 1124 pp., John Wiley & Sons, New York, 1951.

Peltier, L. C., The geographic cycle in periglacial regions as it is related to climatic geomorphology, *Assoc. Am. Geographers Annals, 40,* 214–236, 1950.

Péwé, T. L., Sand-wedge polygons (tesselations) in the McMurdo Sound region, Antarctica—A progress report, *Am. J. Sci., 257,* 545–552, 1959.

Péwé, T. L., Multiple glaciation in the McMurdo Sound region, Antarctica—A progress report, *J. Geol., 68,* 498–514, 1960a.

Péwé, T. L., Glacial history of the McMurdo Sound region, Antarctica, *International Geological Congress, XXI Session, Norden. Part IV, Chronology and Climatology of the Quaternary,* pp. 71–80, 1960b.

Priestley, R. E., Physiography (Robertson Bay and Terra Nova Bay regions), *British Antarctic (Terra Nova) Expedition, 1910–1913,* 87 pp., Harrison and Sons, Ltd., London, 1923.

Priestley, R. E., and T. W. E. David, Geological notes of the British Antarctic Expedition, 1907–1909, *Compt. Rend., congr. géol. intern., XI:E Session, Stockholm, 1910,* pp. 767–811, 1912.

Racovitza, E., General results of the Belgian Antarctic Expedition: Appendix No. 1, in *Through the First Antarctic Night,* edited by Frederick A. Cook, pp. 409–424, Doubleday & McClure Co., New York, 1900.

Ragotzkie, R. A., and G. E. Likens, The heat balance of two antarctic lakes, *Limnology and Oceanography, 9*(3), 412–425, 1964.

Ricker, J. F., Outline of the geology between the Mawson and Priestley glaciers, Victoria Land, *Polar Record, 11*(75), 759–760, 1963.

Rivard, N. R., and T. L. Péwé, Origin and distribution of mirabilite, McMurdo Sound region, Antarctica, *Geol. Soc. Am. Special Paper No. 68,* p. 119, 1962.

Roos, S. E., The submarine topography of the Ross Sea and adjacent waters, *Geograph. Rev., 27,* 574–583, 1937.

Schell, I. I., Recent evidence about the nature of climate changes and its implications, *Ann. N. Y. Acad. Sci., 95* (article 1), 251–270, 1961.

Shepard, F. P., *Submarine Geology,* 348 pp., Harper & Brothers, New York, 1948.

Shepard, F. P., Thirty-five thousand years of sea level, in *Essays in Marine Geology in Honor of K. O. Emery,* edited by T. Clements, pp. 1–10, Univ. of Southern California Press, Los Angeles, 1963.

Shumskiy, P. A., Glaciological and geomorphological reconnaissance in the Antarctic in 1956, *J. Glaciol., 3*(21), 54–61, 1957.

Skinner, D. N. B., A summary of the geology of the region between the Byrd and Starshot glaciers, South Victoria Land, *Polar Record, 11*(75), 761, 1963.

Smith, W. C., The volcanic rocks of the Ross Archipelago, British Antarctic Terra Nova Expedition, 1910, *Geol., 2*(1), 107 pp., 1954.

Speden, I. G., Post-glacial terraces near Cape Chocolate, McMurdo Sound, Antarctica, *New Zealand J. Geol. Geophys., 3*(2), 203–217, 1960.

Speden, I. G., Fossiliferous Quaternary marine deposits in the McMurdo Sound region, Antarctica, *New Zealand J. Geol. Geophys., 5*(5), 746–777, 1962.

Stephenson, A., Graham Land and the problem of Stefansson Strait, *Geog. J., 96,* 167–180, 1940.

Stephenson, P. J., Some geological observations on Heard Island, *Polar Record, 11*(75), 748, 1963.

Stetson, H. C., and J. E. Upson, Bottom deposits of the Ross Sea, *J. Sediment. Petrol., 7,* 55–66, 1937.

Taylor, G., *The Physiography of the McMurdo Sound and Granite Harbour Region, British Antarctic (Terra Nova) Expedition, 1910–1913,* 246 pp., Harrison and Sons, Ltd., London, 1922.

Taylor, G., *Antarctic Adventure and Research,* 245 pp., D. Appleton and Co., New York, 1930.

Tedrow, J. C. F., F. C. Ugolini, and H. Janetschek, An antarctic saline lake, *New Zealand J. Sci., 6*(1), 150–156, 1963.

Thiel, E., Antarctica, one continent or two? *Polar Record, 10*(67), 335–348, 1961.

Thiel, E. C., The amount of ice on planet Earth, *Antarctic Research, Geophysical Monograph 7,* pp. 172–175, American Geophysical Union, Washington, D. C., 1962.

Thiel, E., *et al.,* Oversnow traverse programs, Byrd and Ellsworth Stations, Antarctica, 1957–1958: Seismology, gravity, and magnetism, *IGY Glaciological Report 2,* 1959.

Treves, S. B., The geology of Cape Evans and Cape Royds, Ross Island, Antarctica, *Antarctic Research, Geophysical Monograph 7,* pp. 40–46, American Geophysical Union, Washington, D. C., 1962.

Twenhofel, W. H., *Treatise on Sedimentation,* 926 pp., The Williams & Wilkins Co., Baltimore, 1932.

Twenhofel, W. H., *Principles of Sedimentation,* 2nd ed., 673 pp., McGraw-Hill Book Co., Inc., New York, 1950.

Visher, S. S., *Climatic Atlas of the United States,* 403 pp., Harvard University Press, Cambridge, Massachusetts, 1954.

Warner, L. A., Structure and petrography of the southern Edsel Ford ranges, Antarctica, *Proc. Am. Phil. Soc., 89*(1), 78–122, 1945.

Webb, P. N., and B. C. McKelvey, Geological investigations in South Victoria Land, Antarctica, *New Zealand J. Geol. Geophys., 2*(1), 120–136, 1959.

Wilson, A. T., Evidence from chemical diffusion of a climatic change in the McMurdo Dry Valleys 1200 years ago, *Nature, 201*(4915), 176–177, 1964.

Wilson, A. T., and H. W. Wellman, Lake Vanda: an antarctic lake, *Nature, 196*(4860), 1171–1173, 1962.

Wood, B. L., The geology of Cape Hallett-Tucker Glacier district, *Polar Record, 11*(75), 761–762, 1963.

Woollard, G. P., Crustal structure in Antarctica, *Antarctic Research, Geophysical Monograph 7,* pp. 53–73, American Geophysical Union, Washington, D. C., 1962.

Wright, C. S., *Physiography of the Beardmore Glacier Region, British (Terra Nova) Antarctic Expedition, 1910–1913,* 25 pp., Harrison and Sons, Ltd., London, 1923.

Wright, C. S., and R. E. Priestley, *Glaciology, British Antarctic (Terra Nova) Expedition, 1910–1913,* 581 pp., Harrison and Sons, Ltd., London, 1922.

Zeller, E. J., E. E. Angino, and M. D. Turner, Basal sedimentary section at Windy Gully, Taylor Glacier, Victoria Land, Antarctica, *Bull. Geol. Soc. Am., 72,* 781–786, 1961.

Zhivago, A. V., Outlines of southern ocean geomorphology, *Antarctic Research, Geophysical Monograph 7,* pp. 74–80, American Geophysical Union, Washington, D. C., 1962.

THE ANTARCTIC CLIMATE

WILLIAM S. WEYANT

Environmental Science Services Administration, Washington, D. C.

Abstract. The general climatological characteristics of Antarctica result from its high latitude and high altitude and from the land-sea distribution of the southern hemisphere. The continent may be divided into three broad climatic zones: the interior plateau, the slopes, and the coastal region. The high central plateau, the coldest area of the earth, is characterized by low temperatures, very light snowfall, and generally light winds. On the surrounding slopes, cloudiness and snowfall are greater and strong winds with blizzards more frequent. On the coast, precipitation and cloudiness are still greater, temperatures are higher, and winds are generally strong, particularly near the foot of steep slopes. Soil areas are found along the coast as rocky beaches, snow-free only in summer, and in terrain-shielded areas called antarctic oases, such as the dry valleys of the McMurdo Sound region and the Bunger Hills area of East Antarctica. Because of a different radiation balance, and especially because of the greatly different albedo (reflectivity) of snow in comparison with exposed soil, the soil areas have a local climatology different from their snow-covered environs, being generally warmer and drier, with less cloudiness and precipitation. A few soil-temperature measurements indicate that the depth of permafrost ranges from a few centimeters to over 2 meters (at Mirnyy), with the maximum depth of thaw in late January.

INTRODUCTION

The climate of Antarctica is more rigorous and severe than that of any land area on the entire planet. Much the coldest region of the Earth, the vast interior is completely devoid of any indigenous life. Even along the coast, with the exception of some rudimentary land plants in the relatively small snow-free areas, the only living things are those nourished by the surrounding sea.

Areas of exposed soil probably comprise no more than 5 per cent of the total area of Antarctica, the major portion of the continent being covered by an ice sheet ranging up to 3 km in thickness. The soil areas, both those exposed only in summer and those that are snow-free throughout the year, create, to some extent, their own climates. The general climate of the continent as a whole, however, provides the background upon which are impressed the modifications created by the differing characteristics of snow and soil. The following discussion can, thus, be divided conveniently into two parts: first, a description of the general climate of the continent without special emphasis on the soil areas; second, a discussion of the modifications introduced by the presence of a surface of exposed soil and the resulting climatology of such soil areas.

THE GENERAL CLIMATE OF THE ANTARCTIC CONTINENT

Astronomical and Geographical Considerations

Before detailing the meteorological factors that, considered together, constitute the climate of Antarctica, it is necessary to examine the basic causes for the severity of the antarctic environment. The primary climatological control on each of the Earth's polar areas is exerted through the geometry of the Sun–Earth relationship. In both polar regions the tilt of the Earth's axis to the ecliptic plane results in long summer days and long winter nights, the most important factor in the seasonal variation in climate. Although the Sun is below the horizon for six months at the geographic south pole, the long twilight reduces the dark period to about five months. Owing to refraction by the atmosphere, the Sun may sometimes be visible while still actually below the horizon (Novaya Zemlya phenomenon).

Because of the low, average angle of incidence of the direct solar radiation at higher latitudes, the amount of solar energy received annually by a unit horizontal area of the Earth's surface decreases with increasing latitude to reach a minimum at the geographic poles (Figure 1). At all latitudes,

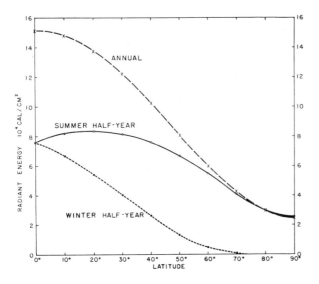

Fig. 1. Direct solar radiation reaching the Earth's surface annually and seasonally as a function of latitude (for atmospheric transmission coefficient 0.6).

owing to the refractive effect of the air, this amount is slightly increased. The eccentricity of the Earth's orbit around the Sun introduces another variation, one which affects the northern and southern hemispheres differently. At the present time, perihelion occurs during early January, when in the southern hemisphere the Sun's rays are most direct. As a result the southern hemisphere receives a little more solar energy during the austral midsummer period than the northern hemisphere receives in its corresponding midsummer. Over the south pole near its summer solstice (about 21 December) the top of the atmosphere receives about 7 per cent more radiation than the atmosphere over the north pole at its summer solstice (about 21 June) and more solar energy on a horizontal surface during a 24-hour period than anywhere else on Earth. All of these astronomical considerations, except for the season of perihelion and aphelion, are the same for the north and south polar regions. To explain the differences in climate between the two areas, it is

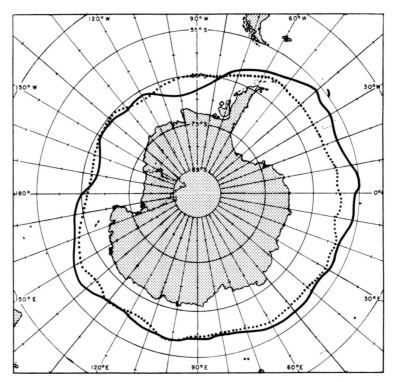

Fig. 2. Pack-ice boundaries from Nimbus I satellite views, 28 August to 22 September 1964; boundaries from (*solid line*) advanced Vidicon Camera System (AVCS) pictures, total area of ice 19.8 × 10⁶ km²; and (*dotted line*) high-resolution infrared radiometer (HRIR) pictures, total area of ice 16.8 × 10⁶ km².

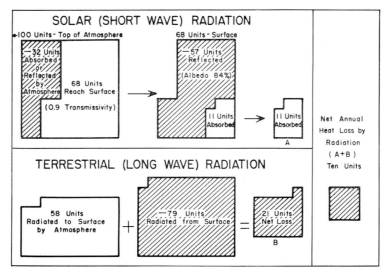

Fig. 3. Typical annual radiation at surface—central antarctic plateau site.

necessary to examine the geographic features of the Arctic and Antarctic.

The primary reason for the climatic differences between the antarctic and arctic regions lies in the distribution of land and sea in the high latitudes of the southern and northern hemispheres. In the north, the arctic basin is an ocean area almost completely surrounded by the land masses of the large northern hemisphere continents. The Arctic Ocean surrounding the north pole, even though largely covered by floating ice, is an ever-present source of heat that helps mitigate the harsh arctic climate. In the southern hemisphere, on the other hand, practically all of the zone from latitude 40°S to the antarctic circle is covered by the 'Southern Ocean,' the largest unbroken expanse of sea in the world. In contrast to the Arctic, the area within the antarctic circle is almost completely filled by the antarctic ice and land mass, the highest mass of any continent. Antarctica, although based on an actual land mass much lower and of lesser areal extent than the present continent [Bentley, 1964], has been transformed by the accumulation of snow over thousands of years to a continent with an area of nearly 14 million km² [Giovinetto, 1964], and with an average height of more than 2 km. In winter, freezing of the sea surface around Antarctica effectively more than doubles the size of the continent [Ostapoff, 1965]. An analysis of photographs taken from the Nimbus I polar-orbiting satellite in late August and September 1964 indicates that the

area of the ice pack surrounding Antarctica at this time is from 17 to 20 million km² (Figure 2).

The difference in mean height of the two polar regions would of itself result in temperatures being higher in the Arctic than in Antarctica, since the average atmospheric temperature fall with height is about 6°C per kilometer. In addition, the source of heat embodied in the open ocean waters is far removed from the central antarctic plateau, particularly at the time of maximum extent of sea ice, when the nearest open water may be nearly 3000 km from parts of central Antarctica (Figure 2).

Although blizzards are a phenomenon of both polar regions, the steep slopes from the central antarctic plateau to the coastal periphery give rise to frequent storm winds and blizzards along and at the base of these slopes. The abundance of loose snow over nearly all the antarctic continent results in the development of blowing-snow or blizzard conditions whenever the surface winds exceed about 10 meters per second.

Radiation Budget and Temperature Regime

The source of all the Earth's energy, except for negligible amounts of geothermal and nuclear energy, is the Sun. Since the Sun is a high-temperature (about 6000°K) source of radiation, its energy lies in the shorter wavelengths of the electromagnetic spectrum, from the ultraviolet through the visible to the near infrared. To maintain an annual balance, the solar radiation absorbed by the Earth during the course of a year is again lost by radiation to space from the Earth; this terrestrial radiation occurs at a relatively low temperature and is in the infrared portion of the spectrum.

The Earth considered in its entirety must achieve an annual radiation balance if its mean temperature is to remain substantially the same from year to year. There are, nevertheless, various areas of the Earth that are regions of radiational excess or deficit as a result of the unequal amounts of radiation they receive and of their differing surface absorptive characteristics. Since the antarctic continent is a region where, during the course of a year, the outgoing terrestrial radiation exceeds the absorbed solar radiation, it is one of the Earth's major heat sinks. Typical values of the various components of the annual surface radiation budget for a point on the central antarctic plateau are shown in Figure 3. For the south pole, one unit on the diagram is approximately equal to 1330 cal cm^{-2} yr^{-1}.

The net radiative loss of heat from the surface

of the antarctic continent results in a strong cooling of the surface and the lowest layers of the atmosphere, and gives rise to the temperature inversions characteristicly found in Antarctica. At the south pole, surface temperatures as much as 30°C below the temperature at a 1-km height have been observed, and the increase of temperature from the surface up to several hundred meters in the atmosphere is a phenomenon observed on the plateau almost all the year around, and in other parts of Antarctica during most of the year.

On a net annual basis heat is lost to space from the surface and overlying atmosphere of Antarctica. Since the temperature of Antarctica remains substantially the same from year to year, this lost heat must be replaced by heat from other sources. The upper layers of snow are not the source of this heat; studies of the temperatures of the upper few meters of snow show an annual cycle decreasing in amplitude from the surface down to a depth of about 10 meters, where the amplitude becomes nearly zero [*Hanson and Rubin*, 1962]. This 10-

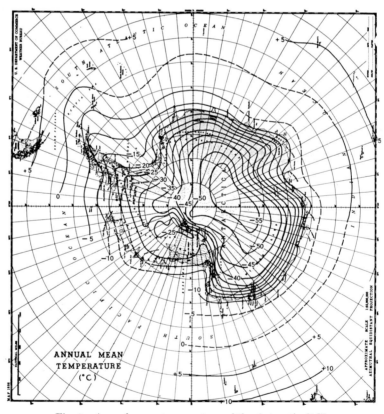

Fig. 4.   Annual mean temperature of the Antarctic (°C).

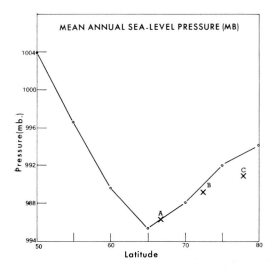

Fig. 5. Mean annual sea-level pressure, 50° to 80° south latitude (based on *Koopmann* [1953]): (*A*) mean pressure, Mirnyy (66°33′S) and Wilkes 66°15′S); (*B*) mean pressure, Hallett (72°18′S); and (*C*) mean pressure, Ellsworth (77°43′S) and McMurdo (77°51′S).

meter snow temperature is a good approximation to the mean annual temperature at snowfield locations, a fact that has made it possible to obtain much information on mean annual temperatures from areas traversed but not permanently occupied.

The heat required to achieve an annual balance over Antarctica must thus be transported from lower latitudes through atmospheric motions, either as sensible heat or as latent heat released through condensation of atmospheric water vapor. An investigation by *Rubin and Weyant* [1963] indicates that the annual heat lost to space through radiational processes is of the order of 10^{22} calories, of which about 90 per cent is replaced by sensible heat transport and 10 per cent by net latent heat transport. Of the sensible heat transport, about 20 per cent is through horizontal eddies and 80 per cent through mean meridional cellular circulation.

Owing to its polar latitude, high altitude, and remoteness from oceanic reserves of heat, the Antarctic is the coldest region of the Earth. A large area of the central plateau has a mean annual temperature below −50°C (−58°F). At the south pole, the lowest temperature thus far recorded, −80.7°C (−113.3°F), occurred in July 1965. The world's record low temperature is held by the Soviet station Vostok (78°27′S, 106°52′E), where a tem-

perature of −88.3°C (−126.9°F) was recorded on 24 August 1960. Mean annual temperatures for the antarctic continent are shown in Figure 4. During the course of a year, temperatures at antarctic stations fall rapidly from the summer maxima to near minimum levels in autumn, but then level off and frequently show several small amplitude maxima and minima during the midwinter period, usually falling again to an absolute minimum in late winter near the time of the first sunrise. This 'kernlose' temperature effect has been observed at both interior and coastal antarctic stations [*Wexler*, 1958].

Storm Tracks, Pressure, and Wind

Over the waters of the southern Atlantic, Pacific, and Indian oceans surrounding Antarctica, great atmospheric cyclones circle the continent in endless procession from west to east, bringing about the meridional exchange of tropospheric air that replenishes the heat lost by radiation from the Antarctic. The energy of these storms is provided by the interaction between the cold polar air and the warmer and moister maritime air of lower latitudes; the great contrast between these two air masses makes this oceanic area one of the stormiest in the world.

A graph of mean annual sea-level pressure for the zone from latitude 50°S to 80°S shows the latitude of minimum pressure to be near 65°S (Figure 5). The strong westerly surface winds, which predominate north of the 65th parallel, are remarkably constant; the latitude belts of the strong westerlies were termed the 'furious fifties' and 'roaring forties' by the old-time sailing-vessel captains. South of 65°S and over the coastal area of Antarctica, winds from a southeasterly direction are predominant.

Over the antarctic continent itself, the use of sea-level pressure as a guide to circulation is meaningless, owing to the great height of most of the continent. Antarctica acts meteorologically, however, much like a cold, stationary anticyclone, largely blocking the passage of low-pressure systems and associated with an outflow of cold air around its periphery. Thus the oceanic cyclones move from west to east in curved paths off the antarctic coast, but rarely move into the high central plateau of Antarctica and only occasionally cross the somewhat lower region of Byrd Land and West Antarctica. These traveling storms are important in the climatology of the slopes and coast of the continent; they account for most of the snowfall and are an important factor in producing the strong winds observed in these areas.

Over most of the antarctic continent, the wind at the surface and in the lower atmospheric layers is not primarily controlled by the pressure distribution. In these lower layers of cold air below the temperature inversion, the slope of the snow and ice surface gives rise to downslope (katabatic) winds, which generally determine the prevailing wind direction at antarctic stations. The direction of these katabatic winds is determined by the direction of the terrain contour gradient and the leftward deflective force due to the Earth's rotation (Coriolis force); such a wind blowing along a surface sloping downward toward the north would thus have both a southerly and an easterly component. The strength of the katabatic effect is proportional to the slope

of the surface, and such winds are particularly strong over and at the immediate foot of the steep slopes from the high interior to the low-lying coastal region of Antarctica, giving rise to the storm winds and frequent blizzards observed at many slope and coastal stations. The isobaric pattern may either reinforce or weaken these katabatic winds, but the net result is an outflow of air from the Antarctic in the lower atmopheric levels. This mass outflow is balanced by an inflow at higher atmospheric levels, and the resulting downward vertical motion, as noted earlier, is an important mechanism for replacing heat lost by radiation.

The katabatic effect results in relatively constant wind direction even where the slope of the surface is small, as it is in most of interior Antarctica, and the constancy of the wind field produces well-defined sastrugi (wavelike patterns on the snow surface). Observations of sastrugi orientation from aerial photographs and by surface traverse parties

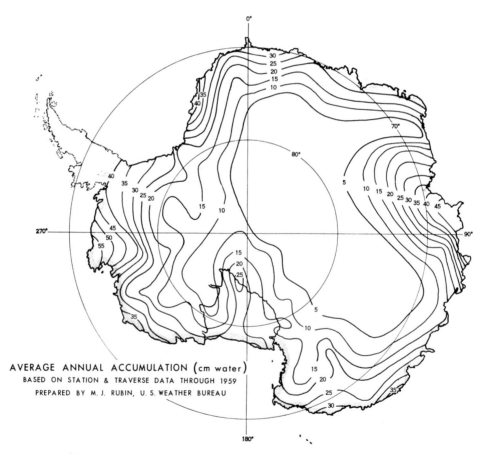

Fig. 6. Accumulation map of Antarctica (after *Rubin* [1953]).

TABLE 1. Vertical Distribution of Atmospheric Water Vapor Transport into Antarctica

Atmospheric Layer (mb)	Per Cent of Total Transport		
	March–August	September–February	Annual
Surface–775	19	−15*	9
775–600	45	51	47
600–400	25	37	29
400–250	4	8	5
250–150	3	7	4
Above 150	4	12	6

* This negative value results from strong net mass outflow, which more than overbalances the relative dryness of southerly winds as compared with northerly winds.

have greatly extended our knowledge of prevailing wind directions in areas where no long periods of wind observations exist.

Water Mass Budget of Antarctica

The antarctic continent is covered by the largest mass of ice on Earth and contains a small but significant fraction of the Earth's entire water mass. The oceans of the world contain about 127×10^{19} kg of water [Rubin and Weyant, 1965], while the antarctic icecap stores about 2.14×10^{19} kg; conversion of the antarctic ice to water (without isostatic adjustment) would produce a rise in sea level of nearly 60 meters [Thiel, 1962]. Observation in Antarctica has been carried on for too few years to permit any reliable determination of a long-period trend of growth or shrinkage of the ice mass, although both extension and retreat of specific glaciers can be inferred from local evidence. Assuming an annual ice-mass balance, the hydrologic cycle in Antarctica consists of the addition to the mass through snowfall over the continent, and the removal of the net mass thus accumulated through oceanic and other melting, calving of icebergs, and ablation of snow to the ocean, all of which takes place in the coastal region. The atmosphere acts as a transport medium in replenishing the ice mass lost around the continental coast, with an annual average net accumulation of 14.5 cm (water equivalent) over the antarctic continent [Rubin, 1962]. The geographic distribution of annual accumulation is shown on the map prepared by Rubin [1962] and reproduced here as Figure 6.

The source of nearly all the atmospheric water vapor precipitated over Antarctica is the open-water area of the oceans of the southern hemisphere. An assessment of the favored areas for and seasonal variation of the atmospheric water vapor transport into Antarctica, by use of a technique similar to that employed by Rubin and Weyant [1963] for heat transport, indicates that about two-thirds of the inflow occurs in the 140° sector between longitude 80°E and 140°W, on the Pacific and Indian Ocean side of the continent. These computations indicate further that about 72 per cent of the inflow occurs during the six-month period from March through August, the winter half-year. Approximately 90 per cent of the total net inflow of water vapor occurs in the troposphere, from the surface up to 250 mb, as shown in Table 1. Since water vapor distributions at the higher levels must, in the absence of direct observations, be assumed, the 10 per cent of the total transport indicated for the topmost two layers may be an overestimate of the stratospheric transport.

Climatological Zones of Antarctica

The antarctic continent, exclusive of the mountainous Antarctic Peninsula, which is essentially a southward extension of the Andes chain, may conveniently be divided into three broad climatological zones: (1) the interior antarctic plateau, (2) the antarctic slopes, and (3) the antarctic coast. The high interior plateau, comprising nearly all of East Antarctica, is a region of less cloudiness, and consequently more sunshine, than the rest of the continent, with light winds, little annual precipitation, comparatively little snowdrift, and extremely low temperature. Plateau stations have a great range of extreme and mean monthly temperatures; temperature extremes at Vostok range from −21°C to −88°C, and at the south pole from −15°C to −81°C. Mean monthly temperatures range 38°C at Vostok and 32°C at the south pole from the coldest month (August) to the warmest month (January). Mean monthly wind speeds are generally in the 10- to 15-knot range at the south pole, and somewhat less at Vostok. Annual precipitation, which annual accumulation (Figure 6) approximates well, is 5 cm (water equivalent) or less over a large portion of the high plateau; the climate may thus be characterized as arid. On the subplateau of

West Antarctica, at an altitude of about 1 to 2 km, the slope of the surface is greater than on the high plateau, and temperatures are higher, winds stronger, and blowing snow and blizzards much more frequent. At Byrd Station (80°S, 120°W), extreme temperatures range from $-1°C$ to $-63°C$, wind speed ranges from 15 to over 20 knots (monthly means), and blizzards occur more often than at any other interior antarctic station [*Morris and Peters,* 1960]. This region comes under the direct influence of the circumpolar cyclones more often than does the high plateau; precipitation at Byrd Station is about 15 cm annually. Surface temperature inversions are very pronounced over the entire plateau area throughout the year.

The climate of the antarctic slopes, although it varies with height, latitude, and the steepness of the slope, is generally severe, with strong katabatic winds, often reinforced by cyclonic activity, and frequent severe blizzards. Cloudiness, precipitation, and temperatures are intermediate between those of the plateau and those along the immediate coast, with strong ascendants of both precipitation and temperature as one moves downward along steep slopes.

In coastal Antarctica, the climate is affected by latitude, nearness to the foot of steep slopes, and the nature of the underlying surface. In general, coastal areas are warmer and have more cloudiness and precipitation than the slopes or the plateau, and are strongly influenced by cyclonic activity. Much of the antarctic coast consists of ice, in the form of glacier tongues or the fronts of ice shelves. Stations situated on permanent ice, such as Little America V on the Ross Ice Shelf and Ellsworth Station on the Filchner Ice Shelf, have generally lighter winds than stations near the foot of steep slopes, where the strong katabatic effect is felt a few kilometers out beyond the slope base. Some of the coast of Antarctica, however, consists of areas where, during the summer season, the snow melts off and the soil is exposed. Penguin rookeries are found on rock and pebble beaches, which are fairly numerous. There are a few areas, such as the dry valleys near McMurdo Sound and the antarctic oases, that, owing to a combination of meteorological and topographic factors, remain nearly or completely free of snow throughout the year.

LOCAL CLIMATOLOGY OF ANTARCTIC SOIL AREAS

Types of Exposed Soil Areas

A dominating feature of the geography of Antarctica is the complete predominance of ice and snow cover on the continent. Only a small percentage of the continental area is composed of soil or rock exposed to the atmosphere. Much of the exposed rock is on the sides of steep mountain ranges or isolated peaks (nunataks) in the interior that are high enough to rise above the surrounding ice sheet, or along the steep slopes of coastal mountains. Other exposed ground is found in narrow strips or beaches along the immediate coast and in the areas known as oases, such as Bunger Hills near Mirnyy in East Antarctica and the dry-valley regions near McMurdo Sound. The local climate of such soil areas is markedly different from that of snow-covered sites at corresponding latitudes, as the soil areas are considerably warmer than their snow-covered environs and, in the case of oases, are characterized by dryness of the air and low precipitation.

Another feature of the antarctic landscape is the almost total lack of vegetation in the exposed areas. Except for a few flowering plants in the extreme northern portion of the Antarctic Peninsula [*Astapenko,* 1960], the many species of plants that have been found in Antarctica consist entirely of mosses, algae, and lichens. Thus, since vegetative cover as a type of underlying surface is not found in the Antarctic, the organic constituents of soil resulting from botanical activity are relatively unimportant. Many of the pebbled beach areas serve as penguin rookeries, and here penguin carcasses and guano may be locally an important soil constituent.

In the antarctic oasis areas, most of the soil is glacial moraine with scattered erratic boulders throughout. The moraine material is largely composed of sand, gravel, and larger fragments, and is characterized by a poverty of finer constituents [*Avsyuk, Markov, and Shumskii,* 1956]. Much of the exposed bedrock shows evidence of glacial polishing and scratching. Since no foreign boulders are evident, the boulders that occur here are apparently of local origin. There is no universally accepted explanation for the formation and existence of the oasis and dry-valley areas, but there is some evidence that geothermal heat or volcanism was of importance in their formation.

Soil-Atmosphere Heat Interchanges

In discussing earlier the thermal regime of the upper layers of snow in interior Antarctica, using a south pole study [Hanson and Rubin, 1962] as an example, it was noted that the annual temperature variation of the atmosphere near the surface produces an annual temperature wave in the snow, a wave whose amplitude decreases with depth until at 10 to 12 meters below the surface it becomes nearly zero. This upper 10 meters of snow might be characterized as the 'active layer,' and the active layer of the soil is that layer in which the daily and yearly variations in soil temperature occur [Chudnovskii, 1948]. The problem of heat transfer and the thermal regime in the soil is complicated by changes in the state of the water present and in the inhomogeneities of the soil, with corresponding variations in its heat-conduction properties.

Since the annual mean temperature of the entire antarctic continent is below freezing (Figure 4), the large-scale features of vertical temperature distribution below the surface in exposed soil areas can be deduced. There is a thick layer of soil and bedrock at temperatures permanently below the freezing point. The lower boundary of this layer, the level at which the temperature again rises above with which we are not greatly concerned here, is the freezing point, owing to the conduction of geothermal heat upward from greater depths in the Earth's crust. Above the top of the permafrost layer, the soil undergoes alternate thawing and freezing; the thickness of this thawing layer in the exposed soil areas of Antarctica varies from a few centimeters to a few meters. The depth below the surface of the permafrost is a function of the mean annual surface temperature, the amplitude of the annual temperature wave at the soil surface, and the heat transmission characteristics of the upper soil layers.

The major differences between the thermal regimes of snow-free and snow-covered areas at similar latitudes stem from differences in the surface radiation budget, and in particular from the differences in albedo of snow and soil. Since the clean snow surface typical of most of Antarctica

has an average albedo of over 80 per cent, less than one-fifth of the incident solar radiation on the surface is converted to heat and absorbed. Since exposed soil has an albedo of, at most, about 20 per cent, more than four times as much solar radiation is generally retained in soil areas and serves to heat the near-surface atmosphere and soil layers. Temperatures in summer in the soil areas can, in extreme cases, rise far above the freezing point. The summer temperatures of the rock surface at the Soviet station Oazis have been reported as high as 15° to 25°C, whereas near Mirnyy a temperature of 30°C has been observed in January [Avsyuk, Markov, and Shumskii, 1956].

Complete data on the surface meteorological and radiation balance for antarctic exposed areas, coupled with measurements of the subsurface temperature profile in the soil and its changes with time, are not available, but observations of surface meteorological conditions, various components of the radiation balance, and partial profiles of subsoil temperatures for some of these areas are available, and some of them are discussed in the following sections.

Hallett Station—An Antarctic Beach Area

Hallett Station, operated jointly by New Zealand and the United States, is located at 72°19'S, 170°18'E, on part of what had been a large Adélie penguin rookery. The soil, which is snow-free only in summer, consists of sand, pebbles, and rock, together with penguin carcasses and guano. Some soil-temperature measurements, taken with resistance thermometers placed at 10 and 50 cm below the ground surface, have been obtained at Hallett [Benes, 1960].

In December and January of both of the summer seasons 1958–1959 and 1959–1960, mean monthly temperatures at −10 cm were above 0°C, but the −50-cm temperature never reached the freezing point, although it closely approached it in early January. The depth of permafrost at Hallett, then, is apparently close to 50 cm below the surface, at least in the specific area of the subsoil-temperature observations. The date of thaw at −10 cm, that is the date on which the temperature first went above 0°C and remained above freezing for a long period, was 5 December in 1958 and 13 December in 1959.

A maximum temperature of 10°C was measured at −10 cm on 17 December 1958. No measurements of the air temperature at the immediate soil surface were taken, although presumably such temperatures would have been somewhat higher than the −10-cm temperatures and would have followed their fluctuations closely. The meteorological 'surface' air temperatures were actually measured about 10 meters distant from the soil-temperature instruments, at a height about 2 meters above the surface in a radiation-shielded shelter. These temperatures did not average above freezing during any month of the two summer periods, which suggests the existence in summer of a strong temperature gradient in the lower 2 meters of the atmosphere.

The Dry Valleys near McMurdo Sound

The part of South Victoria Land that lies to the west of McMurdo Sound is dominated by the Royal Society Range, which rises to over three thousand meters. In the area within about 15 to 75 km of the sea, the terrain is characterized by generally east-west–oriented alternate ridges and valleys, and the land of this region may be the largest ice-free area on the antarctic continent [*Péwé*, 1961]. Many of the snow-free valleys, called dry valleys, contain saline lakes, and, although summer-season scientific studies have been made in a few of these valleys, the studies were not primarily meteorological in nature. Lake Bonney, in the Taylor Valley, has been the site of investigations by summer parties, as has Lake Vanda in the Wright Valley, which parallels the Taylor Valley and lies about 25 km north of it.

At the United States station McMurdo, at the southeast extremity of McMurdo Sound, the annual

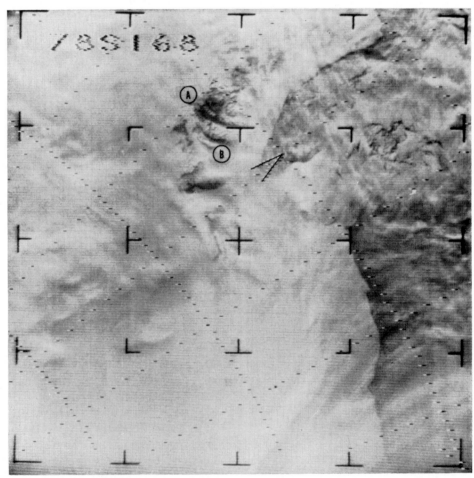

Fig. 7. Nimbus I AVCS photograph of McMurdo Sound area (NASA photo). Dark areas in upper center (*A* and *B*) are dry-valley areas.

mean temperature is −17.7°C, and the relative humidity 57 per cent. Average cloudiness is 61 per cent, and precipitation is about 15 cm (water equivalent) per year. The climate of the west side of McMurdo Sound appears to be somewhat different from that at McMurdo Station: summer temperatures are higher, the air is drier, cloudiness and precipitation less [Péwé, 1961]. No winter observations have been made in the dry valleys.

Most of the area of the Taylor and Wright valleys is snow-free in summer, although the larger lakes along the valley bottoms remain ice-covered throughout the year. It is not certain whether a large portion of the ground surface remains bare in winter. The two valleys can be seen quite clearly in a Nimbus I satellite photo (Figure 7), taken on 16 September 1964. In this photo the tip of the northward-pointing arrow is at the northern edge of McMurdo Sound; to the right of this arrow are Mounts Erebus and Terror. The two elongated, nearly parallel dark areas to the left of the arrow are the Wright (the northernmost) and Taylor dry valleys. The dark area farther south is the region of exposed ground and numerous smaller valleys lying along the northwest side of the Ross Ice Shelf and its confluence with the Koettlitz Glacier.

Although correct interpretation of satellite photographs is not certain, the darkness of the dry valleys in the photo appears not to be entirely the result of a shadowing of the low Sun by the adjoining ridges, but to be due in part to the presence of exposed ground, even on this late-winter date. In spite of winter temperatures, which must be far below freezing, it is quite possible for the dry-valley areas to remain at least partly snow-free during that season. The valley winds are very probably downslope, and the downward motion induced by the surrounding terrain would result in the air being very dry as it blows along the valley floors, permitting considerable sublimation into the air of any snow present. The surrounding high ridges also tend to reduce both low cloudiness and precipitation, so that the amount of snow falling in the dry-valley areas might be considerably less than that falling at the permanent station on the other side of McMurdo Sound. If strong winds also sweep the valleys in winter, then wind ablation would also be an important factor in snow removal. Such questions may be resolved in the future by the establishment of a wintering-over outpost in one of the dry-valley areas.

When, in an investigation of Lake Bonney *Shirtcliffe and Benseman* [1964] calculated the amount of incident solar radiation that in theory would be necessary to account for the temperature distribution in the lake on the assumption that it is a 'solar pond,' they arrived at a value of 80,000 cal cm^{-2} yr^{-1}. Such a large, although quite reasonable, amount of solar radiation incident on a low-albedo surface, such as the soil area surrounding the lake, would produce very high temperatures at the soil surface. A study of Lake Vanda in the Wright Valley [*Nichols*, 1962] indicates that ground temperatures in this area occasionally reach 70°F (21°C) and that temperatures of over 10°C must be quite common at the soil surface in summer.

Colin Bull, in a study of the climatology of the dry-valley areas prepared for a later volume of this *Antarctic Research Series* (personal communication), reports a December temperature of 12.3°C recorded under standard conditions at Lake Vashka, and a mean monthly temperature above freezing for December 1959. The mean temperature for January 1959 was also above freezing at Lake Vanda, and a minimum-temperature thermometer left near Lake Vida during the 1960 winter showed a minimum of −62°C, well below the lowest temperature occurring at the Navy station at McMurdo Sound. In the generally east-west–oriented Taylor and Wright dry valleys, winds generally blow along the longitudinal axis of the valleys, with westerly winds associated with humidities of less than 50 per cent, and easterlies with humidities averaging nearly 70 per cent. Bull estimates the annual net radiation as a gain of about 29,000 ly per yr.

Oazis Station and Mirnyy

The Bunger Hills area is an ice-free region of about 775 km²; it contains three large and 20 smaller lakes and is situated in East Antarctica at about 66°S, 101°E. The Soviet antarctic expeditions have their main base Mirnyy nearby at Mabus Point (66°33′S, 93°E) and during 1957 and 1958 manned Oazis Station, a small station in the central Bunger Hills at 66°16′S, 100°45′E. Both Mirnyy and Oazis Station are near sea level. At Mirnyy there is exposed ground during the summer season, and at Oazis the rock and soil surface is only occasionally snow-covered [*Rubin*, 1965].

At Mirnyy, near the antarctic circle, temperatures show a diurnal variation. Afternoon soil-surface temperatures average above freezing during the two midsummer months, and during five months they rise at times above freezing. In December a soil-surface temperature of 12.5°C has been observed. The surface-air (2 meter) temperature averages 1.4°C lower than the soil-surface temperature over the course of a year, and is considerably lower on mid-summer afternoons. The upper soil layers begin to thaw in early November at Mirnyy, and deepest thawing is noted at the end of January, with a depth of the permafrost a little over 2 meters below the surface [*Grigor'ev*, 1959].

At Oazis Station, the summer air temperatures average 4°–5°C higher than that over the neighboring ice [*Dolgushin*, 1958]. The temperature at the ground surface reaches 35°C, and a local circulation develops over the oasis region in summer, with thick cumulus clouds developing during the day and dissipating toward evening [*Rusin*, 1958]. The air is dry, with the mean annual relative humidity only 60 per cent, and on some summer days humidities as low as 10–15 per cent have been observed. The daily net gain of heat through radiational processes has been measured as 300 calories during a period in January. Owing to the dryness of the exposed soil and rock surfaces, nearly all this heat is used in heating the soil and the air immediately above it, which explains the relatively high soil and air temperatures and the strong convection in the lower atmosphere.

CONCLUSION

The general climate of the antarctic continent is characterized by extreme cold, scanty precipitation, frequent strong winds and blizzards along the slopes, and decreasing cloudiness as one goes away from the coast. The continent is covered by a thick ice shield, with only a very small part of its total area comprised of exposed soil. The soil areas are found as rocky beaches along the immediate coast and in the unique snow-free enclaves aptly termed antarctic oases. The soil areas have a local climate sharply different from neighboring snow-covered

regions, primarily because of the much lower albedo of exposed soil and rock as compared with snow and ice. The greater heat absorption by the soil in summer results in relatively high temperatures and even convective cloud formation; protection by surrounding high elevations leads to a dryness of the air in oasis areas, a reduction of low cloudiness, and less snowfall than elsewhere at similar latitudes.

The interested reader is referred to *Van Rooy* [1957] for a discussion of the climate of subantarctic islands, and to *Astapenko* [1960] for a more detailed discussion of antarctic atmospheric processes from a primarily synoptic point of view.

Acknowledgment. For the preparation of some of the material included in this review of antarctic climatology, the author wishes to express his thanks to the staff of the Polar Meteorology Branch, Atmospheric Analysis Laboratory, which is supported by the Office of Antarctic Programs, National Science Foundation.

REFERENCES

Astapenko, P. D., Atmospheric processes in the high latitudes of the southern hemisphere, *Section II of IGY Program (Met.) No. 3,* Publishing House of the Academy of Sciences of the USSR, Moscow, 1960.

Avsyuk, G. A., K. K. Markov, and P. A. Shumskii, Geographical observations in an antarctic "oasis," *Izvestiya Vsesoyuznogo Geograficheskogo Obshchestva (Moscow), 88*(4), 316–350, 1956.

Benes, N. S., Soil temperatures at Cape Hallett, Antarctica, 1958, *Monthly Weather Review, 88,* 223–227, 1960.

Bentley, C. R., The structure of Antarctica and its ice cover, in *Research in Geophysics,* Vol. 2, *Solid Earth and Interface Phenomena,* edited by H. Odishaw, pp. 335–389, The Massachusetts Institute of Technology Press, Cambridge, Mass., 1964.

Chudnovskii, A. F., *Heat Transfer in the Soil,* Gosudarstvennoe Izdatel'stvo Tekhniko-teoreticheskoi Literatury, Leningrad-Moscow, 1948. (Translation published by Israel Program for Scientific Translations, Jerusalem, 1962.)

Dolgushin, L. D., Geographical observations in the Antarctic, *Izvestiya Akademii Nauk SSR, Seriya Geograficheskaya, No. 1,* 28–47, 1958.

Giovinetto, M. B., The drainage systems of Antarctica: Accumulation, in *Antarctic Research Series,* Vol. 2, *Antarctic Snow and Ice Studies,* edited by M. Mellor, pp. 127–155, American Geophysical Union, Washington, D. C., 1964.

Grigor'ev, N. F., Some results of permafrost investigations in East Antarctica, *Information Bulletin of the Soviet Antarctic Expedition, No. 7,* 288–290, 1959.

Hanson, K. J., and M. J. Rubin, Heat exchange at the snow-air interface at the south pole, *J. Geophys. Res., 67,* 3415–3424, 1962.

Koopman, G., Entstehung und Verbreitung von Divergenzen in der oberflachennahen Wasser bewegung de antarktischen Gewasser, *Deutsche Hydrographische Zeitschrift, Erganzungsheft 2,* p. 14, Deutsches Hydrographishes Institüt, Hamburg, 1953.

Morris, W. R., and N. L. Peters, Inside Antarctica No. 5—Byrd Station, *Weatherwise, 13,* 162–165, 1960.

Nichols, R. L., Geology of Lake Vanda, Wright Valley, South Victoria Land, Antarctica, in *Antarctic Research, The Matthew Fontaine Maury Memorial Symposium,* edited by H. Wexler, M. J. Rubin, and J. E. Caskey, Jr., pp. 47–52, American Geophysical Union, Washington, D. C., 1962.

Ostapoff, F., Antarctic oceanography, in *Biogeography and Ecology in Antarctica,* edited by P. van Oye, J. van Mieghem, and J. Schell, pp. 97–126, Dr. W. Junk (publishers), The Hague, 1965.

Péwé, T. L., Multiple glaciation in the McMurdo Sound region, Antarctica—A progress report in *IGY Glaciological Report No. 4,* pp. 25–49, American Geographical Society, New York, 1961.

Rubin, M. J., Atmospheric advection and the antarctic mass and heat budget, in *Antarctic Research, The Matthew Fontaine Maury Memorial Symposium,* edited by H. Wexler, M. J. Rubin, and J. E. Caskey, Jr., pp. 149–159, American Geophysical Union, Washington, D. C., 1962.

Rubin, M. J., Antarctic climatology, in *Biogeography and Ecology in Antarctica,* edited by P. van Oye, J. van Mieghem, and J. Schell, pp. 72–96, Dr. W. Junk (publisher), The Hague, 1965.

Rubin, M. J., and W. S. Weyant, The mass and heat budget of the antarctic atmosphere, *Monthly Weather Review, 91,* 487–493, 1963.

Rubin, M. J., and W. S. Weyant, Antarctic meteorology, in *Antarctica, A New Zealand Antarctic Society Survey,* edited by T. Hatherton, pp. 375–401, Methuen and Co., Ltd., London, 1965.

Rusin, N. P., Meteorological processes in the surface layer of the atmosphere in Antarctica, in *Contemporary Problems in the Meteorology of the Surface Layer of the Atmosphere,* edited by M. I. Budyko, pp. 5–25, Gidrometeoizdat, Leningrad, 1958.

Shirtcliffe, T. G. L., and R. F. Benseman, A Sun-heated antarctic lake, *J. Geophys. Res.,* 3355–3359, 1964.

Thiel, E. C., The amount of ice on planet Earth, in *Antarctic Research, The Matthew Fontaine Maury Memorial Symposium,* edited by H. Wexler, M. J. Rubin, and J. E. Caskey, Jr., pp. 172–175, American Geophysical Union, Washington, D. C., 1962.

Van Rooy, M. P. (editor), *Meteorology of the Antarctic,* Weather Bureau, Pretoria, South Africa, 1957.

Wexler, H., The 'kernlose' winter in Antarctica, *Geophysics, 6,* 577–595, 1958.

PRELIMINARY MEASUREMENTS OF GROWTH OF NONSORTED POLYGONS, VICTORIA LAND, ANTARCTICA[1]

Thomas E. Berg[2] and Robert F. Black

University of Wisconsin, Madison

Abstract. Nonsorted polygons are common in Victoria Land, Antarctica. Polygons are usually 10–30 meters in diameter and have associated wedges 20–1000 cm in width. The most common wedge filling is a composite of ice, sand, or rubble. In very dry areas with abundant free-running quartz sand, sand wedges are present. In areas of high moisture where cementation of the active layer by ice occurs, ice wedges are found. The wedges go through a predictable sequence of growth, which is reflected at the surface. Youthful wedges less than 75 cm in width are reflected at the surface by troughs as wide as the wedge. Wedges 75–200 cm in width are outlined by double raised-rims bordering troughs that may reach 50–75 cm above the surface. Double raised-rims are usually masked in areas of ice-cored moraine, due to slumping and sublimation of exposed glacial ice. Double raised-rims reach a maximum height of 1.5 meters in Victoria Valley, where wedges 3–10 meters in width are present. Very mature wedges result in a 'pimple' surface consisting of small mounds 1–5 meters in diameter and 1–2 meters high separated by troughs over 4 meters in width. Polygons are also developed in thin-bedded Beacon sandstone.

Preliminary measurements of growth rates of 0.5 to 3.8 mm per year for wedges in Victoria Land permit dating of various geomorphic surfaces. Results for recent surfaces appear to be good and in agreement with dates derived from lichen studies, but they vary markedly from carbon-14 dates. Preliminary results indicate: (1) that Hut Point Peninsula was submerged or under ice about 1000 years ago; (2) that water filled Taylor Valley to a depth of 300 meters as recently as 1500 years ago; (3) increasing aridity in Wright Valley since the last glaciation, as evidenced by retreat of some alpine glaciers 700 years ago, retreat of snowfields 250 years ago, and distinct drying out of surficial material on ice-cored moraines. That the last glaciation is more recent than previously thought is evidenced by a date of 500 years for moraine in front of the Hobbs Glacier and 1300 years for a terrace in Wright Valley.

Although dating by polygonal ground is still subject to uncertainties, owing to an inadequate time base and uncertainties regarding the physical environment of growth, results to date do permit the determination of ages of glacial events of an order of magnitude. Where polygons are present, surfaces are less than 10,000 years old; where polygons are absent and the thickness of the surface dry zone is greater than 1 meter, surfaces may be older.

INTRODUCTION

In Victoria Land, Antarctica, growth of nonsorted polygons is one of the most important factors affecting soil genesis. The ubiquity of polygons in ice-free areas requires the soil scientist to be cognizant of the different kinds of nonsorted polygons that occur and of the various stages through which polygons pass from youth to old age. Polygons with wedges of ice, of sand, and of mixtures of rubble and ice occur. The growth of polygons from youth to old age results in drastic changes in microtopography, drainage and soil moisture, soil mineral content, and soil texture. Importantly, areas of polygonal ground are constantly changing, never static. Irregular, diurnal, and annual cycles of temperature fluctuations set up stresses and humidity gradients in the ground that continually modify the soil zone. The growth rates of wedges, however, are predictable and measurable, and can be used for dating geomorphic events during the last 5,000 to 10,000 years.

This paper presents preliminary measurements of growth rates and describes the sequence of development of nonsorted polygons. Growth rates are

[1] Geophysical and Polar Research Center, Contribution 153, Department of Geology, University of Wisconsin.
[2] Now at Research Council of Alberta, Edmonton, Alberta, Canada.

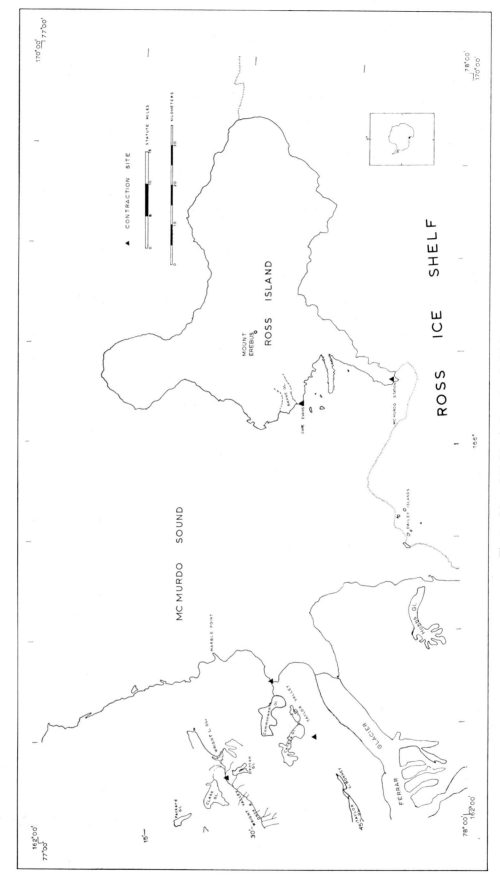

Fig. 1. Map of McMurdo Sound and vicinity.

correlated briefly with the physical environment of the wedges (only a few examples are given here) and with the glacial chronologies proposed by other workers. No attempt is made to present all data accumulated to date on the temperature regime, moisture, lithology, and texture of the permafrost and active layer, nor to discuss exhaustively all findings on the broader aspects of geomorphology and glacial geology as related to the nonsorted polygons. Growth rates cited here are for only 1 to 2 years. That at least 5 to 10 years are needed for reasonably precise values must be emphasized. Nonetheless, as the data are internally consistent, they represent results which can be used within limits. Although preliminary, these results are thus of value now in an area where most dating methods are not widely applicable.

VICTORIA LAND

Victoria Land contains an essentially ice-free area of 28,000 km² near the center of an immense mountain chain that stretches across the entire continent of Antarctica (Figure 1). The area is bounded on the west by the Polar Plateau, with surface elevations of 2000 to 3000 meters and an ice cover of almost equal thickness. On the east is the Ross Sea, the largest indentation in the generally circular outline of the continent.

Dissected fault-block mountains rise to 4000 meters and retard the flow of ice from the Polar Plateau to the Ross Sea, giving rise to numerous east-west–trending ice-free valleys. These valleys, ice-covered during the Pleistocene [Péwé, 1961], form the largest ice-free area in Antarctica.

Several volcanic islands lie close to the west side of the Ross Sea. The largest, Ross Island, is dominated by Mount Erebus (4023 meters), the only active volcano in Antarctica. Ross Island is separated from Victoria Land proper by McMurdo Sound, an arm of the Ross Sea. The sound is covered with ice for much of the year but is usually ice-free for a period of one or two months. The south end of McMurdo Sound, as well as the south side of Ross Island, is bounded by the Ross Ice Shelf, the largest ice shelf in the world (540,000 km²) [Giovinetto and Behrendt, 1964]. Piedmont glaciers, small alpine glaciers, and a few outlet glaciers are present on the mainland, in the 'dry valley' area.

Climate

Victoria Land may be classified as a cold polar desert. Climatic records are few, consisting of approximately 15 years of record spread over the period from 1900 to 1963, including continuous records since the advent (1957) of the International Geophysical Year. Precipitation data have been obtained from snow studies, which provide records for the last century or so.

The average annual temperature at McMurdo, Ross Island, based on twelve years of observation is −17°C [U. S. Navy Weather Research Facility, 1961]. At Scott base, 5 km southeast, the average is −20°C [Gunn and Warren, 1962], due to the proximity of the Ross Ice Shelf. On the Polar Plateau an average temperature of −40°C is recorded in pits at a depth where annual temperature fluctuation is zero [Stuart and Heine, 1961]. The maximum temperature recorded at McMurdo was 6°C and the minimum −51°C for the period 1956–1961 [U. S. Navy Weather Research Facility, 1961]. August is the coldest month, January the warmest. Maximum deviation from the mean occurs during July, in the austral winter. The mean annual wind speed is 22.5 km per hour; a maximum of 155 km per hour was recorded in June 1957 [U. S. Navy Weather Research Facility, 1961].

Precipitation is slight, and, since it occurs as snow, usually during periods of high winds, it is difficult to make an accurate determination of it; only one instance of rain in the area has been re-

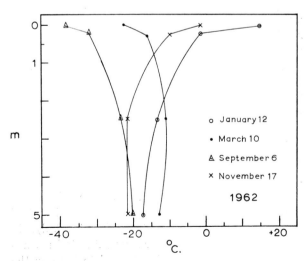

Fig. 2.   Tautochrome of temperatures, 'Windy Crater,' Ross Island.

corded. Snow-accumulation studies show the average water accumulation per year to be 16 cm on the Polar Plateau and 20 cm on the Ross Ice Shelf [*Stuart and Heine*, 1961]. Qualitative observations in Taylor Valley indicate that snowfall near the mouth of the valley is comparable to that on the Ross Ice Shelf but that the amount diminishes rapidly inland (e.g., see aerial photographs of the U. S. Navy, 10 October 1961).

The climate is reflected in seasonal fluctuations of temperature in the upper few meters of the ground (Figure 2), fluctuations fundamental to the concepts of patterned ground described later.

Terminology

Where applicable, the terminology of *Washburn* [1956] is followed. In Antarctica, however, some additional terms are needed, and the classification has to be 'stretched.' Nonsorted polygons [*Washburn*, 1956] are a form of patterned ground in which no sorting of material takes place. Ice-wedge polygons, tundra polygons, fissure polygons, and the like are characteristic, widespread, and best known in the Arctic. Recently, sand-wedge polygons or tesselations were shown to be analogous to ice-wedge polygons [*Péwé*, 1959]. In sand-wedge polygons, wedges are mostly undersaturated sand; in ice-wedge polygons, mostly ice. The origin and development of the two end members are so similar [*Black and Berg*, 1963] that it seems inappropriate to exclude sand-wedge polygons from the general group of nonsorted patterns even though sorting does take place. Moreover, 'composite' wedges—those with supersaturated sand or rubble—are also commonplace and follow the same general origin and development as sand and ice wedges; they may be partly sorted. Other 'sand' wedges may be in large part composed of rubble.

A 'dry' layer of non-cemented unconsolidated rubble overlying ice-cemented material is common in the dry-valley areas of Victoria Land. Thickness of the layer varies from 5 cm to more than 2 meters. This dry layer may or may not coincide with the active layer (i.e., the zone of annual freeze and thaw). It is an easily recognized unit of very low moisture content (undersaturated), in contrast to the saturated or supersaturated permafrost below, and is loosely referred to here as the surface dry zone.

History of Investigation

Péwé [1959] reported that nonsorted polygons had actively growing sand wedges at McMurdo and in ice-free valleys in Victoria Land rather than ice wedges, which are common in patterned ground in the Arctic [*Black*, 1952, 1954]. Black, in a short visit to Antarctica in 1959 under the auspices of the National Science Foundation, excavated numerous polygons at McMurdo and found mostly ice wedges or composite sand and ice wedges. The ubiquitous nature of the nonsorted polygons, the lack of information on their growth rates, and the apparently abrupt transition of sand wedges to ice wedges over short distances prompted Black to submit a proposal to the National Science Foundation for their study. Under the forthcoming grant, Berg and James R. Sullivan started field work in December 1960 at McMurdo, whereas Black remained in the United States.

Berg and Sullivan spent much of the initial summer in reconnaissance of Victoria Land to determine optimum locations for quantitative measurements of growth rates of wedges and of their physical environment. A primary site with ice wedges was chosen close to McMurdo because of easy access during the following winter. A second site with sand wedges was picked in Taylor Valley to contrast with the McMurdo site and to provide a basis for dating geomorphic events in the valley; this site was on an abandoned delta inland from the coast. A third site on an active delta at the mouth of Taylor Valley was established to provide a check on the results of the work. At each site a network of stakes was installed to measure the contraction and expansion of the ground and the growth of wedges.

At McMurdo an attempt was made to adapt indoor thermal recorders to measure ground temperatures at the field site. Unfortunately, the equipment did not stand up to the rigors of the antarctic winter, and no usable data were collected. During the austral winter of 1961, contraction measurements were made at monthly intervals at the site near McMurdo. Ground-moisture conditions were also monitored and ice-fabric studies of ice wedges were undertaken.

During the austral summer of 1961–1962, Black, Berg, and Sullivan controlled additional wedges at the previously established sites and established new sites in Beacon Valley and at Cape Evans. New temperature-monitoring equipment [*Black and Berg*, 1963], set up in February 1962, proved much more reliable than previous equipment. Measurements of the growth rates of nonsorted polygons were begun at 6-month intervals.

Black, Berg, and Peter Vogt returned to the area in October 1962. Part of the summer field season was spent in measuring growth of wedges at existing sites, adding additional stakes in Taylor Valley, and in establishing new contraction sites in Wright Valley, where a great deal of work on the glacial history of the valley had been undertaken [e.g., *Bull, McKelvey, and Webb*, 1962; *Nichols*, 1961*a*]. Four sites were established in Wright Valley to provide control over a variety of geomorphic surfaces in an effort to reliably date the glacial sequences. In addition, moisture and temperature studies were continued, as were investigations into the glacial history of Victoria Land. The study was also expanded geographically when Black and Berg examined the area in the vicinity of Hallett Station and Berg visited many sites on the Antarctic Peninsula. The expanded field operations revealed that the best development of patterned ground was in the area of original operations, i.e., near McMurdo, and investigations were thenceforth confined to this area.

In the summer of 1963–1964 Black and Berg again returned to Victoria Land to continue routine measurements of growth rates, ground temperatures, and soil moisture. Airborne reconnaissance and spot investigations of large ice-free areas served to correlate the patterned ground with the glacial history or geomorphic chronology of events. As the reliability of carbon-14 dates in Victoria Land is questioned [*Berg and Black*, 1964], living algae from various places were collected to check on its carbon-14 balance.

Throughout the investigations, all geologic phenomena related to patterned ground were investigated. These include, among others, thickness of active layer or 'dry zone' on permafrost, salt deposits, moraines, ventifacts, drained lakes and ponds, stream terraces, marine beaches, recent volcanic deposits, and pseudo-volcanic deposits in Taylor and Wright valleys.

NONSORTED POLYGONS

Nonsorted polygons 3–30 meters in diameter are common surface patterns in polar areas. The polygons are formed by intersecting troughs in the surface. Beneath each trough is a wedge—oriented vertically with its apex downward—of ice, sand, or a mixture of the two. Sand and composite wedges are more common in Antarctica, and ice wedges are more common in the Arctic. Their origins and sequence of development are similar. Essential for their formation are permafrost and an average annual temperature usually below −5°C [*Black*, 1952, 1954, 1963; *Black and Berg*, 1963; *Lachenbruch*, 1962].

Theory of Formation

The popular theory of origin of nonsorted polygons was first outlined in detail by *Leffingwell* [1919] and has been accepted by a majority of investigators who have field experience with this phenomena [e.g., *Black*, 1952; *Popov*, 1955; *Washburn*, 1956; *Péwé*, 1959; *Lachenbruch*, 1962]. A few workers doubt the theory [*Taber*, 1943; *Schenk*, 1965].

Leffingwell's basic theory is as follows. During the winter, cold temperatures set up stresses in the ground and result in contraction of the permafrost. When the stresses exceed the tensile strength of the permafrost, cracking occurs and vertical fractures up to 5 cm in width and several meters in depth form in the frozen ground. During the spring the crack may be filled with hoarfrost, melting water, or sand, producing a thin vein extending down into the permafrost. During the following summer horizontal compression is set up by the re-expansion of the permafrost as it becomes warmer. The ground cannot, however, return to its original position due to the addition of the ice or sand in the crack. Upturning of the permafrost at the sides of the vein may occur by plastic or shear deformation. The following winter the vein acts as a zone of weakness, and renewed thermal tension causes cracking at the same place. Repetition of this process over tens and hundreds of years builds up the wedges seen today. The polygonal shape visible on the surface is a natural consequence of the contraction origin, analogous to polygonal cracks in mud, lava, ceramics, and related materials.

Mathematical investigation of Leffingwell's theory is meager. *Dostovalov* [1957] presented a simplified mathematical model that was superseded by the work of *Lachenbruch* [1962]. Lachenbruch used mechanics to develop detailed mathematical models that support the theory and provide a quantitative basis for amount of thermal tension, depth and rate of cracking, crack spacing, and origin of the polygonal network. He distinguished two polygonal systems, orthogonal and nonorthogonal.

Orthogonal systems are those that have a preponderance of orthogonal intersections. They are characteristic of somewhat inhomogeneous or plastic media where cracks form at loci of high-stress concentration. Since the cracks do not all form simultaneously, new cracks tend to join older cracks at orthogonal intersections. Orthogonal systems can be divided into two subgroups:

(*a*) 'Random orthogonal systems,' in which cracks have no preferred directional orientation, and

(*b*) 'Oriented orthogonal systems,' which have preferred directional orientation. They are probably caused by horizontal stress differences generated by horizontal thermal gradients such as those set up by lakes and glaciers. The cracks are oriented parallel and normal to the discontinuity.

Nonorthogonal systems are those having a preponderance of crack intersections at about 120°. Lachenbruch suggests that they result from uniform cooling of very homogenous, relatively nonplastic media. Unlike an orthogonal system, all cracks are generated practically simultaneously. However, where ice or sand wedges are over a few centimeters in width, it is practically impossible from surface inspection to determine whether the system is random orthogonal or nonorthogonal unless appreciable differences in wedge widths exist [*Lachenbruch*, 1962]. Fabric studies [*Black*, 1954, 1963] of ice wedges permit distinction.

Dating with Nonsorted Polygons

Theoretically, by determining the rate of addition of material in contraction cracks in a nonsorted wedge, over a fairly long period of time it should be possible to determine the age of the wedge by dividing its width by the observed growth rate [*Black and Berg*, 1963, 1964]. Since wedges cannot form beneath glaciers or deep lakes, it might be possible by this method to date certain geomorphic events, for example glacial retreat, lake drainage, or marine emergence. *Black* [1952, 1963] determined the feasibility of this method while working with ice-wedge polygons near Point Barrow, Alaska. He suggested an average growth rate of 1 mm per year for wedges in the Barrow area; using this figure he determined the age of the Point Barrow Spit, which was later confirmed [*Péwé and Church*, 1962a] by carbon-14 dating.

There are many unknowns and problems in this method. Minor variations in the physical environment play major roles in the development of the patterned ground. Since not all potential interpolygonal fractures recur every winter, as large a sample as possible is necessary. In addition, the presence of a snow cover may cause a hiatus in growth that cannot be determined. Variability in growth rates is large and may change with age of a wedge. Since ice is much more responsive to temperature changes, growth should become greater as ice wedges widen, i.e., grow older. On the other hand, if a wedge is composed of sand, the growth rate should slow with increasing age. However, as the carbon-14 method of dating is unreliable in Antarctica [*Broecker*, 1963; *Berg and Black*, 1963], dating with patterned ground may prove to be one of the most useful tools, especially for phenomena occurring during the last few millenia [*Black and Berg*, 1963, 1964].

Surficial Expression of Wedges

That nonsorted polygons and their associated wedges go through a predictable sequence of growth from youth to old age has long been recognized [*Leffingwell*, 1919]. As they do so, their surficial expression reflects their age and the kind of material, hydrothermal environment [*Black and Berg*, 1963], and topography in which they are found. In Antarctica, where well-developed polygons are present on most all unconsolidated material and even bedrock, it is convenient to separate those areas of polygons that form in supersaturated permafrost, such as ice-cored moraines where the topography is irregular, from those of undersaturated permafrost, where the topography is usually more regular. Whether the topography is a cause or a consequence is not always clear. Moreover, addition or removal of ice from the perma-

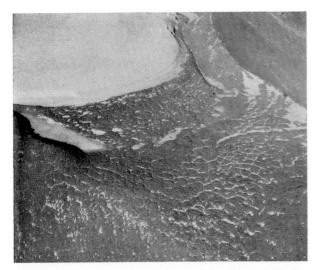

Fig. 3. Ice-cored moraine in front of the Denton Glacier, Wright Valley. Polygonal troughs are 1–2 meters deep; polygons average 10–20 meters across. Notice kettles along former front and two stages of polygons. The youngest set of wedges is developed parallel and perpendicular to the present front. Site A is off the picture to the right.

frost during growth of wedges may produce significant differences in surficial expression.

In ice-cored moraines, such as those of the Hobbs and Denton glaciers (Figure 3), contraction cracks expose buried ice to the atmosphere. Sublimation

occurs due to reversed temperature gradients (Figure 2). The loss of ice by sublimation may equal or exceed the infall of debris from the sides and from above. Thus, a gradual lowering of the trough can take place. Slumping from the sides will then expose ice to sublimation, resulting in a widening of the trough as well. Growth of the wedges, therefore, results in the creation of a high core in the centers of the polygons that slopes down toward the troughs. With time, sublimation of ice will decrease, due to the increased cover of debris, and infall of debris will exceed the amount of ice removal.

As a wedge widens, the adjacent material will be forced up by plastic deformation during expansion of the buried ice or ground. However, either the steep sloping sides of the core will mask the displaced material, or only a slight break in slope may occur at the edges of the wedge (Figure 4). At maturity, troughs up to 4 meters wide separate high-centered cores of the polygons. Reduction in the height of the central core also takes place by sublimation of the underlying glacial ice due to strong temperature gradients. In areas of mature polygons on ice-cored surfaces, migration of the contraction crack, or commonly the subdivision of central polygon cores, will incorporate part of the core in the trough (Figure 5). In old age widely spaced hillocks or 'pimples' are surrounded by low

Fig. 4. Polygonal trough at Site B, Wright Valley. The limits of the trough are marked by the two arrows (left and right). Notice how the upturning of the material adjacent to the wedge is masked by the irregular topography. Looking north toward Site C. Shovel (center) is 54 cm long.

Fig. 5. Migration of contraction cracks on ice-cored moraine at Site B, Wright Valley. Relic troughs are the linear areas containing sand, in contrast to pebble-covered surfaces. Note the irregular topography.

Fig. 6. 'Pimple' moraine approximately 2 km east of the terminus of the 'Loop' moraine, Wright Valley.

Fig. 8. Double raised-rims on a terrace of the Onyx River, Wright Valley, 8 km west of the Wright Lower Glacier.

areas underlain with wedges up to a maximum of 10 meters in width. Well-developed surfaces of this type are visible in Wright Valley immediately east of the terminus of the 'Loop' moraine (Figure 6).

Saturated to undersaturated permafrost usually underlies stream terraces, deltas, beaches, and bedrock. These surfaces are usually flatter, sediments are better sorted and contain less ice than ice-cored moraine. In the youthful stage of the development of wedges, surficial expression consists of narrow troughs formed by slumping from the sides and above into the wedges (Figure 7). Some minor sublimation of ground ice may occur, but a net addition of material into the wedge results. With continued growth, material will be forced to the

Fig. 7. Youthful polygons and troughs at the contraction site on a delta at the mouth of Taylor Valley, looking southeast. (See also Figure 36.)

Fig. 9. Aerial view of polygons with high, double raised-rims in Victoria Valley. In the background are sand dunes and the Packard Glacier.

Fig. 10. Double raised-rim polygons in Victoria Valley. Rims are 1.5 meters above the polygonal centers. The active contraction crack has some recent sand.

Fig. 12. Sand wedge in thin-bedded Beacon sandstone, with marked upturning of the sandstone on the right. Asgard Range. G. I. shovel is 54 cm high.

surface along a wedge by plastic or shear deformation of the adjacent material, forming double raised-rims (Figure 8).

Raised-rims produce low-centered polygons. The rims are exposed to the erosive force of wind which, with work of frost action, gravity, and water, tends to smooth them. The trough between the rims acts as a catchment basin for sand and snow. Snow, accumulating in the troughs and in the lee of the rims, introduces complexities into the thermal and moisture regime that will be discussed later. Growth

Fig. 11. Large polygonal troughs, Victoria Valley. The dunes in the background are in front of the Packard Glacier.

of the rims is rapid and can continue into old age.

As a general rule, double raised-rims do not develop on the surface until a wedge is 75–100 cm wide; with wedges 1–2 m wide, rims commonly reach 50–75 cm above the surface of the polygon. Wedges wider than 2 meters may have still higher rims. The highest double raised-rims known in Victoria Land are in Victoria Valley, 4 km west of the Victoria Lower Glacier (Figure 9). There, rims rise to heights of 1.5 meters above polygonal centers (Figure 10). Distance from crest to crest, across troughs, ranges from 3 to 10 meters (Figure 11), and troughs are 0.5–1.5 meters deep. Where excavated, wedges beneath the troughs are 2–5 meters wide and others are probably larger. All appear active. Wedge fillings consist of structureless sand. Stratified sands and gravels are turned up on edge at the borders of the wedge. Polygons are 20–30 meters in diameter.

Ultimately, if troughs widened indefinitely the raised-rims bordering a polygon should grow inward until a high-centered polygon is formed. None of these high-centered polygons have been observed in Antarctica. It seems clear that sand wedges in particular are limited in maximum width by release of stress entirely within the wedges.

Polygons in thin-bedded Beacon sandstone go through a similar but slower sequence of growth, in which wedges always cause upturning of the flat-

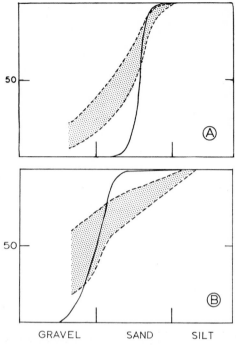

Fig. 13. Size analyses of wedges and adjacent material. Stippled areas cover the range of material in the active layer and permafrost. Solid black line is the sorting profile of wedge material. (*A*) sand wedge, delta, Nussbaum Riegel, Taylor Valley; (*B*) composite wedge, Windy Crater, Ross Island.

TABLE 1.   Moisture Content of Various Geomorphic Features (Per Cent Water by Weight)

Surface	Perma-frost H_2O	Active Layer H_2O	Wedge Type	Wedge H_2O
Ice-cored moraine— recent	Up to 100	0.9–6	Sand Ice	2.5–8 Up to 100
Ice-cored moraine— relic	Up to 100	0.5–4	Sand Composite	2–8 12–30
Terraces	8–15	0.5–4	Sand	5–10
Deltas–relic	5–18	2–6	Sand Composite	2–10 10–50
Deltas—recent	6–13	1.5–8	Sand	6–10
Volcanic ter-rain (Ross Island)	7.5–20	1.2–9	Composite Ice	12–50 Up to 100

Fig. 14.   Cones of depressions from sand runs in polygonal trough perpendicular to the wind at Site B, Wright Valley, view north.

lying beds resulting in single or double raised-rims (Figure 12).

TYPES OF WEDGES

Sand Wedges

Sand wedges are common in Victoria Land [*Péwé*, 1959]. The wedges consist of well-sorted, rounded, fine- to medium-grained quartz sand (Figure 13). The writers have excavated sand wedges in Beacon, Taylor, Wright, and Victoria valleys, as well as in the Asgard Range where some are developed in bedrock. The typical wedge consists of structureless to faintly foliated sand containing little moisture (Table 1). Wedges range in width up to 10 meters, although most are less than 5 meters. They extend at least 2 meters below the surface and, theoretically, in favorable environments some should go to depths of at least 5 meters. Overlying the wedge is a trough that is usually filled with sand (Figure 14), but rubble may be concentrated directly over the active contraction crack (Figure 15). Where sand is the trough filling, depression cones in spring are commonly visible at the surface (Figure 14). Material adjacent to the wedge is usually forced up toward the surface (Figure 16) as wedges grow.

Fig. 15. Composite wedge, Site B, Wright Valley. Foliation is well developed in wedge. Contraction crack in center of photo is filled with sand and covered by a layer of stones. Dry, active layer is light-colored, whereas permafrost is darker from melting of ice. Shovel is 54 cm high.

Fig. 17. Excavation of wedge in Beacon Valley, showing foliation and cobble layer parallel to present contraction crack in foreground. Wedge is 4 meters wide. Boundary of wedge is marked by large boulder in background. Scales are 15 cm long.

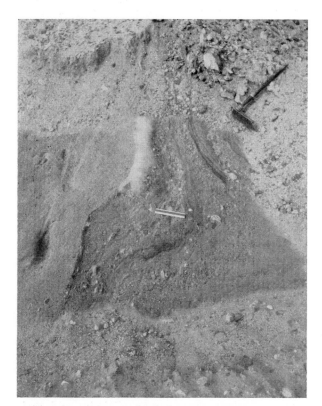

Fig. 16. Upturning of stratified sands (right) adjacent to a sand wedge (left), Wright Valley.

Some sand wedges possess well-developed structure. Foliation from layers of different sand size or other textural or compositional changes are generally parallel to the sides of the wedge or vertical. Differences in moisture from layer to layer are particularly common. Occasional cobbles and rock fragments are incorporated into the upper surfaces of the wedge but generally do not extend to depth, unless the wedge is in ice. Some elongate stones have preferred lineation or foliation. Cross-cutting contraction-crack fillings, fold axes, and shear plane intersections also provide lineations. The structures are in part derived from the periodic filling of contraction cracks and in part from flow and shear in the wedge during expansion of the ground. The deformation fabrics are superposed on the growth fabrics in complex and perplexing array.

Removal of the dry zone above a wedge reveals an interesting microtopography developed on and adjacent to the upper surface of the wedge (Fig-

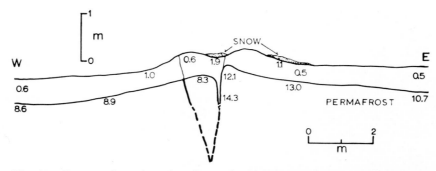

Fig. 18. Cross section of sand wedge and adjacent material on terrace of the Onyx River, 8 km west of the Wright Lower Glacier. The irregular topography is developed on the top of permafrost, and displacement of the surficial expression of the wedge is to the east (i. e., downwind). Values represent percentage of soil moisture by weight, 26 October 1962.

ures 17 and 18). Differences in elevation of 40 cm over the surface of a wedge and adjacent permafrost are common. Pebble zones or concentrations of ice are usually coincident with bumps on the surface. In contrast, ridges 10–30 cm high in permafrost adjacent to wedges (Figure 18) result from the pushing up of adjacent material in summer by plastic deformation and shear and are generally not distinct in regard to texture or composition.

A convenient source of sand for wedge fillings is the Beacon sandstone, which crops out over much of Victoria Land. The sandstone contains clean, rounded, medium-grained quartz sand with a sphericity of 0.6–0.8 [*Angino and Owen*, 1962]. On Ross Island, where the sandstone is absent, sand wedges are also absent.

Wind is an important transporting agent of sand for wedge filling, especially where double raised-rim polygons are present, as the trough between the rims provides an excellent catchment basin. More sand is present in troughs perpendicular to the wind than in troughs parallel to the wind on the terraces of Wright Valley. Whether or not the additional sand is an incentive to faster growth of wedges is not known for certain, but evidence suggests that such is the case. At Site C in Wright Valley (see description later) the relations shown in Table 2 are evident. Site C is an optimum location for measuring wind effects. At other sites where optimum conditions did not exist, results were mixed, as would be expected. Local temperature regime, variability of material, and variation in moisture content also play important parts in causing variation of growth rates of wedges in local areas [*Black and Berg*, 1963].

The mode of origin of sand wedges is simple. Upon formation of the contraction crack, the overlying sand runs into the crack, leaving a cone of depression on the surface. Areas of sand wedges have active layers containing 0.3 to 3 per cent water by weight. Occasionally the sand in the trough is cemented by a small amount of ice (3 per cent or more, Table 1) which prohibits the filling of the crack until the ice is removed by melting or sublimation. The melting or sublimation usually occurs in October or early November, at which time filling will occur. Hoarfrost may have formed in the open crack in the interval between formation and filling due to the reversal of vapor pressure gradients by reversal of temperature gradients [*Black and Berg*, 1963]. The hoarfrost may prevent the sand from filling the crack or may mix with the sand. The continued addition of sand over the years results in sand wedges.

Complications are common. Cobbles and rock fragments in centers of wedges usually constitute a

TABLE 2.   Relation of Polygonal Trough to Wind Direction

	⊥	‖	↗	Average of All
Average trough width (cm)	175	110	140	147
Average growth rate (1 yr) (mm)	1.43	0.96	1.07	1.19
Number of troughs	19	13	14	

Fig. 19. Site of ice-wedge excavation (*at shovel*) in 'Windy Crater,' Ross Island. Shovel is 54 cm high. View east, 4 December 1963.

residual lag concentrate, but their occurrence may indicate a shift in the amount of sand available for filling, due to a lack of the transported sand that fills the trough or to an increased moisture content that causes cementation of the sand. Incorporation of surrounding material into the wedge due to a shift in the zone of contraction cracking is also possible (Figure 15).

Ice Wedges

In Victoria Land, ice wedges are less common and more restricted in environment than sand wedges.

Fig. 20. Ice wedge excavated at 'Windy Crater.' (See also Figure 19.) An ice-cemented zone lies directly above the wedge. Scale is 15 cm long.

On Ross Island and in areas bordering the Ross Sea, where free-running sand is absent [*Black and Berg*, 1963, 1964, 1965], ice wedges are generally present to the exclusions of sand wedges. Composite wedges are, however, commonly associated with both ice and sand wedges. In general, ice wedges in Victoria Land are usually less than 1 meter wide and perhaps 2 meters high (probably because the surfaces in which they are found are comparatively very young). They border polygons of the same general dimensions and configuration as do sand and composite wedges.

Ice wedges have been excavated at several localities in Victoria Land. 'Windy Crater,' Hut Point Peninsula, Ross Island, has ice wedges in volcanic rubble in the lower parts of the crater and composite wedges in bedrock on the rim. One wedge, excavated in the floor of the crater on a small rise between two ponds, is shown in Figures 19 and 20. Volcanic ash and scoria make up the surface. The wedge is 45 cm wide at the top (Figure 20) and was excavated to a depth of 1.2 meters. It was covered with an ice-cemented layer of ash and pebbles 4–10 cm thick and containing 8.6 per cent water by weight. The active layer was 24 cm thick, averaged 3.8 per cent water by weight, and

Fig. 21. Site of excavation in Wheeler Valley. Trough is 170 cm wide, 15 cm deep. Polygons in vicinity are 8–12 meters in diameter. Dolerite ridge in background. Looking west-southwest. 20 January 1964.

Fig. 22. Ice wedge 165 cm wide beneath 42 cm of morainal material in Wheeler Valley. Contraction crack filled with hoarfrost in center of wedge (below 15-cm scale).

was underlain by permafrost with 18 per cent moisture.

Snow fills the troughs on the floor of the crater throughout most of the year. Perennial snowfields cover most of the inner slopes on the east and south sides of the crater. Only a slight increase in accumulation is needed to provide a perennial snow cover over the polygons on the floor of the crater.

Wheeler Valley (77°12′S, 161°42′E) trends northeasterly, is ice-free, and is 33 km from the Ross Sea. Polygons are 8–15 meters in diameter and have troughs 1–3 meters wide. Snow filled the troughs on 20 January 1964 (Figure 21). An excavation was made in a northeast-trending trough, 80 meters east of an ice-covered lake in the center of the valley. The excavation was 5 meters above lake level. An ice wedge was exposed at a depth of 42 cm below the surface, at which point it was 165 cm wide, narrowing to 35 cm wide at a depth of 140 cm (Figure 22). At 140 cm a contraction crack that was 3 cm wide at the top narrowed to 5 mm. Directly above the wedge was a cemented zone of sand, 12 cm thick, containing 10.5 per cent water by weight. Above the cemented zone was a layer of loose sandy morainic material 30 cm thick and containing 4.2 per cent water by weight.

The origin of ice wedges is somewhat similar to that of sand wedges, except that moisture is going into instead of out of the ground. Contraction cracks are formed in permafrost due to cold winter

temperatures. In spring, the thermal gradient in the permafrost is reversed, the ground being colder than the active layer or the air [*Black and Berg,* 1963]. Hoarfrost forms in the crack, if the crack is not filled with sand. During the spring, meltwater from snow banks and other sources may flow into the crack and freeze when subject to the colder temperatures beneath the surface. Additional yearly increments of ice will result in ice wedges. It is evident that the contraction cracks must remain open early in the spring to permit hoarfrost to form or melt water to fill the crack. Ice wedges can therefore form only where there is no filling by sand of the cracks because of:

1. Lack of material to fill contraction cracks: for example, sand, the most common wedge filling, is missing at 'Windy Crater,' and at Wheeler Valley it is contaminated with ice and silt so that it no longer is free-running.

2. Presence of a barrier to movement of sand: at many localities a layer 4–10 cm thick of ice-cemented material or of rubble lies directly above a wedge, retarding sand movements but allowing moisture movement.

Abundant moisture in the air or surface soil is also necessary to produce ice wedges. At most localities, water bodies are in close proximity, snow is common in the troughs throughout most of the

Fig. 23. Composite wedges exposed on south rim of 'Windy Crater,' Ross Island. Active layer removed. Note ice along open contraction crack. Scale is 15 cm long.

year, and, as at Windy Crater, perennial snow-fields are a few meters away.

Composite Wedges

The most common wedge filling in Victoria Land is a composite of ice and sand or rubble. All variations between pure ice and pure sand wedges are present, and gradations occur over short distances. This change is visible at Windy Crater, Ross Island, where well-developed composite wedges are visible on the rim of the crater, and ice wedges are present on the floor. Removal of the dry zone on the south rim of the crater exposed an excellent network of composite wedges, outlined by color variations in the permafrost or bedrock; the undisturbed permafrost or bedrock commonly was dark red-brown, the wedges grayish yellow. Abundant ice was present in the wedges (Figure 23). Ice is added to the wedges generally by the filling of the contraction cracks with hoarfrost or melt water from the surface. Addition of ice may also result from incorporation of surrounding material due to migration of contraction cracks in unconsolidated material during wedge growth (Figure 15).

Alternation of sand and ice in a wedge may possibly indicate slight variations in microclimates, presence or absence of snowbanks, or timing of temperature–humidity changes. The presence of ice could indicate periods of increased moisture, cementation of the active layer, and formation of ice in the contraction crack. Conversely, sand layers are indicative of less moisture, permitting flow of sand into the contraction crack. Since only very minor changes in the moisture regime are needed to change the mode of wedge filling, compositional changes may or may not reflect climatic changes that would cause a variation in glacier activity. The source or cause of the alternations of composition in composite wedges is not yet fully understood.

Composition and Growth

The composition of the permafrost affects the rate of growth of wedges by controlling the width and spacing of contraction cracks [Black and Berg, 1963]. Since the coefficient of thermal expansion of ice is five times that of quartz, the larger an ice wedge or the more ice in the adjacent permafrost

the greater is the response to temperature change, the greater the contraction, and the more likelihood for faster growth. With a sand wedge or a lower moisture in the adjacent permafrost, the reverse should be true. The rate of filling of contraction cracks, however, can more than compensate for the size of cracks. Free-flowing sand can fill a crack entirely, whereas absence of sand or a crack sealed off with ice or rubble precludes growth. Growth of sand wedges usually results in a reduction in the ice content of the permafrost (Table 1), as sand wedges have a much lower moisture content than the surrounding permafrost, especially in ice-cored moraines. Replacement of the permafrost with sand wedge material, therefore, should reduce the response to thermal change. Amount of cracking of the wedge should diminish until thermal changes are not sufficient to permit contraction cracks to form, at which time the wedges would become inactive. Observations of the largest and the oldest-appearing wedges in Victoria Land revealed that all were active.

MEASUREMENTS OF GROWTH RATES

Control for the measurement of growth rate of wedges was accomplished by driving iron stakes into the permafrost on each side of a wedge or within a wedge but as far from an active contraction crack as was practicable. The stakes (Bathy Manufacturing Co.) are light-weight T-shaped benchmark rods pointed at one end and with a small hole at the other end to which a 1.8-cm chrome-plated brass cap can be attached with a screw. Stakes 60 to 120 cm long were used, depending on depth to permafrost. In the McMurdo area 60-cm stakes proved to be most useful. The stakes were driven with a 5-pound sledge hammer into the permafrost 2–12 cm, depending upon the ease of driving and length of stake. Stakes were often bent in driving, making their abandonment and the driving of others necessary. Losses ranged from 10 to 40 per cent per site. The letters UNIV WISCONSIN were stamped on the perimeter and letter designation near the center of each cap. Letters were used to avoid mistakes or confusion between stake designation and growth measurements. A small cross was also marked on the surface of the cap by a diamond pencil or steel knife to provide a fixed point for accurate measurement. When, because of damage during driving, a brass cap could not be affixed to a stake, the stake designation was placed on the side of the stake, and the measuring cross was made at the center of the T of the rod. Stakes with chrome-plated brass caps resist corrosion very well, but stakes without caps are quickly corroded. Nail polish, lacquer, and plastic films on uncapped stakes accelerate corrosion of the steel rod. In spite of corrosion, however, the use of the T-junction should permit a measurement of the rod that would be accurate for the foreseeable future.

After the pairs of stakes were emplaced and marked, the intervals were measured annually, or more often, by bar or tape. An invar-steel meter bar, optically tooled with ½-mm divisions (Sargent Co.) was hand-held by two observers where each pair of stakes was less than a meter apart. Readings were made to tenths of millimeters, using Bausch and Lomb magnifying micrometers or $10\times$ hand lens or both. An optically tooled lovar tape (Keuffel and Esser Serial No. 3437) with an expansion coefficient of 0.0000004 per degree centigrade was used for intervals up to 5 meters. Measurements were read to tenths of a millimeter with the magnifying micrometers. Whenever possible, the tape was supported by stands, and 20 pounds of tension was applied. In many instances this was not possible, owing to the roughness of the topography. In such instances the tape was hand-held and at least three readings made to give an accurate determination.

Sources of Error

Measuring devices. Under normal conditions both the meter bar and the tape are capable of an accuracy far exceeding the 0.1 mm to which readings were made. Owing, however, to wind, which made it impossible to support the lovar tape properly, even with fixed supports, this accuracy for most measurements was reduced possibly to ±0.2 mm. Hand-held tape measurements occasionally provided more anomalous results, as in measurements at Beacon Valley, Site B. There the only records of shrinking wedges were made by tape, and the shrinking in each of two instances was 0.4 mm. These records may be true, or the shrinkage may be zero. Measurements using the meter bar are believed to be accurate generally to less than 0.1 mm. The meter bar proved to be easy to handle and read,

and the expansion factor was insignificant over the temperature and radiation conditions experienced during measurement. The shortness of the field season and lack of suitable measuring conditions made use of the meter bar mandatory whenever possible.

Quality of measuring points. The quality of the measuring points varies considerably. Excellent quality was obtained where chrome-plated caps were present on both stakes of a measuring set and the stakes were level. The use of a diamond pencil or steel knife allowed a fine reference mark to be cut into the cap that was easily read to 0.1 mm. A drop-off in accuracy was experienced where the stakes were not level and the bar or tape could not be placed precisely on the mark. Parallax then presented a problem, but fortunately it was held to a minimum by marking the caps at the point of contact with the measuring device. Results from pairs with parallax are used only where the readings are in general agreement with the majority of readings from a site. Since the lack of caps on stakes also reduces accuracy, deep grooves must be cut into these stakes to counteract corrosion. Grooves up to 2 mm wide were cut into some stakes. In such instances the judgment of the person making the measurement must be relied upon to determine the exact center of the measuring point, although accuracy, of course, is reduced. Such cases are, however, few in number.

Stake movement. Stake movement other than from wedge growth is difficult to determine. Although large inaccuracies could result from stake movement and not be recognized, the reproducibility of results and the narrow range of most measurements indicate that stake movement is not of an over-all importance. Movement occurs from bumping of rods by people, by gravity movements on slopes, or by frost action as related to the growth of the adjacent wedge. For the present all such movement must be ignored.

Personnel factors. Personal factors are also difficult to evaluate. Efforts were made to reduce the errors to a minimum by having the same persons do the same tasks at all contraction sites. In this way reproducibility of measurement at any one time was high. Working conditions, however, were often poor, owing to high winds, cold temperatures, and

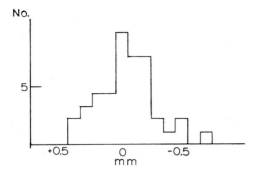

Fig. 24. Variation in width of wedges at the contraction site (delta) near Nussbaum Riegel between 6 December 1963 and 17 January 1964. Average variation was −0.04 mm.

poor visibility, and lack of time made it impossible to recheck all measurements. In 1960 and 1961 Berg and Sullivan made all the measurements, in 1962 Berg and Vogt made most of them, and in 1963 Berg and Black made all of them. Occasionally, logistic problems impressed other personnel into service, and in such instances, accuracy suffered from their inexperience.

Time of measurement. Time of year when measurements are made is probably the most important factor affecting recorded growth rates. Since temperature changes cause constant expansion and contraction of the ground (Figure 2), for maximum reliability of growth rates measurements must be made when the ground affecting the stakes is at its warmest. Unfortunately all measurements could not be made at optimum times due to logistic and personnel problems. Moreover, at the start of this project it was not known how rapidly the ground temperatures changed or when precisely optimum conditions were obtained. Ground temperature studies at McMurdo now show that late December to mid-January is best. For example, wedges measured at Taylor Valley on 6 December 1963 were re-measured on 17 January 1964 (Figure 24). Average variation was −0.04 mm, or within the margin of measuring error. This indicates that closing of contraction cracks has essentially ceased by late December, as the ground temperatures suggest.

Measurements made during October and early November record maximum contraction—not wedge growth. Wedges measured at Windy Crater on 1 March 1962 and re-measured on 29 October 1962 showed an average growth of 3.0 mm (Table 10);

when re-measured 28 November 1963 these wedges had shrunk an average of 1.9 mm.

Other sources. Whenever possible, measurements were carried out on calm, cloudy days. Ideal measuring conditions, however, were the exception rather than the rule. Winds were particularly troublesome in the use of the tape but much less so in the use of the meter bar. Temperatures were monitored continuously during the measurements. Corrections for temperatures were insignificant for the shorter intervals measured with the bar over the temperature range measured, but became important with the tape. Radiational effects, as checked by hand radiometer, are also believed to be insignificant. Condensation upon the magnifying lenses and glasses was troublesome.

Measurements made during the winter required the use of artificial light, and a reduction in accuracy may have resulted.

Accuracy of Measurements Reported in This Paper

All factors considered, in most instances the measurements reported herein are believed to be accurate to ±0.1 mm. Where there is reason to believe that measurements are less accurate, the degree of accuracy is noted. Where errors greater than 0.5 mm are suspected, the data are disregarded. When the error is believed to be between 0.1 and 0.5 mm, the data are included only if they are in general agreement with other measurements at the site.

Wedge Widths

Accuracy of dating by the polygonal ground method is dependent upon two factors: reliable determination of growth rates of wedges, and accurate determination of wedge widths. Problems involved in the determination of growth rates are detailed elsewhere. Determination of wedge widths can be accomplished in two ways. Removal of the surface dry zone permits an accurate delineation of wedge width. At the permafrost surface, wedge boundaries can be recognized by:

1. A change in lithology or texture between the wedge and adjacent material: the presence of ice or clean quartz sand make recognition easy, and

even composite wedges possess better sorting than the surrounding material (Figure 12).

2. Change in moisture content: in sand wedges, adjacent material usually has higher moisture content (Figure 18).

3. Structure: wedges usually have foliation parallel to the axis of the wedge; pebble bands are common in sand wedges.

4. Color: a color difference due to the presence of silt in non-wedge material, or color changes due to oxidation or reduction of iron permit delineation of boundaries in some instances (Figure 23).

Excavation of all wedges is, however, neither practicable nor desirable, and surficial expression of the wedge is therefore most often used in determining wedge widths; a break in slope is usually present directly above the edges of the wedge at the surface. In youthful polygons developed on gentle surfaces, this method is as accurate as excavation. On older surfaces, however, or where the topography is irregular, an accurate determination of the break in slope is not only difficult but, in places, erroneous. Ice-cored moraines, such as those at Site B, Wright Valley, present additional problems, in that migration of the contraction crack may incorporate non-wedge material into the wedge, and cause the result to be an unusually large figure. Where old polygons are present and the surficial materials are very poorly sorted and contain large boulders, as in Beacon Valley, accurate determination of wedge widths becomes very difficult. In such instances investigators seldom agree on wedge widths based on surficial expression. For example, at Site A in Beacon Valley, Berg obtained an average width of 3.2 meters for the wedges. Black, measuring the wedges at Site B, supposedly older, obtained an average width of 2.6 meters. Some of the disparity in widths may be attributed to differences in the method of measuring, e.g., pacing versus taping in the field or measurement of troughs in air photos.

Another problem is also present. Wedge-spacing depends greatly on the moisture and textural properties of the ground. Where moisture content is greater, wedges will be more closely spaced. Site B in Beacon Valley is in a depression where snow accumulation is common, and it may, therefore, have a higher moisture content than Site A. Polygons at Site B are smaller than those at Site A by several meters, and the division of primary polygons by secondary wedges is more common. Secondary wedges cannot give maximum age for a site, as they come in at some later date.

CONTRACTION SITES

Beacon Valley

Beacon Valley (77°48′S, 160°44′E), approximately 15 km east of the Polar Plateau and 70 km west of the Ross Sea, is a southwest-trending valley blocked at the northeast end by a lobe of the Taylor Glacier. The moraine-covered floor of the valley, 17 km long and 3 km wide, rises steadily for 3 km from the Taylor Glacier at 1250 meters to an elevation of 1350 meters. From this point, it continues in a series of undulations to terminate at an elevation of 1900 meters in several cirques cut into the Beacon sandstone (U. S. Geological Survey topographic map, proof sheet). The valley appears to be glacially cut, and moraines hug both walls. Cirques are common on both sides of the valley; on the west side the cirque floors are 200 meters above the valley floor, and on the east side the cirques are graded down to present valley floor. Ice-cored 'rock glaciers' or debris-covered glaciers fill the cirques at the south end of the valley and are level with the valley floor. The cirques are partly controlled by the bedrock [McKelvey and Webb, 1959] consisting of the Beacon sandstone intruded by dolerite sills. Cirques that are cut into the Beacon sandstone are long and narrow; those that cut into the dolerite are shallower and smaller [McKelvey and Webb, 1959]. On the west side of the valley dolerite-capped peaks rise to 2300 meters, and on the east side a Beacon sandstone divide at 2200 meters is prominent. Mount Feather, a dolerite-capped peak, rises to 2985 meters at the south end of the valley.

The climate of Beacon Valley is somewhat different from the large easterly-trending valleys that face on the Ross Sea and make up much of the ice-free area of Victoria Land. From several weeks observations in the valley during the austral summer the following observations are noted:

1. Cloudiness is greater, except for coastal areas where orographic clouds are extremely common.
2. Snowfall is slightly greater.
3. Ground temperatures are lower, due in part to the altitude and in part to the increased cloudi-

Fig. 25. Polygonal trough in moraine on floor of Beacon Valley, near Site B. G. I. shovel marks active contraction crack, and long-handled shovel the west edge of the trough. Trough is over 4 meters wide. Large boulders on the surface are mainly dolerite.

ness. The range of the diurnal temperature change is probably about the same.

4. As expected, winds blow up and down the valley, and have presumably the same velocity as winds in other valleys in the area.

The morainal floor of the valley is extremely rough, with boulders of dolerite and sandstone up to 10 meters in diameter scattered over the surface. The major portion of the surface consists of clean quartz sand overlain by dolerite boulders 0.5 to 1 meter in diameter. Nonsorted polygons are well developed over the entire valley floor.

The larger polygons at the contraction sites are high centered and many have troughs over a meter deep (Figure 25). Secondary wedges subdividing the larger polygons (7–12 meters) are common. Polygon centers are covered with a boulder pavement, but troughs are mostly filled with clean, well-rounded, quartz sand. Occasional pebbles and cobbles lie in the center of the troughs. Snow is present in the troughs throughout most of the year, and because of the prevailing winds, tends to remain longer in troughs perpendicular to the valley than in troughs parallel to the valley and the winds. Depression cones are common in troughs in November, indicating a filling of contraction cracks by the well-rounded quartz sand.

Widths of troughs were measured using as outer limits the break in slope between a trough and the centers of the adjacent polygons. This may not be a true reflection of the width of the wedges, because of slumping or the presence of cobbles or boulders. Excavation of several wedges revealed large differences in width, composition, structure, and color. Some wedges (usually trending northeasterly) are composed entirely of clean, well-rounded quartz sand with an occasional pebble. They are structureless, have a low moisture content (less than 2 per cent by weight), and possess clear-cut boundaries. Others, notably southeasterly-trending troughs, are much more complicated. In these troughs the surface sands possess a slightly higher moisture content (3–4 per cent) from more common snow cover. As a result, the sands are more cohesive and retard the flow of sand into contraction cracks. The number of controlled wedges oriented parallel and normal to prevailing winds is, however, insufficient to quantify this difference at this time. In some wedges the center of the wedge consists of a zone of poorly sorted material approximately 50 cm wide adjoined by clean quartz sand. The inner zone, directly below the center of the trough, possesses strong foliation from textural changes parallel to the sides of the inner wedge (Figure 17). The clean quartz sand adjoining the inner wedge is also foliated but less so. Pebble bands, oriented parallel to the trend of a wedge, are common throughout the zone of quartz sand.

What the inner wedges represent is a matter of conjecture. They may represent an increase in the amount of snow present in the trough or an increase in duration of snow cover. This would suggest less availability of sand. Less snow would reduce water to bind the sand, and an abundant supply of sand would therefore be available for filling of the contraction crack.

The presence of a glacial front—a series of apparently recessional moraines dividing the valley floor into areas of different age—and ubiquitous polygons should make Beacon Valley ideal for contraction measurements. Logistic problems, large boulders, marked surface relief, apparent variation in original ice content across moraines, and the difficulty of determining actual widths of wedges, make for a less than ideal setup.

The writers made an initial effort to establish a site at the glacier front where two sets of polygons

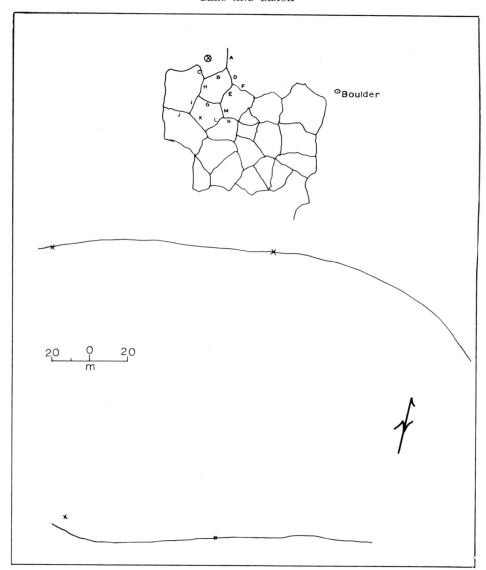

Fig. 26.   Map of contraction Site A, Beacon Valley.

are present. The oldest set has wedges 2.5 meters wide and is not controlled (aligned orthogonal) by the ice front. The second set possesses wedges only 10–20 cm wide, and they are aligned orthogonal to the glacier front. The solidly ice-cemented bouldery moraine, however, defeated our efforts to drive control stakes for growth measurements.

Contraction sites were established on both sides of the prominent moraine 500 meters southwest of the Taylor Glacier. Site A (Figure 26), established 12 November 1961, consists of 14 controlled wedges and lies between the moraine and the ice front. Site B (Figure 27), established 18 November 1962,

consists of 18 controlled wedges and is to the south of that moraine. Contraction measurements to date are given in Tables 3 and 4. At Site A (Table 3) wedges averaged 1.03 mm growth between 12 November 1961 and 18 November 1962, and 0.95 mm between 18 November 1962 and 1 December 1963, for an average of 0.99 mm per year during the 2-year period; wedge B was not included in the average because of an obvious error in measurement. Maximum growth of any wedge was 2.2 mm in 1961–1962 and 2.6 mm in 1962–1963, both from wedge K. Minimum growth was +0.1 mm (wedge N) in 1961–1962 and —0.3 mm (wedge D) in 1962–

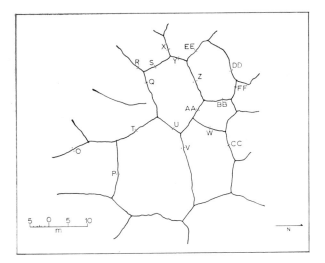

Fig. 27. Map of contraction Site B, Beacon Valley.

1963. From field observations and growth measurements, wedges D and N appear to have been inactive during the period; no cones of depression or other evidence of growth were visible in the troughs. Wedges D and N were, however, included in the calculations in order that an average growth rate would take into account periods of reduced growth. Variation of growth between the 1961–1962 results and the 1962–1963 results for any one pair of stakes averaged 0.3 mm. Maximum variation in growth

TABLE 3. Contraction Measurements (cm), Site A, Beacon Valley

Wedge	12 Nov. 1961 18 Nov. 1962	18 Nov. 1962 1 Dec. 1963	Interstake Measurement 1 Dec. 1963
A	+0.16	+0.16	89.60
B	UNR	UNR	94.80
C	+0.08	+0.02	95.49
D	+0.02	−0.03	88.08
E	+0.08	+0.04	83.65
F	+0.18	+0.21	90.96
G	+0.10	+0.13	88.28
H	+0.12	+0.08	89.03
I	+0.19	+0.17	87.28
J	+0.04	+0.06	80.10
K	+0.22	+0.26	91.55
L	+0.05	+0.08	89.29
M	+0.09	+0.06	89.25
N	+0.01	0.00	83.44
Growth	1.03 mm/yr	0.95 mm/yr	

UNR = unreliable.

TABLE 4. Contraction Measurements (cm), Site B, Beacon Valley

Wedge	18 Nov. 1962 1 Dec. 1963	Interstake Measurement 1 Dec. 1963
O	+0.07	72.00
P	+0.10	99.75
Q	+0.06	86.69
R	+0.07	89.00
S	+0.27	62.09
T	+0.22	97.53
U	−0.04	118.42
V	+0.23	86.61
W	−0.04	121.35
X	+0.19	89.94
Y	+0.12	82.24
Z	+0.07	80.32
AA	+0.07	96.10
BB	+0.17	89.01
CC	+0.08	94.97
DD	+0.12	90.01
EE	+0.40	91.26
FF	+0.04	97.29
Growth	1.22 mm/yr	

was 0.6 mm (wedge C). At a site where stake movement might be expected, and where relief of stress may take place entirely within the wedges, these results are remarkably consistent. In addition, the time of year when the measurements were made is not the best period for making such measurements, because the ground is still warming up, closing unfilled cracks. A previous estimate of the growth rate for the first year [*Black and Berg,* 1964] included a correction for time of measurement for an average annual growth rate of 0.78 mm. The additional year's data and the consistency of the results suggest that the average growth rate of 0.99 mm per year is more nearly correct.

The wedges at Site A average 3.2 meters in width (field data of Berg). As has been pointed out, accurate estimates of wedge width are very difficult in Beacon Valley. Assuming, however, that Berg's wedge widths are accurate and that growth rates over the entire life of the wedges are uniform, an age of 3230 years is obtained for Site A.

At Site B, between 18 November 1962 and 1 December 1963, the 18 wedges grew an average 1.22 mm. Sixteen had positive growth rates; the maximum was 4.0 mm (wedge EE). Two shrank 0.4 mm (wedges U and W), but these two were also

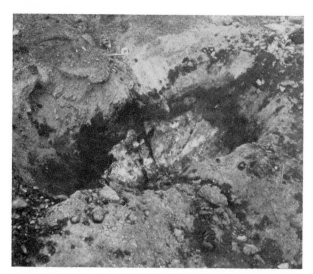

Fig. 28. Excavation of ice wedge at Cape Evans, Ross Island, 30 meters south of the 'Ramp.' A thin layer of moraine lies on ground ice.

the only measurements made by hand-held tape. Average width of the wedges at Site B is 2.6 meters, according to measurements by Black. Maximum width, 4.2 meters, is similar to that of Site A; three secondary wedges average 1.5 meters in width. Assuming a uniform growth rate over the life of the wedges, an age of 2130 years is indicated for Site B.

According to field evidence, Site B is interpreted to be older than Site A, but the wedges suggest the opposite. Differences in growth rates between Site A and Site B may reflect time of measurement rather than any significant actual differences. Moreover, ages of the wedges are reflected in the width measured, which in Beacon Valley can lead to significant error. The widths recorded by Berg for Site A one year and those recorded by Black for Site B a year later may not actually be so different. The indicated disparity between ages may thus not, in fact, be so great.

Considering the small sample, the short time of growth, and the difficulty in obtaining reliable measurements of wedge widths, the agreement is fair. At least the ages are believed to represent the correct order of magnitude.

Cape Evans

Cape Evans (77°38'15"S, 166°25'E) on the west flank of Mount Erebus on Ross Island is triangular

in shape and is bounded on the northeast by the Barne Glacier and on the other sides by McMurdo Sound. Volcanic flows and morainic debris make up the ice-free portion of the cape. The volcanics are thought to be kenytes [*Treves*, 1962] containing phenocrysts of feldspar. The kenyte is easily eroded, resulting in pitted rocks, with the feldspars standing out in relief. The flows form knobs and ridges between which are numerous shallow ponds and small lakes scattered over the cape. Morainic material consists of poorly sorted black volcanic debris, with a coating of white-yellow salts below the surface. Ground ice is present 20–50 cm below the morainic material near the base of the ice-cored moraine of the Barne Glacier (Figure 28). The ice-cored moraine, known as the 'Ramp,' consists of glacier ice covered by 40–80 cm of volcanic moraine. Debris cones up to 9 meters high are common on the moraine.

Because of the relatively high snowfall and irregular topography that provides catchment basins, water is abundant [*Loewe*, 1963]. Winds blow from the southeast 60 per cent of the time at an average yearly velocity of 9 meters/second [*Loewe*, 1963], and gales blow from the southeast 97 per cent of the time. In summer the active layer has a moisture content of 2.3 to 4.3 per cent, reflecting the abundance of moisture available.

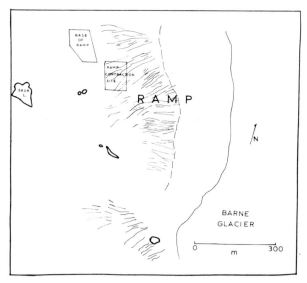

Fig. 29. Sketch of troughs on the 'Ramp,' Cape Evans, Ross Island. From U. S. Navy Aerial Photograph, CAM 31–164, 3 November 1959. Scale approximately 1:3750.

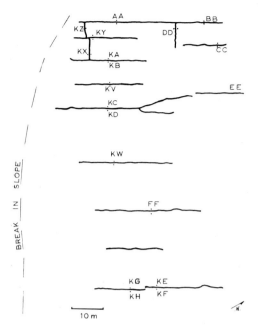

Fig. 30. Sketch map of contraction site on the 'Ramp,' Cape Evans, Ross Island.

Aligned orthogonal polygons are common on the 'Ramp' and on adjacent parts of the cape. On the 'Ramp' and parallel to the strike of the 'Ramp,' wedges 15–80 cm wide, averaging 55 cm, are normal (Figure 29). Troughs, 10–20 cm deep, are irregular and discontinuous, running 10–20 meters between interruptions of from some centimeters to a meter. At the base of the 'Ramp' the wedges are 25–60 cm wide, average 40 cm wide, and have troughs 10–20 cm deep. Polygons are 5–15 meters wide and flat-centered.

Two contraction sites were established at Cape Evans, one on the top of the 'Ramp' (Figure 30), the other at the base. Fifteen wedges were controlled on the 'Ramp,' 12 wedges at the base (Table 5). From 30 December 1961 until 13 November 1962 the wedges on the 'Ramp' grew 2.7 mm and at the base 5.58 mm. These values, however, are too high, because at the time of measurement the ground was still expanding and closing partially filled cracks. Between 13 November 1962 and 15 December 1963, the wedges grew 1.05 mm on the 'Ramp' and 1.97 mm at the base. Average growth rates over the 2-year period are 3.8 mm per year for wedges at the base of the 'Ramp' and 0.85 mm per year for wedges on the 'Ramp.'

Maximum growth at the base of the 'Ramp' was 13.7 mm over the 2-year period, and minimum growth 3.0 mm. On the 'Ramp,' maximum growth was 6.0 mm whereas maximum shrinkage was 2.8 mm—a variance of 8.8 mm. Three wedges parallel to the strike of the 'Ramp' had an average growth rate of 2.1 mm per year over the measured period, while the 12 wedges that were perpendicular to the strike of the 'Ramp' had growths averaging 0.5 mm per year. Five of 11 troughs perpendicular to the strike had negative values; one was zero. From these data it seems apparent that the ice is moving perpendicular to the strike of the 'Ramp' and that the troughs perpendicular to the strike of the 'Ramp' probably reflect tension in the ice rather than wedge growth.

Results at the base of the 'Ramp' appear reliable. Uniformity of wedge size and consistency of growth measurements are good. The presence of ground ice supports the high growth rates. Assuming a uniform growth rate over the life of the wedges (3.8 mm per year), the 40-cm-wide wedges at the base of the 'Ramp' should be only 100 years old.

Taylor Valley

Taylor Valley is one of a series of east-west–trending, ice-free valleys that are characteristic of central Victoria Land. The west end of the valley is filled by the Taylor Glacier, which drains from the Polar Plateau. The east end is bounded by McMurdo Sound. On the south the Kukri Hills rise to heights of 1800 meters, and small valleyside glaciers, originating on the upland, cling to the valley wall. The Asgard Range has peaks up to 2150 meters and separates Taylor Valley from additional ice-free valleys to the north. Two large glaciers, the Canada and the Commonwealth, flow from uplands on the north down onto the valley floor.

From McMurdo Sound the floor of Taylor Valley rises gradually westward reaching 500 meters in elevation at the base of Nussbaum Riegel, a glacially eroded rock knob in the center of the valley. West of Nussbaum Riegel, the valley floor drops sharply down to 38 meters above sea level at Lake Bonney. A narrow gorge separates Nussbaum Riegel and the north side of the valley.

In the central part of the valley a series of nearly vertical, north-northwest–striking, metasedimentary rocks of the Ross System [*Angino, Turner,*

TABLE 5. Contraction Measurements (cm), Cape Evans, Ross Island

Wedge	29 April 1961 31 Aug. 1961	31 Aug. 1961 30 Dec. 1961	30 Dec. 1961 13 Nov. 1962	13 Nov. 1962 15 Dec. 1963	30 Dec. 1961 15 Dec. 1963	Interstake Measurement 15 Dec. 1963
			Ramp			
KA–KB	0.00	+0.12	−0.10	+0.05	−0.05	50.92
KC–KD	+0.81	−0.69	+0.66	−0.09	+0.57	76.92
KE–KF	+1.10	−1.17	+0.31	−0.21	+0.10	61.52
KG–KH	+0.91	−0.75	−0.05	−0.06	−0.11	86.62
KV	—	—	−0.15	−0.13	−0.28	59.05
KW	—	—	+0.05	+0.05	+0.10	81.76
KX	—	—	+0.21	−0.10	+0.11	62.33
KY	—	—	+0.39	0.00	+0.39	73.36
KZ	—	—	+0.53	+0.01	+0.54	57.13
AA	—	—	+0.66	−0.30	+0.36	68.06
BB	—	—	+0.39	−0.26	+0.13	83.92
CC	—	—	−0.09	+0.02	−0.07	33.62
DD	—	—	+0.55	+0.05	+0.60	62.39
EE	—	—	+0.45	−0.50	−0.05	80.65
FF	—	—	+0.26	—	—	—
Average	+7.0 mm	−6.2 mm	+2.7 mm	+1.05 mm	+0.85 mm/yr	
			Base of Ramp			
KO			+0.66	+0.07	+0.73	54.44
KP			+0.72	+0.21	+0.93	43.49
KQ			+0.30	0.00	+0.30	56.50
KR			+0.73	+0.01	+0.74	50.81
KS			+0.45	+0.35	+0.80	45.77
KT			+0.38	+0.06	+0.44	53.45
KU			+0.21	+0.99	+1.20	51.89
GG			+0.39	+0.12	+0.51	43.41
HH			+0.29	+0.04	+0.33	56.70
II			+1.04	+0.10	+1.14	52.03
JJ			+0.65	−0.08	+0.57	46.08
KK			+0.88	+0.49	+1.37	51.30
Average			+5.58 mm	+1.97 mm	+3.8 mm/yr	

and Zeller, 1962] crops out. Most of the lower part of the valley is blanketed with morainal material and glacial lake deposits [*Péwé*, 1959]. Only limited climatic data for the valley have been published [*Angino, Armitage, and Tash*, 1962] but numerous reports on Lake Bonney are out [e.g., see *Hoare et al.*, 1964].

Nussbaum Riegel–delta. The contraction site with the most controlled wedges in Taylor Valley is on a thin delta in the center of a depression in bedrock 4 km east of Nussbaum Riegel (77°39′27″S, 162° 53′33″E). It is surrounded by moraines [*Angino, Turner, and Zeller*, 1962]. The delta, which slopes gently toward the north, was formed at a time when the shallow fresh-water pond northeast of the delta

was greatly enlarged and occupied the whole depression. Abandoned high beaches are south of the delta, and an outlet channel 20 meters above the delta crosses the bedrock ridge and moraine to the east.

Polygons on the surface of the delta are flat-centered, average 10 meters in diameter, and have abrupt troughs averaging 75 cm wide (Figure 31). The surface is covered with a desert pavement of pebbles one layer thick (Figure 32). Numerous excavations and temperature studies in the area reveal a true active layer averaging 25 cm thick, with a moisture content of 2–3.5 per cent in summer. Permafrost in the delta contains 10–15 per cent moisture. Wedges are mainly composite with more sand

Fig. 31. Contraction site at delta near Nussbaum Riegel. Control rods are visible in left foreground. Windmill generator and boxes are part of an automatic temperature-recording station. Glaciers in background were the main source of water for former lake in which delta was built. View to the southwest.

than ice. Removal of the active layer reveals a typical double raised-rim along wedges at a depth of 25–30 cm, although the rims do not show at the surface. These rims are characteristic of young flat-centered polygons.

Average growth of 49 wedges over a 2-year period from 13 December 1961 to 6 December 1963 was 1.0 mm, or a mean growth of 0.5 mm per year (Table 6, Figure 33). Maximum growth of a wedge during the period was 3.5 mm; maximum shrinkage, 5.6 mm. Forty-three wedges grew, one did not change, and 5 shrank. Although the shrinkage of 5.6 mm is high, it is not a result of measurement error, because the wedge was measured before and after the measurements during which the shrinkage occurred. The other four wedges shrank 0.1 to 0.4 mm. From 13 December 1961 to 8 November 1962 the wedges grew an average of 1.17 mm. Forty-four wedges widened, one did not change, and 3 shrank. The three that shrank appeared to be inactive. The 1.17-mm growth rate for the 11 months is too large, because in early November the ground had not warmed sufficiently to expand and close partly filled contraction cracks. A second set of measurements was made on 6 January 1963. During the 2-month interval, all wedges shrank an average of 0.88 mm. An average growth rate of 0.3 mm per

year (the net average growth from 13 December 1961 to 6 January 1963) was, therefore, used for this site, and correction factors were applied to other sites [*Black and Berg*, 1964]. Between 6 January 1963 and 6 December 1963 the 49 wedges grew an average of 0.72 mm, ranging from a maximum of 2.5 mm to a minimum of —5.6 mm. Forty wedges had positive values; 3 had negative values. A second measurement on 17 January 1964 showed an average change of only —0.04 mm, which is less than our measuring error, and suggested that the 2-year average of 0.5 mm per year will probably only be modified slightly with additional measurements over a longer time period. Assuming the growth rate is uniform over the entire span of the 75-cm wedges, an age of 1500 years is obtained for the delta, presumably when the lake level dropped below the delta surface.

Immediately west of the delta is a moraindal surface that rises up onto bare rock surfaces 1 km distant, where it is covered with eolian material. No break or change is seen in the size of wedges from the ground or from air photos [*Black and Berg*, 1964]. Larger polygons with double raised-rims 1 to 3 meters apart are present 3 km west-northwest of the lake on the east slope of Nussbaum Riegel (Figure 34). These wedges are probably several thousand years older than the wedges on the surface of the delta. From ground observations and aerial photographic studies, wedge widths elsewhere in the lower half of Taylor Valley are comparable to those on the delta.

Fig. 32. Troughs on surface of delta near Nussbaum Riegel outline flat-centered polygons which have a desert pavement on the surface.

TABLE 6. Contraction Measurements (cm), Delta, Nussbaum Riegel, Taylor Valley

Wedge	13 Dec. 1961 8 Nov. 1962	8 Nov. 1962 6 Jan. 1963	6 Jan. 1963 6 Dec. 1963	13 Dec. 1961 6 Dec. 1963	6 Dec. 1963 17 Jan. 1964	Interstake Measurement
A	+0.22	−0.22	−0.56	−0.56	−0.03	89.95
B	+0.03	−0.08	+0.09	+0.04	−0.02	87.52
C	+0.08	−0.05	+0.06	+0.09	+0.01	51.40
D	+0.08	—	—	−0.04	—	—
E	+0.13	−0.06	−0.01	+0.06	0.00	96.07
F	+0.12	−0.05	+0.05	+0.12	0.00	86.31
G	+0.06	−0.10	+0.10	+0.06	+0.03	82.29
H	+0.08	−0.06	+0.01	+0.03	−0.02	91.13
I	+0.04	−0.03	+0.16	+0.17	0.00	65.22
J	+0.09	−0.11	+0.01	−0.01	+0.02	85.57
K	+0.03	0.00	+0.04	+0.07	0.00	49.40
L	+0.07	−0.02	+0.10	+0.15	+0.02	63.93
M	+0.18	−0.11	+0.05	+0.12	+0.01	77.17
N	+0.34	−0.31	+0.03	+0.06	−0.02	76.30
O	+0.22	−0.11	+0.04	+0.15	−0.07	85.75
P	+0.46	−0.27	+0.14	+0.33	0.00	81.61
Q	+0.13	−0.09	+0.11	+0.15	−0.01	80.61
R	+0.03	−0.11	+0.09	+0.01	+0.02	96.89
S	−0.02	−0.06	+0.13	+0.15	−0.01	68.49
T	+0.18	−0.16	+0.13	+0.15	−0.04	71.60
U	+0.18	−0.07	+0.12	+0.23	−0.01	69.95
V	+0.12	—	—	0.00	—	—
W	+0.18	−0.08	+0.22	+0.32	+0.02	55.63
X	+0.15	−0.05	+0.25	+0.35	−0.02	98.83
Y	+0.10	−0.08	+0.10	+0.12	0.00	68.60
Z	+0.16	−0.06	+0.13	+0.23	0.00	55.45
AA	+0.03	−0.06	+0.16	+0.13	+0.03	70.44
BB	+0.22	−0.11	+0.07	+0.18	−0.02	99.59
CC	+0.08	−0.01	+0.05	+0.12	+0.04	88.00
DD	—	—	+0.01	+0.03	+0.03	79.78
EE	+0.14	−0.07	+0.06	+0.13	−0.02	68.13
FF	+0.31	−0.14	−0.04	+0.13	0.00	71.11
GG	+0.08	−0.01	+0.07	+0.14	−0.05	67.32
HH	+0.24	−0.14	+0.09	+0.19	+0.01	82.31
II	+0.09	−0.09	+0.05	+0.05	0.00	69.84
JJ	0.00	−0.08	+0.05	−0.03	−0.01	85.91
KK	+0.15	−0.07	+0.05	+0.13	−0.01	64.25
LL	+0.10	−0.08	+0.04	+0.06	−0.05	66.18
MM	+0.05	−0.03	+0.11	+0.13	−0.10	67.64
CE-CF	+0.08	—	—	+0.08	—	—
CH-CI	+0.04	—	—	+0.10	—	—
CJ-CK	+0.12	—	—	+0.21	—	—
CM-CN	+0.20	−0.13	+0.18	+0.25	−0.01	94.18
CO-CP	−0.03	−0.07	+0.08	−0.02	—	—
CQ-CR	+0.05	−0.05	+0.10	+0.10	+0.04	60.81
CS-CT	+0.06	−0.03	+0.16	+0.19	−0.03	86.67
CU-CV	+0.11	−0.08	+0.08	+0.11	—	—
CW-CX	−0.02	−0.11	+0.14	+0.01	−0.02	88.10
CY-CZ	+0.07	—	—	—	+0.01	69.56
Growth (mm)	+1.17	−0.88	+0.72	1.00, 2 yr 0.5, 1 yr	0.04	

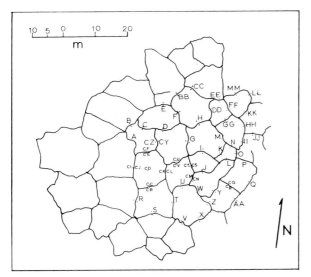

Fig. 33. Map of contraction site on the delta 4 km east of Nussbaum Riegel.

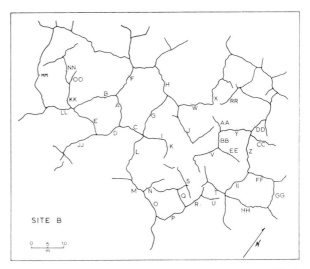

Fig. 35. Map of contraction site on moraine-covered bedrock ridge 1 km east of the delta at Nussbaum Riegel.

Nussbaum Riegel–hillsite. To provide additional control on growth rates in the area 42 wedges were controlled on the top of a moraine-covered bedrock ridge 1 km east of the delta (Figure 35). The ridge, 450 meters above sea level, consists of a metamorphic complex [*Angino, Turner, and Zeller,* 1962] overlain by a thin veneer of morainal debris. Topography is irregular, large glacial erratics are common, and thickness of the dry zone averages 30 cm.

Fig. 34. Double raised-rim polygons 3 km west–northwest of the lake east of Nussbaum Riegel. G. I. shovel is 54 cm high. Looking north.

A salt-rich layer is locally present 7–12 cm beneath the surface. The dry zone contained 2–3 per cent water by weight, whereas the permafrost was locally supersaturated with ice. Moisture contents greater than 50 per cent by weight were measured. Wedges contained 10–15 per cent water by weight.

Wedge widths ranged from 50 to 160 cm and averaged 75 cm. Growth from 12 November 1962 to 6 December 1963 averaged −0.01 mm (Table 7). Seventeen wedges shrank as much as 1.1 mm; nineteen wedges grew as much as 1.0 mm; and one wedge did not change.

The results are not a reliable indication of growth rate because November turns out to be a very poor time for measurement. The measurement interval is somewhat similar to that on the delta between 8 November 1962 and 6 January 1963. During that period those wedges shrank 0.88 mm, even though the average annual growth rate at the site is 0.5 mm. A proportional relation between the delta and this site would indicate that wedges here should have a growth rate of around 0.75 mm per year. Since, however, control is too poor to use this figure, the results are disregarded for the present. The presence of only a shallow morainic cover on bedrock and the lack of moisture due to the exposed position of the ridge would suggest a rate of growth at the site that is less than 0.5 mm per year.

Mouth of valley. Growth of wedges in the abandoned delta at Nussbaum Riegel may be compared

TABLE 7.   Contraction Measurements (cm),
Hill Site, Nussbaum Riegel, Taylor Valley

Wedge	12 Nov. 1962 6 Dec. 1963	Interstake Measurement 6 Dec. 1963
A	−0.09	81.67
B	−0.01	58.92
C	−0.06	89.97
D	−0.04	77.63
E	−0.04	65.94
F	−0.06	86.09
G	—	101.48
H	−0.11	74.40
I	+0.07	88.32
J	—	82.53
K	+0.10	72.98
L	+0.02	97.05
M	−0.01	97.50
N	−0.09	88.31
O	+0.01	89.95
P	+0.04	46.85
Q	−0.01	84.86
R	−0.01	94.23
S	+0.03	96.90
T	+0.06	99.30
U	−0.05	84.87
V	+0.01	61.91
W	—	156.99
X	+0.06	72.11
Y	—	105.65
Z	+0.04	85.95
AA	+0.01	88.13
BB	0.00	85.88
CC	+0.02	87.64
DD	+0.05	97.85
EE	+0.02	74.35
FF	—	134.29
GG	+0.02	97.12
HH	+0.01	92.68
II	−0.02	80.12
JJ	−0.03	71.55
KK	−0.09	82.35
LL	−0.05	78.10
MM	−0.01	89.36
NN	+0.10	91.69
OO	—	114.70
PP	No stakes	—
QQ	+0.04	99.78
RR	+0.03	68.30

Fig. 36.   Contraction site at the mouth of Taylor Valley. Commonwealth Glacier in upper left. Aligned orthogonal polygons are developed normal and parallel to the stream channel.

Glacier that enters New Harbor at the northeast end of Taylor Valley (Figure 36).

The site is divided into two sections (Figure 7), one on the delta proper and another on the adjoining moraine. On the delta the wedges are developed

with that of the wedges of an active delta 1–3 meters above sea level at the mouth of Taylor Valley (77°33′30″S, 163°30′55″E). The delta has been formed by a stream from the Commonwealth

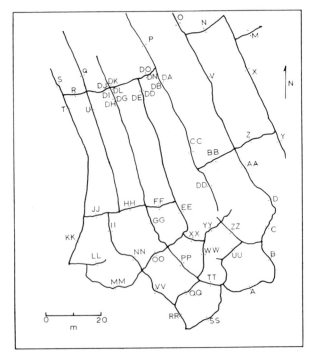

Fig. 37.   Map of contraction site at the mouth of Taylor Valley.

in a rectangular net with polygons 5–12 meters wide and 30–50 meters long, parallel and normal to the stream channel (Figure 37). Troughs average 70 cm in width. Gravelly sand of the delta is covered with a pavement of pebbles.

Snowfall is greater at the mouth of Taylor Valley than further inland at Nussbaum Riegel. Snowbanks are common at the junction of the moraine and the delta throughout most of the year (Figure 38). The active layer on the delta contains 2–9 per cent water, depending on the time of year and prox-

TABLE 8. Contraction Measurements (cm), Delta, New Harbor, Taylor Valley

Wedge	23 Dec. 1961 12 Nov. 1962	12 Nov. 1962 14 Dec. 1963	23 Dec. 1961 14 Dec. 1963	Interstake Measurement 14 Dec. 1963
M	+0.31	−0.09	+0.22	71.03
N	+0.61	−0.14	+0.47	62.21
O	+0.44	−0.31	+0.13	62.21
P	+0.42	−0.30	+0.12	63.46
Q	+0.39	−0.02	+0.37	64.36
R	+0.41	−0.04	+0.37	63.77
S	+0.10	+0.12	+0.22	63.64
T	+0.16	+0.03	+0.19	57.77
U	+0.33	+0.12	+0.45	55.51
V	+0.37	−0.19	+0.18	73.87
W	+0.04	−0.03	+0.01	56.28
X	+0.33	−0.11	+0.22	68.76
Y	+0.64	0.00	+0.64	55.27
Z	+0.40	−0.11	+0.29	64.88
AA	+0.45	+0.34	+0.79	62.94
BB	+0.69	−0.43	+0.26	68.60
CC	+0.51	−0.11	+0.40	54.41
DD	+0.47	+0.02	+0.49	47.75
EE	+0.72	UNR	UNR	55.66
FF	+0.40	−0.21	+0.19	56.10
GG	+0.71	UNR	UNR	55.46
HH	+0.93	−0.50	+0.43	53.66
II	+0.71	−0.29	+0.42	59.23
JJ	+0.56	−0.28	+0.28	55.39
KK	+0.50	+0.02	+0.52	40.61
DA–DB	—	—	+0.05	125.90
DD–DE	—	—	−0.14	82.61
DG–DH	—	—	+0.22	80.28
DI–DJ	—	—	+0.18	127.98
DI–DL	—	—	+0.18	111.53
DJ–DK	—	—	+0.09	114.09
DL–DK	—	—	+0.18	127.42
DN–DO	—	—	+0.21	129.66
Ave.	+4.64 mm	−1.1 mm	1.7 mm/yr	

UNR = unreliable.

TABLE 9. Contraction Measurements (cm), Moraine, New Harbor, Taylor Valley

Wedge	23 Dec. 1961 12 Nov. 1962	12 Nov. 1962 14 Dec. 1963	23 Dec. 1961 14 Dec. 1963	Interstake Measurement 14 Dec. 1963
LL	+0.66	—	—	Undersnow
MM	+0.54	+0.03	+0.57	52.32
NN	+0.39	+0.19	+0.58	61.76
OO	+0.70	+0.05	+0.75	53.66
PP	+0.26	UNR	UNR	46.32
QQ	+0.05	−0.03	+0.02	47.77
RR	+0.39	+0.12	+0.51	61.28
SS	+0.25	+0.08	+0.33	59.05
TT	+0.24	+0.08	+0.32	57.61
UU	+0.42	+0.14	+0.56	58.21
VV	+0.23	+0.05	+0.28	64.57
WW	+0.42	+0.07	+0.49	62.34
XX	+0.61	+0.26	+0.87	47.73
YY	+0.88	+0.22	+1.10	53.52
ZZ	+0.13	+0.03	+0.16	53.55
A	+0.19	+0.12	+0.31	60.46
B	+0.16	−0.03	+0.13	69.09
C	+0.30	+0.20	+0.50	59.75
D	+0.25	+0.14	+0.39	60.90
Ave.	3.72 mm	+0.9 mm	2.1 mm	

UNR = unreliable.

imity to snow. Permafrost contains 10–15 per cent moisture. Wedges are mainly sand, with double raised-rims developed on top of the permafrost but not reflected at the surface.

Between 23 December 1961 and 12 November 1962, 25 measured wedges on the delta expanded 4.64 mm; 8 wedges were not measured on 12 November 1962 because tape was not available (Table 8). Maximum expansion was 9.3 mm, and minimum expansion 0.4 mm. The expansion is largely due to the time of measurement and does not indicate actual growth. Between 12 November 1962 and 14 December 1963, 23 of the 25 wedges shrank an average of 1.1 mm; 17 wedges shrank with a maximum of 5.0 mm, and 6 wedges expanded as much as 3.4 mm; two wedge measurements were unreliable and thus not included. Of the 33 wedges measured on 23 December 1961 and 14 December 1963, 30 wedges widened, one shrank 1.4 mm, and two were not usable. Growth rate for the 2-year period averages 2.78 mm or 1.4 mm per year. Assuming growth is uniform over the life of the 70-cm wedges, they are 500 years old.

Fig. 38. Snow cover at contraction site at the mouth of Taylor Valley. Snowbank is on moraine at edge of delta. 14 December 1963.

Immediately to the south of the delta and adjoining it is a moraine which rises to 8 meters above sea level. Polygons are 5–15 meters in diameter with troughs averaging 70 cm in width. The surface of the moraine is drier than that of the delta except near the junction of the two, where snow is usually present. The active layer contains 1–3 per cent moisture, and the permafrost 12 per cent moisture (one sample). Wedges are filled with sand. On the moraine, 17 wedges grew an average of 3.72 mm from 23 December 1961 to 12 November 1962 (Table 9). This figure is too high, owing to the early measurement. Maximum contraction during this period was 8.8 mm; the minimum was 0.5 mm. Between 12 November 1962 and 14 December 1963 the wedges grew an average of 0.9 mm. Maximum growth was 2.6 mm; two wedges shrank 0.3 mm. Again these figures are suspect because of the time of measurement. The rate should be somewhat low, because on 12 November contraction cracks would still be open. That the first year's results were too high and the second too low is shown by the 2-year average of 2.1 mm per year and our knowledge of the thermal changes of the ground. On 14 December 1963, snow up to 0.5 meter deep covered most of the site and probably affected the readings. It was necessary to burrow down to some stakes; we were not able to find one set of stakes. Until additional measurements are made the average

growth rate of 2.1 mm per year should be treated with caution. However, using the above figure and assuming uniform growth throughout the life of the wedges, they are 333 years old.

Undoubtedly the moraine is slightly older than the delta, yet the wedges imply that the delta is over a hundred years older than the moraine. Possible reasons for the discrepancy include:

1. Interruptions of growth on the moraine due to perennial snow cover: Figure 38, taken on 14 December 1963, shows the abundant snow cover over the area and the large snowbank that persists through much of the year at the junction of the delta and the moraine. A slight increase in accumulation could result in a perennial snow cover with a resultant cessation of growth. Wedge widths and growth rates in the snowbank area, however, are not significantly different from those given above.

2. Stake movement on moraine due to slope angle: stake movement is difficult to assess, but uniformity of growth rates suggests that it is not important.

3. Error in measurement: nothing suggests such error and in fact all evidence indicates actual values are correctly measured.

4. Measurements made between 23 December 1961 to 12 November 1962 showed an average growth of 4.6 mm on the delta and 3.7 mm on the moraine, but between 12 November 1962 and 14 December 1963 wedges on the moraine expanded an average of 0.9 mm whereas wedges on the delta shrank an average of 1.1 mm. This indicates that

Fig. 39. Air photo of 'Windy Crater,' Hut Point Peninsula, Ross Island, looking southwest. McMurdo Station in background. 22 December 1960.

the moraine warms up faster than the delta in the austral spring (October–November) and closes the contraction cracks in the moraine while the cracks in the delta are still open. Although this affected the November readings it should not materially affect the late December readings. Timing can, however, be very critical, and at least part of the difference may be attributed to the short time of measurement. Moreover, in the moraine, loose sand tends to fill cracks more readily than in the delta, where less loose sand was available at that time because of cohesion by water and partial filling by snow. Although wedges at both localities are composed of sand, the active layer on the delta has a higher moisture content, and the filling of the wedge may not have taken place due to cementation of the active layer.

'Windy Crater'

'Windy Crater' (77°50′30″S, 166°40′30″E) is a recent volcanic cone on Hut Point Peninsula, Ross Island. The cone is 160 meters above sea level and 300 meters in diameter. The floor of its double crater is 30 meters below the highest point on the rim. The cone is one of a series of Pleistocene to Recent volcanic deposits [Harrington, 1956] that form a rim around the United States base at McMurdo. Crater Hill, another volcanic cone and the highest point (310 meters) on the peninsula, lies to the east of 'Windy Crater' and forms a barrier to the storm winds that blow across the Island from the Ross Ice Shelf. No moraines are visible on the rim of the crater, but they do exist on the east and south outer sides of the cone. Moraines in a small pass to the south of 'Windy Crater' were deposited after the formation of the cone [Wellman, 1964]. Erratics of quartzite, sandstone, and granite in the volcanic rubble on the rim of the crater are thought by Wellman [1963] to be wind-blown from the mainland, but they may be glacial or glacio-marine erratics. Olivine is derived by weathering from xenoliths in the volcanics. Beach gravel near the summit of Crater Hill indicates possible Recent uplift of Ross Island. Forbes and Ester [1964] reported east-trending glacial striae on top of Observation Hill (227 meters above sea level), indicating an enlarged ice shelf that covered Observation Hill and that correlates with moraines at 244 meters at Cape Royds, 30 km north.

The contraction site covers part of the east rim and the interior of the crater (Figure 39). Two small sites were established in 1960, one on the east rim, the other on the west rim. Contraction measurements were carried out through the winter of 1961 and the following summer. Unfortunately the site on the west rim was destroyed in February 1962. In the austral summer of 1962–1963, the site was expanded to its present state. 'Windy Crater' is not only the largest contraction site, but it also has an extensive ground-temperature measurement installation.

A pavement of volcanic rubble, mainly scoria, covers the surface of 'Windy Crater.' The scoria is black to reddish brown but on the underside of the rocks whitish coatings of mirabilite are common. Beneath the pavement is a layer of yellow volcanic ash from 1 to 10 cm thick. Beneath it is another layer of silt [loess, re Wellman, 1964] or ash which is 15–20 cm thick, reddish, and very friable at all times of the year. Since moisture content in this layer ranges from 1 to 2.5 per cent water by weight, it is not cemented by ice. Beneath this layer is a poorly sorted layer, 5–7 cm thick, containing 4–8 per cent water, that grades into permafrost which contains 10–60 per cent water by weight. Salt layers 1–5 cm thick are very locally present 5–15 cm below the surface.

Polygons are 5–10 meters in diameter and have scoria-filled troughs 5–20 cm deep. Wedges range from pure ice wedges at the floor of the cone (Figure 20) to composite wedges (Figure 23) with as much as 60 per cent sand and silt on the higher insides and rim of the crater. No appreciable difference in growth rate was noticed between wedges on the floor of the crater and wedges on the insides and rims of the crater. Only 9 wedges on the lowermost floor of the crater are, however, controlled.

Ten wedges were measured throughout the austral winter of 1961. From 15 April to 11 May the wedges grew an average of 0.9 mm; 9 were positive, one shrank 0.2 mm. From 16 May until 15 June the wedges gave mixed results: 6 wedges expanded, the maximum 1.0 mm, and 4 shrank, one 1.4 mm. Data for July suggest shrinkage of some and expansion of others. For the period 15 June to 9 September, 9 of the 10 wedges grew and one shrank 0.8 mm, for an average growth of 0.8 mm. From 15 April to 9 September, 9 wedges grew and one shrank 0.8

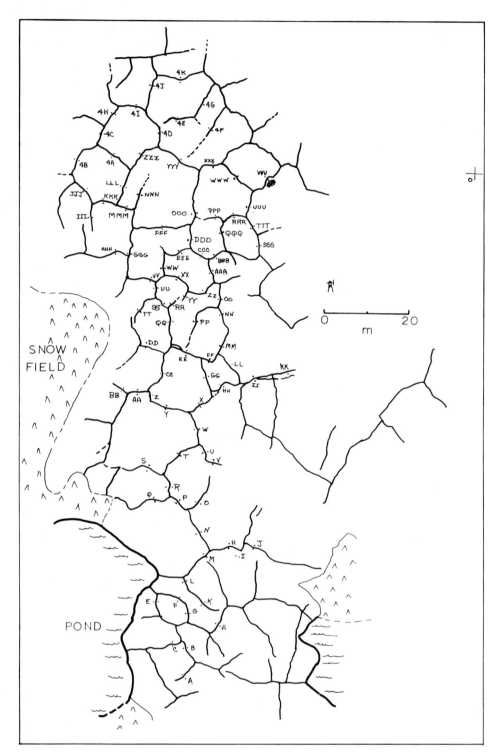

Fig. 40.   Map of contraction site at 'Windy Crater,' Hut Point Peninsula, Ross Island.

TABLE 10. Contraction Measurements (cm), 'Windy Crater,' Hut Point Peninsula, Ross Island

Wedge	1 March 1962 29 Oct. 1962	29 Oct. 1962 28 Nov. 1963	1 March 1962 28 Nov. 1963	Interstake Measurement 28 Nov. 1963	Wedge	1 March 1962 29 Oct. 1962	29 Oct. 1962 28 Nov. 1963	1 March 1962 28 Nov. 1963	Interstake Measurement 28 Nov. 1963
A	+0.21	+0.03	+0.24	53.28	TT	+0.16	−0.18	−0.02	53.20
B	+0.20	−0.01	+0.19	48.30	UU	+0.25	−0.16	+0.09	64.54
C	+0.17	−0.10	+0.07	50.91	VV	+0.37	−0.18	+0.19	54.80
D	+0.30	−0.09	+0.21	42.62	WW	+0.58	+0.45	+0.13	45.83
E	+0.18	−0.04	+0.14	94.74	XX	+0.17	−0.08	+0.09	51.67
F	−0.58	−0.05	−0.63	43.44	YY	+0.07	−0.06	+0.01	66.75
G	+0.23	+0.04	+0.27	51.68	ZZ	+0.33	−0.25	+0.08	66.07
H	+0.57	+0.04	+0.61	76.76	AAA	+0.29	0.00	+0.29	62.49
H′	−0.15	−0.14	−0.29	92.25	BBB	+0.12	−0.02	+0.10	42.50
I	—	—	−0.11	55.13	CCC	+0.79	−0.57	+0.22	67.11
J	+0.44	−0.26	+0.18	53.41	DDD	+1.52	−0.60	+0.92	61.00
K	+0.27	−0.11	+0.16	50.69	EEE	+0.19	−0.06	+0.13	39.61
L	+0.40	−0.74	−0.34	47.59	FFF	—	−0.20	—	51.18
M	+0.59	−0.65	−0.06	81.46	GGG	+0.46	−0.24	+0.22	54.34
N	+0.52	−0.28	+0.24	63.94	HHH	+0.74	−0.11	+0.63	53.65
O	+0.34	−0.28	+0.06	56.47	III	+0.19	−0.04	+0.15	47.05
P	+0.67	−0.63	+0.04	60.55	JJJ	+0.29	−0.17	+0.12	49.53
Q	+0.35	−0.59	−0.24	66.81	KKK	+0.21	−0.09	+0.12	57.62
R	+0.32	−0.24	+0.08	64.35	LLL	+0.27	−0.13	+0.14	60.35
S	+0.46	−0.26	+0.20	68.65	MMM	+0.20	−0.01	+0.19	61.29
T	+0.39	−0.38	+0.01	67.10	NNN	+0.40	−0.27	+0.13	60.15
U	+0.16	−0.13	+0.03	53.33	OOO	+0.50	−0.26	+0.24	57.39
V	+0.16	0.00	+0.16	62.16	PPP	+0.17	−0.13	+0.04	57.32
W	+0.35	−0.06	+0.29	56.69	QQQ	+0.14	−0.08	+0.06	49.65
X	+0.44	−0.42	+0.02	63.30	RRR	+0.19	−0.19	0.00	58.78
Y	+0.24	−0.09	+0.15	48.42	SSS	+0.30	−0.18	+0.12	43.30
Z	+0.26	+0.02	+0.28	46.51	TTT	+0.35	−0.28	+0.07	50.68
AA	+0.38	−0.25	+0.13	57.46	UUU	+0.33	−0.15	+0.18	59.59
BB	+0.20	+0.01	+0.21	53.79	VVV	+0.16	−0.11	+0.05	62.58
CC	+0.30	−0.21	+0.09	60.78	WWW	+0.26	−0.13	+0.13	66.14
DD	+0.34	−0.24	+0.10	48.90	XXX	+0.45	−0.40	+0.05	69.20
EE	+0.54	−0.16	+0.38	58.08	YYY	+0.46	−0.15	+0.31	57.62
FF	+0.15	−0.12	+0.03	59.80	ZZZ	+0.37	−0.19	+0.18	62.50
GG	+0.18	−0.13	+0.05	75.07	4-A	+0.38	−0.16	+0.22	56.22
HH	+0.30	−0.12	+0.18	60.76	4-B	+0.38	−0.21	+0.17	54.72
II	+0.40	−0.20	+0.20	58.93	4-C	+0.30	−0.12	+0.18	60.79
JJ	+0.34	−0.08	+0.26	59.52	4-D	+0.41	−0.23	+0.18	63.88
KK	+0.51	−0.46	+0.05	67.59	4-E	+0.06	−0.03	+0.03	46.12
LL	+0.30	−0.37	−0.07	67.23	4-F	+0.17	−0.23	−0.06	60.97
MM	+0.29	−0.25	+0.04	74.47	4-G	+0.18	−0.15	+0.03	57.63
NN	+0.35	−0.09	+0.26	70.21	4-H	−0.32	−0.20	−0.52	71.20
OO	+0.30	−0.07	+0.23	52.95	4-I	+0.25	−0.17	+0.08?	52.26
PP	+0.10	−0.04	+0.06	63.06	4-J	+0.40	−0.21	+0.19	60.19
QQ	+0.38	−0.28	+0.10	57.20	4-K	+0.35	−0.22	+0.13	54.65
RR	+0.15	−0.09	+0.06	57.40	Ave.	3.0 mm	−1.9 mm	+1.2 mm	
SS	+0.20	−0.03	+0.17	57.00					

mm, for an average growth of 1.75 mm. These data indicate that the initial cracking occurs before 15 May and that throughout much of the winter growth or shrinkage is dependent upon the temperature regime. All the above wedges are composites.

Eighty-nine wedges were measured at Windy Crater over the period from 1 March 1962 until 28 November 1963 (Figure 40). From 1 March 1962 until 29 October 1962, 88 wedges grew an average of 3.0 mm; 3 wedges shrank (Table 10). One pair of contraction stakes labeled H' is no longer usable, as the contraction crack that it measured has become dormant; contraction now takes place 50 cm to the south of the wedge and is measured by the contraction stakes labeled H. The calculations, therefore, do not include H'. Maximum expansion was 15.2 mm. The measurements were too late in summer and too early in spring to represent a normal year's growth, but they show the rapid changes taking place. The wedges were measured again on 28 November 1963. Between 29 October 1962 and 28 November 1963, 5 wedges expanded, one did not change, and 82 shrank; all wedges collectively shrank an average of 1.9 mm. Over the period from 1 March 1962 until 28 November 1963, the 88 wedges grew an average of 1.2 mm, or about 0.6 mm per year. The maximum growth was 9.2 mm, the minimum —5.2 mm. Eleven wedges shrank and 3 wedges grew less than 0.1 mm. As the initial measurement was made too late in the year and the last too early, the true growth rate is probably slightly less than 0.6 mm. Assuming an average annual growth rate throughout the life of the wedges of 0.5 mm per year, with an average wedge width of 50 cm the wedges should be approximately 1000 years old.

Wright Valley

Wright Valley, one of the major valleys in Victoria Land, reaches from the Polar Plateau 70 km eastward toward the Ross Sea, where it is filled by the Wilson Piedmont Glacier and its tributary, the Wright Lower Glacier. To the south the peaks of the Asgard Range rise to heights of 2400 meters; on the north the valley is bounded by the Olympus Range with peaks around 2000 meters. The floor at the east end of the valley is 200 meters above sea level and slopes westward, reaching its lowest point

at Lake Vanda 70 meters above sea level. The Onyx River flows westward for 3 to 6 weeks in the summer from the Wright Lower Glacier to Lake Vanda into which it empties.

The valley walls display a series of bedrock benches, some of which may have been formed by glaciers moving eastward early in the glacial history of the valley [Bull, McKelvey, and Webb, 1962, 1964]. Moraines are also present along the valley walls. Numerous small alpine glaciers flow down into the valley from the Asgard Range, each possessing its own group of small moraines. Wright Valley is probably better known geologically than any other valley in Antarctica. The geologic setting is similar to that in Taylor Valley. Steeply dipping metasediments of Pre-Cambrian or Lower Paleozoic age form the valley walls and are often capped by dolerite of Cretaceous or Jurassic age. West of Bull Pass, Beacon sandstone caps the summits [Gunn and Warren, 1962; McKelvey and Webb, 1962]. The floor of the valley is covered with morainal deposits except near the east end of Lake Vanda where gneiss and granodiorite outcrop. Glacial sequences specifically for the valley have been postulated by Bull, McKelvey, and Webb [1962] and Nichols [1961a]. A comparison of the Wright Valley sequences with Péwé's regional sequence is provided in Table 11 [from Black and Berg, 1964]. In an effort to date these moraines and other features, four contraction sites were established in Wright Valley in 1962.

The highest and apparently oldest moraine along the south side of the valley does not have polygonal ground visible on its surface, except very locally. This moraine [Nichol's Loop (?) moraine] has a surface covering of silt and sand and some stones that contains less than 1 per cent moisture by weight. This dry zone blankets the surface to a depth of at least 2 meters, and is much thicker than the true active layer. Its original moisture content is unknown, but a progressive drying-out of the material is inferred. Salts are abundant and indicative of a net transport of water from the ground to the air. A long period of dessication, of the order of more than 5000 years, is implied. In swales where the material possesses a more normal moisture content (3–10 per cent), patterned ground is weakly developed. Excavations here have not been sufficiently extensive to prove whether polygons existed

TABLE 11. Correlation and Synopsis of Glaciations in Victoria Land

McMurdo Sound Region [Péwé, 1960]	Wright Valley and Victoria Valley System [Bull et al., 1962]	Wright Valley [Nichols, 1961a; Bull et al., 1962]
Koettlitz Glaciation Multiple advances by plateau glaciers and shelf ice were more extensive than advances by alpine glaciers. Ice-cored moraines with knob and kettle topography are characteristic. Lake and delta beds are common. No ventifacts have formed. Radio-carbon dating of dried algae from ablation moraine in front of Hobbs Glacier indicates a minimum age of 6000 years for the Koettlitz glaciation. *Fryxell Glaciation* Fryxell glaciation was less extensive than preceding glaciations. Fair- to well-preserved moraines with well-developed ventifacts are cut by small, ephemeral streams. Some alpine glaciers expanded onto floor of Taylor Valley depositing moraine loops; others in the region advanced only 100 m. Glacial-lake shorelines are weakly developed up to 45 m above sea level in Taylor Valley. *Taylor Glaciation* Subdued moraional blanket of granitic and metamorphic rocks extends up to 300 m above sea level in Taylor Valley and other localities on the west side of McMurdo Sound. Small alpine glaciers left deposits 0.8 to 3 km beyond their present fronts. Well-developed ventifacts and desert pavements are common. Ice-dammed lakes left shorelines 300 m above sea level in Taylor Valley, and laminated silts and dissected deltas are abundant in the valley. *McMurdo Glaciation* Scattered and highly weathered drift without moraional form lies on deeply etched bedrock benches 600 to 900 m in Taylor Valley and around McMurdo Sound. On Nussbaum Riegel in Taylor Valley, granitic and metamorphic rocks lie on marble. Boulders have no fresh faces, and most are abraded to ground level. Basic dikes on Nussbaum Riegel are etched out in relief 0.9 to 2.4 m by weathering since retreat of the ice.	*Fourth Glaciation* Minor advances of the plateau outlet glaciers in the western part of the area. Thick boulder moraines have intense frost heaving. Ventifact fields are not developed. Depressions close to the sides and snouts of present-day alpine glaciers and the Wright Lower and Victoria glaciers may be contemporaneous with other Fourth glaciation moraines. *Third Glaciation* Following the second glaciation, land-locked lakes were reduced in area by evaporation and sublimation, leaving the Wright–Victoria area largely deglacierized. The third glaciation was marked by glacier advances into the valleys from the inland ice plateau and from the Wilson Piedmont Glacier. Alpine glaciers descended from the ranges to the valley floors. Thick terminal and lateral moraines are often covered with a surface veneer of ventifacts. Depressions in the moraine are filled by evaporite deposits and lake silts. Glacial melt lakes were less extensive compared with those associated with the preceding glaciation. Moraines are deeply dissected by later fluvio-glacial action. *Second Glaciation* This glaciation was less extensive than the preceding glaciation. Plateau glaciers flowed through this area to McMurdo Sound. Deposits are preserved as dune sands, gravels, polished boulders, and ventifact fields and as scattered drift on erosion levels up to 800 m above sea level. During retreat, ice-dammed lakes flooded the central parts of Wright Valley, cutting high-level lake shorelines. *First Glaciation* A major glaciation, responsible for cutting benches, accordant cirques, and floors up to 1500 m above sea level across the entire width of the present-day deglacierized area. Sparse, highly abraded moraines lie on these levels. These features are prominently developed along the Asgard, Olympus, and St. Johns ranges, and on the tabular summits of Insel Range, Dais, and Labyrinth. More recent glacial erosion has dissected these features at many localities.	*Trilogy Glaciation* Small discontinuous indistinct end moraines in the valley about 8 km west of the Wright Lower Glacier can be traced into lateral moraines 300 m above the valley. A prominent and extensive end moraine was built 5 km east of the above advance, and ice-cored moraines lie immediately in front of the Wright Lower Glacier. All deposits show a small amount of wind-cutting, an absence of odd-shaped erratics weathered to ground level, many upstanding boulders, and only minor staining. Dating of an elephant seal in a raised beach at Marble Point indicates the oldest advance occurred more than 7000 years ago. *Loop Glaciation* The type deposit is about 13 km west of the Wright Lower Glacier. It is a prominent-looped, steep-sided end moraine about 75 m high. Deposits show ventifacts from which more than 30 cm of rock have been removed, odd-shaped boulders from which more than 90 cm of rock have weathered off, a high proportion of boulders weathered to ground level, and a pronounced yellow stain. *Pecten Glaciation* Stratified gravels about 40 km west of the Wright Lower Glacier contain pecten shells dated at more than 35,000 years by radioactive carbon. The shells are considered to have been brought in by glacial ice and meltwater streams from the floor of Mc-Murdo Sound at a time when 1000 m of ice lay in the Sound. Bull [1962] regards this as outwash from the Loop or Third glaciation. —— (*Unnamed Glaciation*) Carving of the bedrock basin of Lake Vanda by an outlet glacier moving eastward.

Fig. 41. Site A, Wright Valley, looking west down valley. The wide size-range of the surficial material and lack of ventifacting is typical.

throughout the moraine and are now masked at the surface, or whether polygons ever existed on the moraine. In any event the next youngest moraines of Nichol's Trilogy glaciation had to be used. Three sites were established on them and one on a stream terrace of the Onyx River, approximately 6–7 km west of the Wright Lower Glacier (77°27′S, 162°31′ 15″E).

Site A. Site A, 7 km west of the Wright Lower Glacier and 200 meters above the valley floor, is near the base of a steep bedrock hill, the top of which is rimmed by moraine of the Denton Glacier. The area is mapped as oldest Trilogy by *Nichols* [1961a]. The surface is covered with poorly sorted material (Figure 41) that ranges in size from boulders several meters in diameter to silt. The surface is very youthful in appearance, with little ventifacting or staining of the soil with the iron oxide that is common elsewhere. No salts were seen in the subsurface. The contraction site slopes northward and westward. Polygons are 10–20 meters in diameter; troughs are 70–120 cm wide (averaging 90 cm) and 15–40 cm deep. Troughs and wedges are filled with free-running sand, and cones of depression are common in the spring. The area is quite dry; the active layer, 20–30 cm thick, contains 1.5–3.0 per cent moisture, the permafrost 10 per cent moisture.

From 29 December 1962 to 17 December 1963, 42 wedges grew an average of 1.3 mm (Table 12); 40 wedges widened, the maximum being 3.2 mm, and 2 wedges shrank, one 3.8 mm.

TABLE 12.   Contraction Measurements (cm), Site A, Wright Valley

Wedge	29 Dec. 1962 17 Dec. 1963	Interstake Measurement 17 Dec. 1963
A	+0.26	72.34
B	+0.11	96.68
C	+0.03	94.27
D	+0.07	97.62
E	+0.31	98.78
F	+0.09	72.16
G	+0.15	95.10
H	+0.04	99.12
I	+0.19	77.00
J	+0.07	75.30
K	+0.04	89.21
L	+0.16	95.85
M	+0.14	94.94
N	+0.24	78.28
O	+0.26	94.19
P	−0.03	98.20
Q	+0.19	87.91
R	+0.03	97.23
S	+0.02	87.88
T	+0.15	98.55
U	+0.34	56.32
V	+0.05	97.15
W	+0.18	99.51
X	+0.26	84.50
Y	+0.18	84.75
Z	+0.10	95.89
AA	+0.26	84.36
BB	+0.08	90.91
CC	+0.16	77.71
DD	+0.16	83.58
EE	+0.05	85.55
FF	+0.15	96.57
GG	+0.20	94.35
HH	+0.06	99.21
II	−0.38	85.29
JJ	+0.10	81.79
KK	+0.16	89.88
LL	+0.13	76.91
MM	+0.16	99.62
NN	+0.20	76.86
OO	+0.15	93.81
PP	+0.20	97.37
Growth	1.3 mm/yr	

Assuming the growth rate to be correct and uniform over the life of the wedges, the wedges should be about 690 years old.

Site B. Site B is 6 km west of the Wright Lower Glacier on an ice-cored moraine 20 meters above and south of the Onyx River (Figure 42). The surface of the moraine is extremely irregular, with only 30–80 cm of morainic rubble over dead glacial ice. High-centered polygons are 10–20 meters in diameter. Troughs up to 4.5 meters wide and 70 cm deep divide the surface. Troughs are filled with free-running sand, and cones of depression are well developed in the spring (Figure 12). Migration of contraction cracks has occurred during the past, as evidenced by relic troughs separated by sections of ice-cored moraine (Figure 13).

The morainic material above the glacial ice is quite dry, averaging 2 per cent water by weight. A thin layer of cemented morainal material is present directly above the ice. The wedge excavated at the site was a composite wedge, but the ice in the wedge appeared to have been forced up from below (Figure 13). Loose sand was present in the active contraction crack to a depth of 60 cm.

The wedges averaged 2 meters in width and ranged in size from 175 cm to 330 cm. Actual

Wedge	30 Dec. 1962 17 Dec. 1963	Interstake Measurement 17 Dec. 1963
A	+0.35	66.02
B	+0.23	65.78
C	+0.93	71.72
D	+0.43	64.09
E	+0.54	65.73
F	−0.09	87.54
G	−0.01	76.51
H	+0.32	91.43
I	+0.16	77.20
J	+0.21	68.08
K	+0.33	78.37
L	+0.31	66.70
M	+0.40	66.00
N	+0.19	91.60
O	0.00	84.39
P	+0.17	74.03
Q	+0.22	81.44
R	+0.42	71.50
S	+0.45	73.70
T	+0.32	76.73
U	+0.32	77.49
V	+0.08	74.87
W	+0.18	72.43
X	+0.36	76.56
Y	+0.40	68.93
Z	+0.19	73.29
AA	+0.20	60.59
BB	+0.42	86.80
CC	+0.30	74.20
DD	+0.68	80.14
Growth	3.0 mm/yr	

TABLE 13. Contraction Measurements (cm), Site B, Wright Valley

Fig. 42. Site D, Wright Valley, is in left center beyond perennial snowfield in immediate foreground. Site B is on the ice-cored moraine in center and south of the Onyx River, which flows left through the center of the photo. Site C is on the terrace in center and north of the Onyx River. View north. 18 December 1963.

wedge widths were very difficult to determine due to the migration of contraction cracks and resulting incorporation of non-wedge material into the wedge. Thirty wedges averaged 3.0 mm growth during the period between 30 December 1962 and 17 December 1963 (Table 13). Twenty-seven wedges expanded with a maximum of 9.3 mm, one wedge did not change, and 2 wedges shrank, the greater being 0.9 mm. Using wedge widths of 2 meters and uniform growth rates during the life of the wedges, they should be about 670 years old. Migration of contraction cracks and difficulty in determining actual wedge widths, however, makes this age somewhat too young.

Site C. Site C is on a sandy terrace of the Onyx River (Figures 42 and 43) 3 meters above the pres-

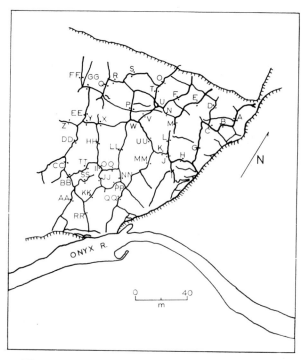

Fig. 43.   Map of contraction Site C, Wright Valley.

ent floodplain. It is directly across the river and north of Site B. Well-developed double raised-rim polygons 10–30 meters in diameter have troughs averaging 150 cm wide. The dry zone, 25–35 cm thick, contains 1–2 per cent water by weight. Well-developed sand wedges are present. Trough widths are highly variable, ranging from 20 cm to 410 cm. Troughs below 100 cm in width are probably secondary. A decrease in wedge size, however, is apparent as one moves away from the river. The north end of the contraction site is bounded by a steep incline where the terrace has been cut into ice-cored moraine. The incline acts as a site of snow accumulation, and an increase in the size of the snowbank could cover some wedges and interrupt their growth. This theory is substantiated by the presence of salt efflorescence on the surface near the incline. As noted earlier, wind also has an effect on wedge growth.

Forty-seven wedges had a growth rate that averaged 1.15 mm for the period 31 December 1962 to 17 December 1963 (Table 14). Forty-three wedges grew during this period, the maximum growth being 2.4 mm. Three wedges shrank, the maximum shrinkage being 0.7 mm, and one did not change. Assuming a uniform growth rate throughout the life of

the wedges of 2.4 mm per year, with an average wedge width of 150 cm these wedges are 1300 years old.

TABLE 14.   Contraction Measurements (cm), Site C, Wright Valley

Wedge	31 Dec. 1962 17 Dec. 1963	Interstake Measurement 17 Dec. 1963
A	+0.08	85.70
B	+0.06	79.11
C	+0.07	88.43
D	+0.08	75.94
E	+0.06	78.93
F	−0.02	81.11
G	+0.33	75.20
H	+0.10	81.66
I	+0.19	90.79
J	+0.17	90.61
K	+0.05	88.58
L	+0.08	79.07
M	+0.20	71.61
N	+0.09	66.76
O	+0.07	74.51
P	+0.16	73.70
Q	+0.18	67.25
R	+0.12	80.31
S	+0.07	75.46
T	+0.03	76.00
U	+0.16	76.61
V	+0.26	61.61
W	+0.17	72.49
X	+0.22	88.39
Y	+0.24	67.37
Z	−0.01	79.40
AA	+0.10	74.11
BB	+0.06	78.54
CC	+0.06	79.83
DD	+0.19	78.19
EE	+0.22	81.62
FF	+0.09	86.53
GG	+0.09	71.70
HH	+0.24	76.89
II	+0.12	75.81
JJ	+0.07	72.47
KK	+0.14	69.42
LL	+0.12	87.68
MM	+0.17	83.61
NN	+0.16	73.90
OO	+0.08	83.28
PP	+0.12	78.49
QQ	+0.05	77.34
RR	+0.09	74.30
SS	0.00	72.44
TT	+0.10	83.67
UU	−0.07	81.29
Growth	1.15 mm/yr	

The terrace on which Site C is located had to be formed later than the ice-cored moraine on which Site B is located, because the terrace is cut into the moraine. The age for the terrace is thought to be more reliable than the age for Site B because (1) wedge widths can be determined with greater accuracy, (2) there has been no incorporation of non-wedge material into the wedge due to migration of contraction cracks, (3) there was less variation in growth rates of individual wedges, and (4) there were no complications due to the presence of clean ice directly below the surface rubble.

Site D. Site D is on the top of a morainic ridge, 100 meters above the valley floor at the point where the ridge merges into another morainal deposit higher up on the south side of the Wright Valley (Figure 42). At present little water flows through the area, but the presence of channels and the waterlaid deposits attest to an increased flow in the past. The surface of the site is covered with a desert pavement of pebbles and cobbles. A concentration of cobbles along the sides of the polygonal troughs reflects selective sorting and movement of finer material into the wedges.

Fig. 44. Trough at Site D, Wright Valley, shows youthful appearance and desert pavement. Perennial snowbank in background presumably covered site about three centuries ago. View south. 18 December 1963.

TABLE 15.   Contraction Measurements (cm), Site D, Wright Valley

Wedge	17 Dec. 1963 1 Jan. 1963	Interstake Measurement 17 Dec. 1963
A	+0.27	57.60
B	+0.24	62.68
C	+0.23	68.20
D	+0.25	69.58
E	+0.16	77.00
F	−0.01	57.15
G	+0.22	74.73
H	+0.23	76.21
I	+0.22	76.32
J	+0.05	73.28
K	+0.08	63.55
L	+0.02	79.42
M	+0.02	70.91
N	+0.18	66.42
O	+0.07	62.20
P	+0.24	75.61
Q	+0.20	51.90
R	+0.13	55.56
S	−0.01	60.28
Growth	1.4 mm/yr	

The polygons are youthful, flat-centered, and with shallow troughs averaging 40 cm in width (Figure 44). The dry zone is 15–25 cm thick, containing 2–4 per cent moisture. The maximum trough width measured was 80 cm, the minimum 15 cm.

From 1 January 1963 to 17 December 1963, 19 wedges had an average growth rate of 1.47 mm per year (Table 15). Maximum growth was 2.5 mm. Two of the wedges appeared inactive, which is borne out by growth measurements, both wedges shrinking 0.1 mm in 1963. Two secondary wedges are included in the average of the contraction measurements (Figure 45): both are 20 cm wide; one is inactive, the other had a growth rate of 0.8 mm in 1963. Excluding the two secondary wedges, the growth rate was 1.6 mm per year. With troughs 40 cm wide and a uniform growth rate of 1.6 mm per year throughout the life of the wedges, the wedges are, therefore, about 250 years old. Whether the surface became exposed about 250 years ago or whether aperiodic growth has occurred is not known. It is assumed that the snowbank to the south once covered the area and during the last three centuries retreated to its present position.

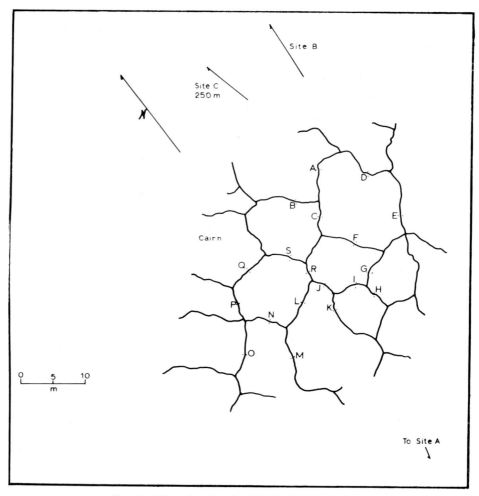

Fig. 45.   Map of contraction Site D, Wright Valley.

DISCUSSION OF RESULTS

Contraction measurements over a period of 1 to 2 years in a wide variety of situations in Victoria Land show that growth rates of nonsorted wedges vary between 0.5 and 3.8 mm per year. Age determinations of wedges using these figures vary from 100 years for wedges adjacent to an active ice front at Cape Evans to 3230 years for mature wedges in Beacon Valley. Other wedges not measured are likely to be somewhat older. All dated wedges are believed to also date the surfaces in which they are found, with certain variances or exceptions that are discussed later. These youthful age determinations are in marked disagreement with published chronologies of the glacial history of Victoria Land. Moreover, the dates derived from nonsorted polygons conflict with carbon-14 dates [*Péwé*, 1959; *Nichols*, 1961b]. Although a complete discussion of the glacial chronology is beyond the scope of this paper, a cursory attempt is made to place the contraction dating method into its proper perspective and to compare its results with those of the carbon-14 and other methods.

Beacon Valley

The age of the morainal complex in Beacon Valley has been the subject of controversy over the past several years. The well-developed moraines and patterned ground have been discussed at length in the literature, but little field work has been done. The polygons were first described by *McKelvey and Webb* [1959], who distinguished two different forms. These workers describe polygons on the valley floor that are up to 7.5 meters across; the polygons have concave surfaces and peripheral troughs as deep as 1.2 meters. Polygons on the surface of the morainal shoulder on the east side of the valley have subdued relief, and peripheral troughs are either lined or filled with small rock fragments and sand. No age correlations were made.

Harrington and Speden [1960] described moraines on the floor of Beacon Valley and correlated them tentatively with the 1820, 1850, and 1890 moraines of the European Alps and New Zealand. Polygonal ground was not mentioned, although an accompanying photograph showed well-developed polygons. In reference to this report, *Blake and Hollin* [1960] used the polygonal network to substantiate their theory that the moraines were laid down a long time ago and that the patterned ground developed when the ice edge was at its present position or farther back. They contended that, since the patterned ground was uniformly well developed over the entire valley floor, polygons had to be of the same age. In a reply to Blake and Hollin, *Harrington and Speden* [1961] described the polygonal network in greater detail and proposed a cycle of youth, maturity, and old age. They indicated that the polygons become increasingly vague and irregular away from the present ice front and interpreted these changes to represent stages in the cycle from youth closest to the ice front toward maturity. They believed the polygons to be of the sand-wedge variety described by *Péwé* [1959].

Péwé [1962] disagreed with Harrington and Speden and correlated the moraines with the late Fryxell Stage (early Wisconsin) and believed the moraines to be 'thousands of years old.' Evidence for the antiquity of the moraines was:

1. Photo study of glacier fronts elsewhere in Victoria Land indicated no appreciable changes in 50 years.
2. Radiocarbon dates from 600 to 2600 years B.P. of seal carcasses scattered throughout the dry valleys.
3. The presence of widespread ice-cored moraines adjacent to the fronts of many glaciers, which were believed from radiocarbon dates to be at least 2500 to 6000 years old.

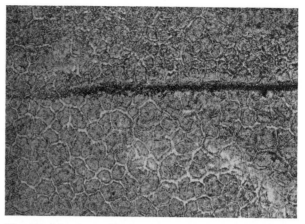

Fig. 46. Moraine of Taylor Glacier, Beacon Valley. Notice control of polygons by the moraine. Variation in size of polygons is probably a reflection of moisture content of the ground. North is at the top of the photo.

4. Péwé's contention that it would take thousands of years to have the intersecting trenches of the polygons widen to 1–2 meters, measured crest to crest.

From only 14 wedges and one year's growth rate, *Black and Berg* [1964] determined that the age of the wedges in the center of Beacon Valley was about 3000 to 5000 years. Another year's data and 18 more wedges support that general order of magnitude.

Widths of wedges increase from the front of Taylor Glacier to the southwest and show some orientation control at each of four distinct moraines crossed (Figure 46). In the oldest of the four moraines that cross the valley floor and presumably were laid down by the Taylor Glacier, wedges are 4–5 meters in width; near the present ice front width of the wedges averages 2.5 meters. By extrapolation of the 1 mm per year growth rate measured, the age of the oldest moraine should be about 5000 years and that of the moraine near the ice front about 2500 years.

A youthful set of polygons controlled by the Taylor Glacier front and 10–20 cm in width indicate a stillstand of the ice front of about 200 years, using a 1 mm per year growth rate. More ice is in the active layer, wedges, and permafrost at the ice front than up valley, but more snow also covers the wedges. This situation could alter growth rates somewhat, but the age of the stillstand should be within 100–300 years. This means that the Taylor

Glacier advanced over a surface exposed for almost 2000 years before stagnating one to three centuries ago.

The largest wedges in Beacon Valley are 4–6 meters wide and were deposited by ice moving from the southwest toward the Taylor Glacier. Greater ventifacting, disaggregation, and staining are present on associated boulders than on those of the oldest moraines of the Taylor Glacier, which suggests an older age for the largest wedges. Surface morphology also suggests that the area is an ice-cored moraine similar to that of the Taylor Glacier moraines. No exploration of the subsurface has been carried out, so its composition and the rate of wedge growth are speculative. Assuming comparable growth rates, the wedges should be about 6000 years old [*Black and Berg*, 1964]. Even if the wedges are too young by a factor of 100 per cent, the maximum expected, the age of the surface cannot be 'early Wisconsin' [*Péwé*, 1962], which is tens of thousands of years ago.

Cape Evans

Cape Evans was mapped by members of the British Antarctic Expedition of 1910–1913. Comparison of their map and 1957 aerial photographs shows no appreciable difference in ice boundaries on the cape. However, the scale of the map (1 cm = 125 meters) and lack of detail in regard to ice fronts prevent an accurate determination of ice fluctuation. Comparison of ground photographs taken by members of the expedition and the present position of the 'Ramp' do not reveal any marked fluctuation, but again control is poor. Shrinkage of many ponds since 1910 has, however, occurred [*Llano*, 1959].

Llano [1959], in his investigation of lichens in the area, concluded that much of the cape had been free of ice for a relatively short time (less than 500 years) due to the absence of lichens and mosses.

Accuracy of the contraction measurements and the uniformity of the wedge widths lead us to believe that the date of 100 years for the wedges at the base of the 'Ramp' is reliable. Snow could have covered the contraction site during the past, but retreat of the 'Ramp' seems the most likely reason for exposure of the contraction site. A retreat of at least 25 meters has taken place during the past 100 years. Other parts of the cape farther from the

'Ramp' should be somewhat older, but no more than a few centuries.

Taylor Valley

Péwé [1961] has proposed a fourfold glacial sequence for Taylor Valley (Table 11) and has tentatively correlated the sequence with the North American chronology. The earliest and most extensive glacial advance recognized in Taylor Valley is named the McMurdo glaciation and is thought to be pre-Illinoian. Péwé notes the presence of old drift near the top of Nussbaum Riegel, and cites lack of morainal form, planation of boulders and cobbles by wind, and etching of diabase dikes as evidence of extreme antiquity. *Angino, Turner, and Zeller* [1962], however, discovered chatter marks and grooves on the higher slopes of Nussbaum Riegel. Preservation of these features seems unlikely if the McMurdo glaciation is indeed pre-Illinoian in age. The contraction sites east of Nussbaum Riegel were covered by ice at this time and at no other, according to Péwé.

The next recognized glacial advance into Taylor Valley was Péwé's Taylor glaciation. Ice reached 300 meters above sea level in Taylor Valley but did not cover the Nussbaum contraction sites, having stopped a short distance east of the contraction site on the moraine-covered bedrock ridge. It is logical to suppose that a lake covered the contraction site on the delta at this time, owing to the abundance of ice in the area. It was during the waning of this glaciation that Glacial Lake Washburn filled Taylor Valley to an elevation of 300 meters (see below).

Later glaciations, the Fryxell and Koettlitz, were less extensive than previous glaciations, and in Taylor Valley were confined to expansion of the alpine glaciers and the Taylor Glacier. Supposedly, therefore, the contraction sites east of Nussbaum Riegel were covered with ice only once, that is during the McMurdo glaciation of *Péwé* [1961].

Glacial lakes were common in Taylor Valley [*Péwé*, 1961; *Angino, Turner, and Zeller*, 1962]. Shorelines up to 300 meters above sea level attest to the former presence of a large glacial lake (Glacial Lake Washburn) thought by Péwé to have formed during and immediately following the Taylor glaciation (Table 11) by a glacial ice dam at the east end of the valley. The Taylor glaciation

Fig. 47. Perched boulders on the south wall of Taylor Valley. Scale = 15 cm.

has tentatively been correlated with the Illinoian stage of the North American glacial sequence [*Péwé*, 1961]. Lake deposits and beaches formed at 45 meters and below are part of Péwé's Fryxell glaciation, correlative with the early Wisconsin of North America. Minor lakes were formed during the Koettlitz glaciation, at least 6000 B.P. [*Péwé*, 1961].

There is considerable evidence of glacial lakes in Taylor Valley. In addition to the aforementioned beaches the following occur:

1. Lake silt deposits are widespread throughout the valley [*Péwé*, 1961].

2. Ventifacted boulders perched atop other ventifacted boulders are found irregularly distributed at elevations up to 800 meters (Figure 47). The composition and the size of the boulders are varied, being usually 10–100 cm in diameter and including dolerite, granite, and metasediments. The perched boulders are probably the result of ice-rafting. Some may be from ice-push along lake shores. Gravity movement of some but not all boulders downslope during times of greater snow cover is also possible. Even these boulders, however, indicate that movement of ventifacts after formation occurs. Other boulders show removal of weathered surfaces by present ventifacting. Spalling and frost disintegration are also evident. Differences in micrometeorological conditions can affect the degree of weathering and ventifacting [*Angino, Turner, and Zeller*, 1962], and the use of weathering surfaces and ventifacting as indicators of age should, therefore, be used with caution.

3. Mummified seals are abundant on the floor of Taylor Valley [*Péwé*, 1959], and Black found one on Nussbaum Riegel at an elevation of about 600 meters. The remains are usually found in dried-up stream channels or lake beds, and may be as far as 30 km from the present sea. Migration of the seals into Taylor Valley during periods of higher lake levels is a possibility.

4. Polygonal ground is remarkably uniform over the floor of the valley, except for recent stream channels, terraces, and floodplains. Sand wedges cut and contort the stratified lake deposits of Glacial Lake Washburn [*Péwé*, 1961], but no appreciable difference in wedge widths occurs over the floor of the valley or on moraines formed by the Canada and Commonwealth glaciers before and during the Fryxell glaciation, except within a few hundred meters of present ice fronts where smaller wedges occur. Uniformity of the pattern implies formation of all polygons at about the same time. This could only be accomplished by removal of a lake or similar water body after the conspicuous moraines were formed.

The removal of the water body in Taylor Valley must have been before the formation of the present floodplain at the mouth of Taylor Valley and, therefore, more than 400–500 years ago. The lake in which the delta formed, on which the contraction site 4.5 km east of Nussbaum Riegel is situated, was probably contemporaneous with but at least 150 meters above Glacial Lake Washburn. This is suggested by the uniformity of wedge size. The lake should have disappeared about 1500–2000 years ago, according to contraction studies. Polygons at 500 meters on the east slope of Nussbaum Riegel appear to be several thousand years older than those on the valley floor, which suggests that the lake existed that long.

The presence of a water body 300 meters deep in Taylor Valley may be due to: (1) an ice dam at the east end of the valley, or (2) sea water invasion of the valley due to a rise in sea level or a lowering of the valley floor. The scope of this paper does not permit discussion of these two possibilities to say that for either to have occurred in the past 1500 years seems unlikely. It, however, also seems extremely unlikely that Glacial Lake Washburn was an Illinoian event as postulated by *Péwé* [1961] [*Black and Berg*, 1964]. Dating with patterned ground does not have the proper time base at present for extrapolation into the distant past, but the dates should not be more in error than by a factor of 2 or 4. It seems reasonable to infer, therefore, that the floor of Taylor Valley was covered with a glacial lake or arm of the sea sometime between 1500 and 10,000 years ago and not over 100,000 years ago as postulated by Péwé.

Results from the contraction site on the bedrock ridge above the delta are not considered valid growth rates. Growth of the wedges must be slow, owing to the thin morainal cover over bedrock, and the exposed position of the ridge prevents accumulation of sand and snow in troughs. Because the time of measurement was poor and the interval only one year, the results are not good enough to determine now the actual growth rate at this site.

Wright Valley

All contraction sites in Wright Valley lie behind the maximum extent of the Trilogy glaciation [*Nichols*, 1961a]. Age agreement between the various geomorphic surfaces dated by patterned ground is fair. The moraine at Site A, mapped as the oldest Trilogy, is dated at 700 years B.P. Ice-cored moraine at Site B, below site A, is dated at 650 B.P. A terrace cut into the ice-cored moraine by the Onyx River is dated at 1300 years B.P. A set of recently uncovered youthful polygons on a fan on a morainal ridge at Site D is about 250 years old.

The discrepancy in the dates could be due to:

1. The migration of the contractions crack in ice-cored moraines resulting in higher than normal growth rates: The wedges at Site B are over twice as large as those on the terrace cut into the moraine. A condition ascribable to the difference in composition of the surficial mantle. The shifting surface of the ice-cored moraine does not make it as receptive to dating by the contraction method as would more stable surfaces.

2. The presence of a permanent snow cover retards or prevents growth of wedges [*Black and Berg*, 1964]: Recognition of a hiatus caused by a snowfield is extremely difficult. At Site D the presence of salt efflorescence on the rocks, the evidence of surface runoff, and the remnant snowbank 100 meters south suggest that a snowbank did cover the area. In the Asgard Range, the presence of active

wedges in older inactive wedges may indicate a period of snow cover [*Black and Berg*, 1963]. Criteria for delineation of former snowfields remain meager and often ephemeral. In the interpretation of the age of polygonal areas strict attention must be paid to a possible snow cover.

3. On steep slopes soil creep could result in erroneous growth rates. No measurement of this phenomenon has been made to date, but at Site A it is a factor that could be important.

4. At Site A the youthfulness of the surface is in contradiction to the ascribed age of oldest Trilogy. A morainic-covered bedrock ridge 200 meters north and 20 meters lower than Site A has abundant ventifacting, cavernous weathering, and iron staining of the soil profile, in contrast to Site A where none of these characteristics are present. Site A is directly downslope from a moraine of the Denton Glacier that caps the hilltop to the south (Figure 3). Retreat of the glacier is recent, as evidenced by the youthful ice-cored moraine at the hilltop. At the time the moraine was deposited on the hilltop, increased downslope movement of material would occur, and Site A would receive most of the material. The wedges at Site A, therefore, may date the retreat of the Denton Glacier, which would lessen downslope movement and stabilize Site A to permit wedge growth. Thus the date of 700 years would apply to the retreat of the Denton and not to the oldest Trilogy, a more logical conclusion in view of the lack of weathering phenomena at Site A.

The formation of the terrace 1300 years ago obviously postdates the full bodied stage of the Trilogy glaciation, which *Nichols* [1961a] believes occurred over 7000 years ago. Since the weathering of material, accumulation of salts, and thickness of the dry zone of the terrace and of the Trilogy moraines are not significantly different, they should be about the same age.

Since the retreat of the Trilogy glaciers, aridity has persisted in Wright Valley, as evidenced by the retreat of the Denton Glacier perhaps 650–700 years ago, retreat of some snowfields 250 years ago, and the distinct drying-out of surficial material on ice-cored moraines and other surfaces.

'Windy Crater'

The straie on the top of Observation Hill are developed in trachyte that is easily weathered through physical disintegration; this implies a fairly recent ice cover for the area. From the distribution of lichens on Hut Point, *Llano* [1959] concluded that the area had been free of ice for about 500 years, and that the presence of lichens within 30 cm of permanent icefields suggests that the ice front is as far advanced now as it has been for some time and that the front is now stationary.

Paucity of salts in the active layer, lack of ventifacting, weakly developed talus slopes, and only a slight modification of primary volcanic forms attest to the recency of 'Windy Crater' and support the date of 1000 years for the wedges.

Evidence for a greater thickness of the Ross Ice Shelf or recent uplift of the land is abundant on Ross and surrounding islands. Glacial straie at 227 meters on Observation Hill [*Forbes and Ester, 1964*], beach deposits at about 300 meters on Crater Hill, moraines at 244 meters on Brown Island, striations at 182 meters on Black Island [*Speden, 1962*], and marine muds at 60 meters on Cape Evans and 50 meters on Cape Royds indicate that the past history of the area is complex and

Fig. 49. Moraine of the Hobbs Glacier showing youthful, oriented orthogonal polygons and abundant kettles.

multicyclic. 'Windy Crater' lies below the striations on Observation Hill and the beach deposits on Crater Hill. The presence of fragile sponge spicules, shell fragments, and possible marine ostracods indicate that the cone was formed prior to encroachment of the Ross Sea. If so, the 1000-year-old wedges date the uplift of the area or retreat of the shelf. Movement of the fossils to their present position might also have been accomplished by wind. For a discussion of the implications of such problems as the variation in the thickness of the Ross Ice Shelf and changing sea level, see *Hollin* [1962].

Hobbs Glacier

Péwé [1961] used a radiocarbon date of 5900 ± 140 years (L-462) from samples of dried algae buried 10 feet beneath the surface of the ice-cored moraine of the Hobbs Glacier as the cornerstone for his proposed glacial chronology of Victoria Land. A date of 2480 ± 120 years (L-462A) for algae from ablation moraine at the lower end of Garwood Valley was used to fortify the radiocarbon date. A minimum age of 6000 years for the Koettlitz (or youngest) glaciation was proposed.

Broecker [1963] showed that marine organisms in antarctic waters could be too old by 800–2000 years; *Berg and Black* [1964] suggested that this date for fresh-water algae was much too old. Recent measurement of three samples of living algae from the moraine of Hobbs Glacier show variations ranging from +54 to −114 per cent δ carbon-14 (Rubin, personal communication, samples W-1492 to W-1495).

Fig. 48. Active contraction crack with ice wedge below cutting through mirabilite, Hobbs Glacier moraine.

The moraine of the Hobbs Glacier consists of 30–40 cm of morainal material over stagnant glacial ice. Abundant salts, mainly mirabilite, are incorporated in the glacial ice, as are the aforementioned algae. A well-developed uniform polygonal pattern occurs over the surface of the moraine, with troughs 50–80 cm wide. Wedges are youthful in appearance, and some cut through the salts (Figure 48). No migration of contraction cracks (Figure 49) has occurred, in contrast to wedges developed on older ice-cored moraine as in Wright Valley (Figure 5). The surface dry zone is very thin. Assuming a growth rate similar to that at Cape Evans, where somewhat similar conditions exist, the polygonal network is less than 500 years old.

The discrepancy between the date from the wedges and the radiocarbon date may be accounted for as follows:

1. The radiocarbon date may be in error by as much as 2000 years.

2. The radiocarbon date does not date the present surface of the moraine, nor possibly even the moraine itself, as the dated material was buried in the glacial ice and does not necessarily have to have been formed on the surface of the moraine. Ponds are abundant throughout the area and incorporation of pond fillings by an advancing glacier is not unlikely. Algal material found below the surface is usually greatly contorted, indicating movement.

Marble Point

The presence of numerous raised beaches, marine muds, and shell deposits in the McMurdo Sound area indicate that the coast has recently been submerged. The presence of a very high block-faulted mountain chain and an active volcano in the immediate vicinity indicate that the area is tectonically unstable and subject to movement.

Whether the beaches and other evidences of marine transgression are due to tectonic factors, isostatic rebound, or eustatic changes in sea level are beyond the scope of this paper, but we feel that certain features relating to the problem of dating by the polygonal ground method must be discussed.

An elephant seal, carbon-14 dated at 4600 ± 200 years, was buried in beach gravels 13.4 meters above

sea level at Marble Point [*Nichols*, 1961*b*]. Nichols used this seal to date the beach and to indicate that the maximum extent of the Trilogy glaciation (Nichol's youngest) occurred more than 7000 years ago [*Nichols*, 1961*a*]. Polygonal ground is well developed on elevated beaches in the Marble Point area. Troughs on the highest beaches (19 meters above sea level) range from 25 to 100 cm in width and decrease progressively downslope to the present beaches. The small troughs (25 cm) occur adjacent to and under snowbanks, and are probably anomalous. Troughs 80–100 cm in width are found in areas where little snow accumulates today, and they should reflect the true age of the surface. Sand is the common wedge filling. Assuming a comparable growth rate with that of wedges on the floodplain at New Harbor, the highest beaches would be around 700–900 years old. Discrepancy between the carbon-14 date and dating by patterned ground is evident. The carbon-14 date is presumed to be accurate, as compensation for the reduced amount of carbon-14 in antarctic waters has been made. That wedges at Marble Point are about 30 cm wider than wedges on the floodplain at the mouth of Taylor Valley, indicates that they are probably about 200 years older than the wedges on the floodplain, assuming a comparable growth rate. Their differences in elevation range from 15 to 18 meters. This would imply uplift of 9 mm per year for the beaches at Marble Point, a not unreasonable figure. However, problems are many. Raised marine beaches are not well developed in Taylor Valley. *David and Priestley* [1914] report finding *Pecten* shells at more than 6 meters in Taylor Valley but no distinct beaches. Poorly developed beaches up to 15 meters above sea level are present at Cape Bernacchi halfway between Taylor Valley and Marble Point. Whether the presence of beaches at Marble Point and not in Taylor Valley is indicative of an open sea at Marble Point and not at Taylor Valley, a condition present today, or some other cause is unknown. The whole problem must be reviewed carefully and fully before the disparity and conflicts are resolved.

CONCLUSIONS

Although dating by the use of polygonal ground is in its infancy and must be treated with caution, and a more substantial time base on which to calculate growth rates will result in greater accuracy, at present, the polygonal ground method appears to date recent geomorphic surfaces, such as flood-plains, deltas, and terraces, quite accurately. At the present stage of investigation, ages of morainic sur-faces are not so reliable but do permit the determi-nation of ages to an order of magnitude (i.e., mor-ainal surfaces are 10,000 years old rather than 100,000). Remeasurement of contraction sites at 5- to 10-year intervals will be of inestimable value in accurately determining growth rates of polygons and dating various geomorphic surfaces.

In addition, observations of the morphology of polygons and the activity of the associated wedges permits a reliable interpretation of subsurface con-ditions. Youthful wedges under 1 meter in width and without double raised-rims indicate a surface dry zone of about 25 cm, minor subsurface salts, and little iron staining. Mature polygons 1–4 meters in width have a thicker dry zone (25–80 cm) and abundant subsurface salts. Where polygons are ab-sent, dry zones over 1 meter thick are present.

Wedges with low growth rates, 0.5 mm per year or less, appear to be indicative of lack of free-running sand or of very low moisture in the dry zone and in permafrost. Active wedges with growth rates of 2 mm per year or more suggest the presence of an ice core. Hummocky surfaces with deep polygonal troughs are also indicative of ice-cored moraine.

Observations of polygonal ground can prove ex-tremely useful to the soil scientist and others in determining the environment and history of an area, providing the limitations of the method are realized and proper care is taken in interpretation.

Acknowledgments. James Sullivan and Peter Vogt were able and congenial field assistants. Bruno Wohl and Paul Dayton made field measurements during the antarctic winter at great personal discomfort. Financial and logistic support for the work was provided by National Science Foundation grants G-13232, G-17906, G-23801, and GA-55. The officers and men of U. S. Naval Air Development Squadron-6 (VX-6) provided invaluable logistic support and cooperation. The support of U. S. Navy Deep-Freeze personnel is gratefully acknowledged.

REFERENCES

Angino, E. E., K. B. Armitage, and J. C. Tash, Air tempera-tures from Taylor Glacier Dry Valley, Victoria Land, 1961, *Polar Record, 11,* 283–284, 1962.

Angino, E. E., and D. E. Owen, Sedimentologic study of two members of the Beacon Formation, Windy Gully, Vic-toria Land, Antarctica, *Trans. Kansas Acad. Sci., 65,* 61–69, 1962.

Angino, E. E., M. D. Turner, and E. J. Zeller, Reconnais-sance geology of lower Taylor Valley, Victoria Land, Antarctica, *Bull. Geol. Soc. Am., 73,* 1553–1561, 1962.

Berg, T. E., and R. F. Black, Validity of C¹⁴ dates in Vic-toria Land, Antarctica, *Geol. Soc. Am. Special Paper 76,* 13–14, 1964.

Black, R. F., Growth of ice-wedge polygons in permafrost near Barrow, Alaska, *Bull. Geol. Soc. Am., 63,* 1235–1236, 1952.

Black, R. F., Permafrost—A review, *Bull. Geol. Soc. Am., 65,* 839–856, 1954.

Black, R. F., Les coins de glace et le gel permanent dans le Nord de l'Alaska, *Annales de Géographie, 391,* 257–271, 1963.

Black, R. F., and T. E. Berg, Hydrothermal regimen of patterned ground, Victoria Land, Antarctica, *Intern. Assoc. Sci. Hydrol., Comm. Snow and Ice, Publ. 61,* 121–127, 1963.

Black, R. F., and T. E. Berg, Glacier fluctuations recorded by patterned ground, Victoria Land, Antarctica, *SCAR Geol. Symposium,* Cape Town, 1964.

Black, R. F., and T. E. Berg, Patterned ground in Antarc-tica, *Proc. Intern. Conf. Permafrost, Natl. Acad. Sci. Natl. Res. Council,* 1965.

Blake, W., Jr., and J. Hollin, Recent moraines of a lobe of the Taylor Glacier, Victoria Land, Antarctica, *J. Glaciol., 3,* 1165, 1961.

Blake, W., Jr., and J. Hollin, Recent moraines of a lobe of the Taylor Glacier, Victoria Land, Antarctica, *J. Glaciol. 3,* 1165, 1961.

Broecker, W., Radiocarbon ages of antarctic materials, *Polar Record, 11,* 472–473, 1963.

Bull, C., B. C. McKelvey, and P. N. Webb, Quaternary glaciations in southern Victoria Land, Antarctica, *J. Glaciol., 4,* 63–78, 1962.

Bull, C., B. C. McKelvey, and P. N. Webb, Glacial benches in south Victoria Land, *J. Glaciol., 5,* 131–132, 1964.

David, T. W. E., and R. E. Priestley, Glaciology, physiog-raphy, stratigraphy, and tectonic geology of south Victoria Land, *British Antarctic Expedition, 1907–09, Report Sci. Invest. Geol. 1,* London, 1914.

Dostovalov, B. N., Iz menenie obshchema rykhlykh gornykh porod pri promerzanin i obrazovanie morozoboynykh treshchin [Change in volume of unconsolidated ground during the freezing and formation of frost cracks], 41–51 i Materialy po laboratornyn isseldovaniyan merzlykh gruntov, *Akad. Nauk, S.S.S.R., Sbornik, 3,* 323 pp., 1957.

Forbes, R. B., and D. W. Ester, Glaciation of Observation Hill, Hut Point Peninsula, Ross Island, Antarctica, *J. Glaciol., 5,* 87–92, 1964.

Giovinetto, M. B., and J. C. Behrendt, The area of ice shelves in Antarctica, *Polar Record, 12,* 171–173, 1964.

Gunn, B. M., and G. Warren, Geology of Victoria Land between the Mawson and Mulock glaciers, Antarctica, *Trans-Antarctic Expedition 1955–58, Sci. Rept. 11,* 157 pp., 1962.

Harrington, H. J., The Cenozoic volcanoes of Ross Dependency and their petrology, *Ross Dependency Geol. Rept. 7, Roy. Soc. New Zealand, Antarctic Res. Comm.,* 8 pp., 1956.

Harrington, H. J., and I. G. Speden, Recent moraines of a lobe of the Taylor Glacier, Victoria Land, Antarctica, *J. Glaciol., 3,* 652–653, 1960.

Harrington, H. J., and I. G. Speden, Recent moraines of a lobe of Taylor Glacier, Victoria Land, Antarctica, *J. Glaciol., 3,* 946–948, 1961.

Hoare, R. A., *et al.,* Lake Bonney, Taylor Valley, Antarctica: A natural solar energy trap, *Nature, 202,* 886–888, 1964.

Hollin, J. T., On the glacial history of Antarctica, *J. Glaciol., 4,* 173–196, 1962.

Lachenbruch, A. H., Mechanics of thermal contraction cracks and ice-wedge polygons in permafrost, *Geol. Soc. Am. Special Paper 70,* 69 pp., 1962.

Leffingwell, E. de K., The Canning River region, northern Alaska, *U. S. Geol. Survey Profess. Paper 109,* 251 pp., 1919.

Llano, G. A., Antarctic plant life, *Trans. Am. Geophys. Union, 40,* 200–203, 1959.

Loewe, F., The scientific observations of the Ross Sea party of the Imperial Trans-Antarctic expedition of 1914–1917, *Ohio State Univ., Inst. Polar Studies Rept. 5,* 43 pp., 1963.

McKelvey, B. C., and P. N. Webb, Geological investigations in South Victoria Land, Antarctica, 2, Geology of upper Taylor Glacier region, *New Zealand J. Geol. Geophys., 2,* 718–728, 1959.

McKelvey, B. C., and P. N. Webb, Geological investigations in Victoria Land, Antarctica, 3, Geology of Wright Valley, *New Zealand J. Geol. Geophys., 5,* 143–162, 1962.

Nichols, R. L., Multiple glaciation in the Wright Valley, McMurdo Sound, Antarctica (abstract), *Tenth Pacific Science Congress of the Pacific Science Association,* 317 pp., 1961a.

Nichols, R. L., Coastal geomorphology, McMurdo Sound, Antarctica, Preliminary report, *Reports of Antarctic Geological Observations, 1956–1960, IGY Glaciol. Rept. 4,* 51–101, 1961b.

Péwé, T. L., Sand-wedge polygons (tesselations) in the McMurdo Sound region, Antarctica—A progress report, *Am. J. Sci., 257,* 545–552, 1959.

Péwé, T. L. Multiple glaciation in the McMurdo Sound region, Antarctica—A progress report, *Reports of Antarctic Geological Observations, 1956–1960, IGY Glaciol. Rept. 4,* 25–50, 1961 (see also *J. Geol., 68,* 498–514, 1960).

Péwé, T. L., Age of moraines in Victoria Land, Antarctica, *J. Glaciol., 4,* 93–100, 1962.

Péwé, T. L., and R. E. Church, Age of the spit at Barrow, Alaska, *Bull. Geol. Soc. Am., 73,* 1287–1292, 1962a.

Péwé, T. L., and R. E. Church, Glacier regimen in Antarctica as reflected by glacier-margin fluctuation in historic time, with special reference to McMurdo Sound, *Intern. Assoc. Sci. Hydrol., Comm. Snow and Ice, Publ. 58,* 295–305, 1962b.

Popov, A. I., Materialy k osnovam vcheniya o merzlykh zonakh zemnoi kory [The origin and evolution of fossil ice], *Inst. Merzlotovedeniya, Akad. Nauk., S.S.S.R., 2,* 5–25, 1955.

Schenk, E., The origin of ice-wedges, *Proc. Intern. Conf. Permafrost, Natl. Acad. Sci. Natl. Res. Council,* 1965.

Speden, I. G., Fossiliferous Quaternary marine deposits in the McMurdo Sound region, Antarctica, *New Zealand, J. Geol. Geophys., 5,* 746–777, 1962.

Stuart, A. W., and A. J. Heinie, Glaciology, Victoria Land Traverse, 1959–60, *Ohio State Univ. Res. Found. Rept. 968–1,* 1961.

Taber, S., Perennially frozen ground in Alaska, its origin and history, *Bull. Geol. Soc. Am., 54,* 1433–1548, 1943.

Treves, S. B., The geology of Cape Evans and Cape Royds, Ross Island, Antarctica, in *Antarctic Research, Geophysical Monograph 7,* pp. 40–46, American Geophysical Union, Washington, D. C., 1962.

U. S. Navy Weather Research Facility, Climatology of McMurdo Sound, *Dept. of the Navy Rept. NWRF 16–1261–052,* 67 pp., 1961.

Washburn, A. L., Classification of patterned ground and review of suggested origins, *Bull. Geol. Soc. Am., 67,* 823–866, 1956.

Wellman, H. W., Transport of pebbles over smooth ice in Antarctica, *Nature, 197,* 681, 1963.

Wellman, H. W., Later geological history of Hut Point Peninsula, Antarctica, *Trans. Roy. Soc. New Zealand, 2,* 147–154, 1964.

TERRESTRIAL VEGETATION OF ANTARCTICA: PAST AND PRESENT STUDIES[1]

EMANUEL D. RUDOLPH

Department of Botany and Plant Pathology and Institute of Polar Studies
Ohio State University, Columbus

Abstract. The historical discoveries of antarctic terrestrial vegetation, the current under-standing of the composition of this vegetation, and recent ecological and physiological research on plants in Antarctica are discussed. An experiment that resulted in the first successful growth of plants from seeds for any length of time within the continental antarctic climatic zone is described. Soil and air temperature data are provided and correlated with germination and growth of *Poa pratensis* L.

Are there any plants in Antarctica? To this question most people would probably have one of two reactions: (*a*) that no plants would grow there, since Antarctica is a continent covered by a huge ice cap; or (*b*) that plants and vegetation of Antarctica are very similar to those of the northern arctic land regions. Both conceptions are erroneous. There are plants in Antarctica, but the vegetation found there is of a type quite different from that found in any other part of the world.

The plant kingdom is composed of many different groups of plants, the largest and most conspicuous of which is the group that contains those plants that produce seeds. In most places in the world, including the Arctic, the dominant vegetation falls into this group. The spore-producing plant groups (algae, fungi, lichens, mosses, liverworts, and ferns and their relatives) are worldwide in distribution, but they rarely constitute the dominant vegetation of any one area. In striking contrast to other areas in the world, the vegetation of the Antarctic, found only in the summer snow-free areas along the coast and inland, which, together, represent much less than 5 per cent of the 14 million km² antarctic land mass, is composed almost entirely of spore-producing plants, or the cryptogams. Two seed plants, a grass and a member of the pink family, are found in Antarctica but only on the northern end of the Antarctic Peninsula opposite South America, mostly outside of the antarctic circle [*Skottsberg*, 1954].

[1] Contribution 80, Institute of Polar Studies, The Ohio State University.

Thus Antarctica is truly the land of the crytogamic plants, one where the vegetation is composed of species of lichens, algae, mosses, and fungi.

HISTORY OF BOTANICAL COLLECTING

The first antarctic plants collected, discounting the three lichens, a moss, and a grass found by James Eights, M. D., in the South Shetland Islands in 1829 [*Eights*, 1833], were those gathered by the botanist J. D. Hooker when he accompanied Sir James Clark Ross on the famous antarctic voyages of 1840–1843. In 1841, on the way to the Ross Ice Shelf at latitude 78°S, this expedition explored the Ross Sea, stopping at two small islands off the Victoria Land coast, but no plant collections were made and, indeed, no plants were seen. 'The coast was lined with ice, but interspersed with fallen masses of stone, rocks and sand, and it was impossible to advance a yard into the interior; but far as eye could reach and glasses could range, not a particle of vegetation existed' [*Hooker*, 1843, p. 270].

In the South America sector of Antarctica, Hooker had more botanical success. On Cockburn Island, off the northeastern tip of the Antarctic Peninsula, latitude 64°12′S, longitude 56°50′W, he collected cryptogamic plants only. 'The flora of Cockburn Island contains nineteen species, all belonging to the orders, Mosses, Algae, and Lichens. Twelve are terrestrial; three inhabit either fresh water or very moist ground; and four are confined to the surrounding ocean. . . . The greatest amount of novelty is found here . . . for example, of the Mosses, two out of five are new. There are seven Algae, and two of them, or less than a third, are new. Of six species of Lichen, four are already described' [Hooker *in* Ross, 1847, as quoted by *Turrell*, 1953].

Further plant collections were not made until fifty-two years later, when plants on the antarctic continent proper were seen for the first time. In 1895 Borchgrevinck gathered some lichens at Cape Adare in Victoria Land at latitude 71°17′S [*Bull*, 1896], and from then on most expeditions to the antarctic continent collected plants. The men of these expeditions were not, for the most part, botanists, but it became apparent to the botanists who worked on the collections from the expeditions that a terrestrial flora of Antarctica was to be found in some of those areas where rocks, gravel, or sand are, in summer, snow-free. Today the botanical exploration of Antarctica continues in a systematic way to cover the many areas of the continent as yet unexplored. Identification and correlation of collections are still major problems, and there is need for detailed taxonomic studies. A number of papers summarize the current state of our knowledge of the various plant groups in Antarctica [*Wille*, 1924; *Llano*, 1956, 1961, 1965; *Drouet*, 1961; *Steere*, 1961; *Greene and Greene*, 1963; *Greene*, 1964a, 1964b].

PLANT LIFE IN ANTARCTICA

Over a century of sporadic botanical collecting activity has produced basic information about the composition of the antarctic flora and some details about the aspects of the vegetation. Over 350 species of lichens, nearly all crustose rock-inhabiting ones, constitute the major elements of the flora. Of all the floristic elements, lichens occupy the largest geographical areas and are found farther south than any other plants. They are found in the Horlick Mountains at 86°09′S [*Wise and Gressitt*, 1965], at latitude 85°48′S (verified by the author from specimens collected by the Ohio State University expedition 1961–1962), and in the Queen Maud Mountains at latitude 86°03′S [*Siple*, 1938]. The fresh-water algae amount to about 200 species found in lakes, melt pools, and wet soil. Less than 75 species of mosses from the continent are de-

scribed as growing in moist habitats, some as far south as 84°40′ [*New Zealand Antarctic Society*, 1964] and 84°42′ [*Wise and Gressitt*, 1965]. Only four of the larger fungi have been described [*Singer and Corte*, 1964], but some of the microscopic groups are now being isolated and studied, and over 35 kinds have been described [*Di Menna*, 1960; *Flint and Stout*, 1960; *Soneda*, 1961; *Tubaki*, 1961; *Meyer et al.*, 1962; *Boyd and Boyd*, 1963; *Corte and Daglio*, 1963, 1964; *Rudolph and Wetmore*, in preparation]. Six liverworts [*Steere*, 1961; *Corte*, 1962] and two flowering plants have been found on the Antarctic Peninsula north of Marguerite Bay, where climatic conditions are the most moderate for the continent. *Holdgate* [1964a] calls this area the 'oceanic antarctic zone' in contrast to his 'continental antarctic zone.' A liverwort on the coast of eastern Antarctica has been reported by *Steere* [1965]. It is significant that there are no ferns or fern allies and no gymnosperms on the continent, although both these groups are well represented in the fossil record [*Plumstead*, 1962, 1964; *Cranwell*, 1963].

Land vegetation on the continent is never over a few inches in height. The attached marine algae are large and abundant, but since their environment is very different from that of the land plants they are not considered in this discussion. *Dodge* [1964] points out that the lichens in Antarctica are much smaller in size than those of the same genera farther north. Modifications of mosses favoring vegetative propagation have been reported [*Savicz-Ljubitzkaja and Smirnova*, 1961; *Matsuda*, 1964b]. *Brown* [1927] indicates a lack of flowering by the two antarctic seed plants that do flower farther north, but Stanley Greene (in a letter) says that these plants flower regularly in most localities, probably setting seed every year in many of them. *Holdgate* [1964a] states that, even on the South Orkney Islands, 'While inflorescences are developed, it is unlikely that seed is often set,' although *Corte* [1961b] at Cabo Primavera found between 7 and 15 per cent germination of the two native flowering plants. Reduced sexual reproductive capacity is probably a characteristic of Antarctic plants. The vegetation of the Antarctic, compared with that of the high Arctic, is much more scarce. In many places in the Antarctic one must search carefully to find a plant and, if found, the plant will be of very small size and hidden in the cracks of rocks. Owing to the extremely arid environment [*Phillpot*, 1964] and the short growing season, the vegetation of the Antarctic is indicative of an extreme desert.

Bacteria, considered to be plants by most biologists, represent yet another group of land flora, and are discussed by *Boyd et al.* [1966] in this volume.

Many aspects of botany in Antarctica are only just beginning to be studied and to be correlated with other sciences. To acquire detailed information about the distribution of individual species it will be necessary to evaluate carefully all collections, and in many instances, to make many more field collections. When such information becomes available, we will be in a much better position to attack the problems of the origin of the antarctic flora [*Dodge*, 1964, 1965]. *Skottsberg* [1912] and *Siple* [1938] have given us some detailed basic observational ecological information, but no studies of the problems related to the ecology and physiology of antarctic plants have been reported. A vegetation map of a small area in the northern Ross Sea sector of Victoria Land has been published [*Rudolph*, 1963], and for this area *Janetschek* [1963] has described two ecosystems, 'Chalikosystem,' of bare rubble, and 'Bryosystem,' with soil mosses and lichens. *Lamb* [1948] provides an ecological classification for that group of lichens that he studied in the Antarctic Peninsula region. The relationship of the vegetation to the chemical composition of its substrata, however, is still not understood for Antarctica.

Although a high degree of endemism (species restriction to a limited area) is indicated in the literature for certain antarctic organisms [*Brown*, 1928; *Cailleux*, 1961; *Dodge*, 1964], it seems premature to assume that this is equally true for all of the flora.

Along physiological lines, the blue-green algae, particularly *Nostoc*, have been shown to fix nitrogen under antarctic conditions [*Holm-Hansen*, 1963; *Boyd and Boyd*, 1963]. In studies of the primary productivity of fresh-water lakes by *Goldman et al.* [1963], an interesting inhibition and injury of the photosynthetic mechanism by high light-intensities were discovered. In an attempt to find out whether the endogenous, circadian (approximately 24-hour) rhythms found in some organisms are related to the stimulus provided by the Earth's rotation, *Hamner*

[1962] studied selected organisms on turntables at the geographical south pole. Bean plants, in which leaf-drooping follows a circadian rhythm, and the mold *Neurospora crassa*, in which zonation of growth also illustrates 24-hour periodicity, were used. Using revolving turntables, some to eliminate the Earth's rotational effect and others to provide new rotational times, no change in the intervals of these circadian responses was induced. The experimenter concluded that the biological clock mechanism of these organisms is not related to the rotation of the earth.

In the past few years the plant environment has begun to be studied quantitatively. For a year *Matsuda* [1964*a*] studied a moss community at the Japanese base on the Queen Maud Land coast. As part of the National Science Foundation Antarctic Research Program, from their studies of soil arthropods *Pryor* [1962], *Gressitt et al.* [1963], and *Janetschek* [1963] have published some information about the microclimate that is applicable to the plants upon which these animals feed. In the terrestrial habitat, the food chain is very simple, with but one animal link, the arthropods.

MICROCLIMATE AND PLANTS AT HALLETT STATION

As part of a 3-year study of the ecology of antarctic lichens, the writer has carried on extensive microclimatic study in the vicinity of Hallett Station, a joint United States–New Zealand station in the

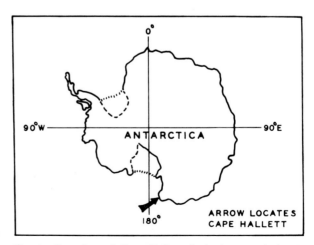

Fig. 1. Location of Cape Hallett, latitude 72°13′S, longitude 170°19′E.

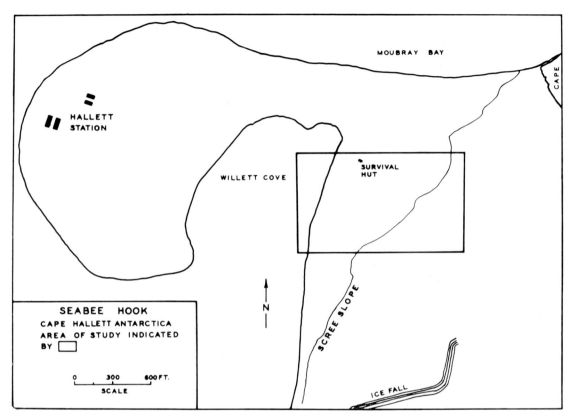

Fig. 2. Seabee Hook and Cape Hallett study area.

Fig. 3. Seabee Hook with Cape Hallett, 7 February 1961, from air; Hallett Station
in foreground. Official U. S. Navy photograph.

Fig. 4. Study area at base of Cape Hallett taken from scree slope; tip of Seabee Hook in midground; Admiralty Mountains on Victoria Land coast in background.

Ross Sea region at latitude 72°13′S, longitude 170°19′E. The station is located on a gravel hook projecting from the north end of Cape Hallett (Figures 1 and 2). The hook is mostly snow-free during late spring and summer (Figure 3) and is the location of a fairly large Adélie penguin rookery of over a hundred thousand birds [*Reed*, 1963]. Mountains surround the station except northward toward the bay entrance. The Cape Hallett headland is over 300 meters high; the level area at its base is composed of beach gravels and cliff talus that *Harrington et al.* [1963, 1964] called Seabee Hook Gravels.

For the study of the ecology and microclimate of lichens, the area outside of the rookery was selected. Indeed, except for a few types of algae, no plants are able to grow in the penguin rookery. The area selected, at the base of Cape Hallett within short walking distance of the station, is an area of gravel, pebbles, and rocks (Figure 4) in which the vegetation is, for Antarctica, quite lush [*Rudolph*, 1963]. This area also provides a variety of microhabitats, owing to varying amounts of moisture, organic material from the nesting activities of the

Fig. 5. Skua debris in study area: penguin eggshells and chick remains.

south polar skua (Figure 5), and exposure provided by the scree slope of the Cape. The area was selected, too, for its easy accessibility at all times on foot, the presence of ample plant life, and the fact that it is snow-free relatively early in the spring. The vegetation in the study area at the base of Cape Hallett consists of three components: algae, mosses, and lichens. The most conspicuous alga found in wet places was the sheet-like green alga *Prasiola crispa* (Light f.) Menegh. that covers the ground in midsummer with an almost continuous covering of brilliant emerald green that resembles the marine sea-lettuce *Ulva lactuca* L. In spots there are concentrations of a filamentous green alga *Ulothrix* sp. and other microscopic green, blue-green, and diatomaceous algae. The blue-green alga *Nostoc commune* Vauch. is abundant in a few places as blackish clumps that resemble small pieces of rubber innertube. The moss, *Bryum argenteum* Hedwig, grows in places that are less wet than where algae grow but where it receives melt water. The moss forms small to large clumps with an accumulation of a fair amount of spongy peat below them; a few of the clumps are several feet in diameter. Although lichens occasionally grow on the mosses, they grow most frequently on rocks and stones in the drier localities. A number of leafy and crustose forms [*Xanthoria mawsoni* Dodge, *Parmelia coreyi* Dodge & Baker, *Rinodina frigida* (Darb.) Dodge, and *Polycauliona pulvinata* Dodge & Baker] that form orange, gray-green, or black crusts on the rocks are commonly found. The orange leafy *Xanthoria* is particularly abundant in those places where skua debris of organic nature is available. None of the plants is any more than a centimeter in height. The lichens are more abundant in the wind-protected surfaces among the rocks.

Continuous records of the weather bureau for Hallett Station are available for the period February 1957 through January 1964 (U. S. Weather Bureau, Polar Meteorological Research Project). Beginning in 1964 the meteorology program was discontinued for the winter season. The record, however, is complete for a 7-year period and does provide an indication of the station's macroclimate. Although an analysis of a small portion of this period has been published [*Benes*, 1959; *Sabbagh*, 1962; *U. S. Dept. of Commerce, Weather Bureau*, 1962–1964], most of the data remain to be analyzed.

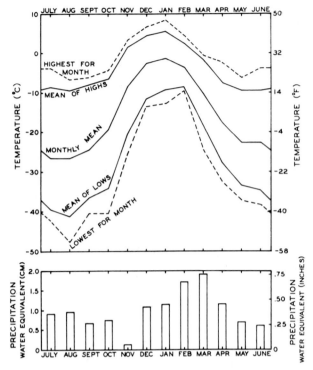

Fig. 6. Hallett Station monthly temperatures and precipitation, 7-year record, February 1957 through January 1964.

Sabbagh [1962] includes Hallett in his Ross Sea marginal subregion classification, based on temperature and pressure regimes. The lowest temperature at Hallett recorded during the 7-year period was −47.8°C in August 1959, and the highest 8.3°C in January 1959 (Figures 6 and 7). Although the Sun does not set during the summer, part of each night it dips below the mountains, which significantly reduces the amount of radiation received and causes heavy surface-soil freezing almost every day during a normal summer season. The mean annual temperature is −15.5°C, and the summer (December–February) mean temperature is −2.4°C. The yearly precipitation (as water equivalent) is 11.99 cm, and the summer precipitation amounts to 3.96 cm. All precipitation is in the form of snow (Weather Bureau Station climate data), and the amount may be overestimated because of considerable snow drifting.

Microclimate measurements of temperatures were continuously recorded on lichen, rock, or moss surfaces as well as at 2 feet in the air for two successive November through January seasons. Relative humidities at 2 feet were also recorded. Rock tem-

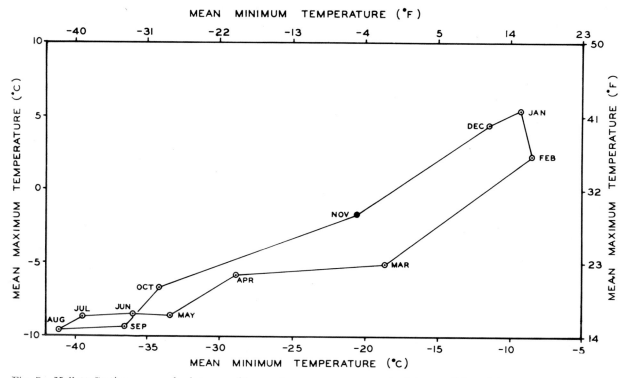

Fig. 7. Hallett Station, mean absolute monthly maximum *versus* mean absolute monthly minimum temperatures for 7-year period, 1957–1963.

Fig. 8. Microclimate-recording equipment. House contains generator, crates contain recorders, and weather boxes contain humidity sensors and thermographs.

Fig. 9. A single microclimate recording station, showing recorder and weather box.

peratures were sensed with copper-constantan (type T, 30-gage) thermocouples, humidities with Hydrodynamics wide-range-resistance humidity sensing units. Both parameters were recorded on a dual-channel recorder run on power supplied by a 2.5-kw field generator. The air temperatures at 2 feet were measured with clock-driven thermographs placed in weather boxes in which the humidity sensing units were located (Figures 8 and 9).

The daily amplitude of variation for the microclimate temperatures was found to be greater than that of the station macroclimate measured at 5 feet [*Rudolph*, 1966]. Figure 10, a summary of the daily minimum temperatures for the 1963–1964 season, illustrates these amplitude differences and also the greater maximums of temperatures that can be expected on rock surfaces where plants, particularly lichens, are growing. Similar results

were obtained by *Matsuda* [1964a] in his summer-season measurements. The summer season at Hallett in 1963–1964 was milder than in 1962–1963, and this mildness is reflected in the higher minimums and the closer correspondence of the minimums of the microclimatic and macroclimatic measurements. As in the 1962–1963 season, during the 1963–1964 season the maximum rock-surface temperatures at times exceeded 32°C; relative humidities were usually low but those of the microclimate exceeded those of the macroclimate.

From such microclimatic measurements it is possible to obtain an indication of the actual conditions under which antarctic plants are growing. Apparently plants experience a milder climate than macroclimatic data alone would indicate; this relates especially to the small size of antarctic plants and their growth in relatively protected habitats. It must be pointed out, however, that the plants experience a very great daily variation in temperature, one that is greater than would be expected on the basis of macroclimatic records alone. Further analysis of Hallett microclimate and its relation to vegetation is in progress.

The plants growing in Antarctica are able to survive the rigors of the climate for a number of reasons. Since the plants are small and closely appressed to the substratum, they benefit greatly from the heating affect of solar radiation upon the rocks and soil and from wind velocities that are reduced considerably near the ground. All are perennial plants, which, when conditions are favorable, can grow immediately. The growing season may consist of very short favorable periods. All seem able to withstand being frozen at least once daily and able to survive winter temperatures that usually exceed —40°C for extended intervals. They can stay alive under the extreme drying conditions of the antarctic atmosphere and can grow with very little water. Finally, these plants can grow in places where there is very little or no accumulation of organic matter in the soil or in the substrata on which they grow (see Table 1, page 119). One can truly say these are hardy plants.

ANTARCTIC ENVIRONMENT AND PLANT ESTABLISHMENT

One of the fascinating questions about antarctic vegetation is: How do plants become distributed

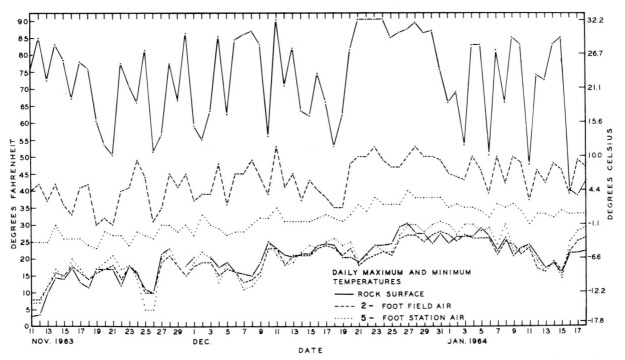

Fig. 10. 1963–1964 daily absolute maximum and minimum temperatures from data for three rock surfaces, four 2-foot weather boxes, and the one 5-foot Hallett Station weather box.

and established in the very rigorous environmental conditions that now exist and that probably have been even more extreme in the recent past? Either the plants survived from a much earlier and warmer period and were easily available for recolonization, or they were introduced anew to the coastal and mountain regions after the retreat of the ice. If the latter is the case, as *Hoppe* [1963] believes, then how did plant propagules happen to arrive in Antarctica?

It is significant, I think, that the plants now growing in Antarctica are predominantly cryptogams and thus propagated by minute spores and/or small vegetative fragments of the plant body. The two flowering plants, found only on the northern end of the Antarctic Peninsula, have small seeds, and might easily have been introduced by birds [*Greene and Greene*, 1963] from nearby South America. In fact, *Taylor* [1954] reports the introduction of flowering plants to Macquarie Island by sea birds. These propagules might also have been carried to Antarctica in the upper atmosphere. Although prevailing surface wind in Antarctica is from the south, the katabatic winds sweeping continually down from the high, cold, polar icecap,

there is in the upper atmosphere a southern movement of warmer air that replaces the displaced polar-cap air. Propagules might be moved in this upper atmosphere and then enter the lower air circulation to reach the potential substratum. *Gressitt* and his colleagues [1960, 1961, 1963], who have been actively studying the possibility of insect dissemination in the Antarctic upper atmosphere, have found a few indications that such a mechanism is a possibility. In respect to more local distribution [*Rudolph and Wetmore*, in preparation], the air in vegetated areas apparently does contain plant propagules, both fragments and spores, which would readily be available as disseminules. *Siple* [1938] believes that wind plays a very important role in the local dissemination of plants, and *Fritsch* [1912] reports the presence of *Podocarpus* pollen in red snow on the South Orkney Islands that must have blown from South America.

Once a plant propagule arrives in Antarctica is it possible for it to become established? *Corte* [1961a] reports the introduction and establishment of a grass (*Poa pratensis* L.) at a point at the south side of Cierva Cove, latitude 64°10′S, longitude 60°57′W, on the Antarctic Peninsula. The plants were in some soil brought from Tierra dal Fuego and contained two kinds of southern beech trees that did not survive the transplanting. The introduction of the grass was due no doubt to the placement of its perenniating parts in the antarctic location. For seed plants to have been introduced naturally by this means seems very unlikely. *Greene and Greene* [1963] list three flowering plants that have been introduced by man to the South Shetland and South Orkney Islands. *Brown* [1928] relates an unsuccessful attempt to germinate seeds of 22 arctic plant species in the South Orkney Islands, and *Holdgate* [1964*b*] reports on Lamb's unsuccessful attempt to introduce Falkland Islands plants to the antarctic continent. On the Pacific side of the antarctic continent, attempts have been made to grow flowering plants without success [*Taylor*, 1913; *Rudolph*, 1966], although when soil from these localities is placed in warmer environments, seeds and bulbs will grow in it [*Brown*, 1927; *Rudolph*, 1966].

FLOWERING PLANT SEED GERMINATION AT HALLETT STATION

At Hallett Station during the 1963–1964 summer season, the writer planted seeds of Kentucky bluegrass (*Poa pratensis*), Scott's strains 'Park' and 'Delta,' and the arctic-alpine plant *Diapensia lap-*

ponica L. in 2- by 2½-foot plots. The bluegrass strains were those especially selected for growth in northern United States and Canada; the seeds of the arctic-alpine plant had been collected on Mount Washington in New Hampshire. The seeds were planted on 11 November 1963 and the experiment was terminated on 23 January 1964, a total experimentation time of 73 days.

The plots were located where the larger stones had been removed from the sandy soil (Figure 11). Chemical and mechanical analysis of this soil and that of a nearby area rich in lichens, particularly *Parmelia coreyi* and *Xanthoria mawsoni*, and that under moss patches are shown in Table 1.

Minimum-temperature thermometers were placed into the soil of the plots on 5 December 1964, and thereafter minimum and mid-afternoon temperatures were recorded each day throughout the experiment. Since the locality near the survival hut at the base of Cape Hallett (Figure 2) was one in which *Bryum argenteum* grew, moist conditions in this locality during mid-summer are indicated [*Rudolph*, 1966]. The native flowering plants on the Antarctic Peninsula are frequently found growing among mosses [*Skottsberg*, 1954; *Follmann*, 1964]. At the end of the experiment, except for voucher specimens all the seeds and seedlings were destroyed.

Fig. 11. Plots in which seeds were planted on the level area at the base of Cape Hallett. Each plot is a 2- by 2½-foot rectangle.

TABLE 1. Analysis of Soil at Level-Area
Base of Cape Hallett

Constituent*	Soil in Grass-Plot Area	Soil in Lichen Area	Soil under Mosses
Particle size†		per cent	
Very coarse sand (2–1 mm)	15.7	55.1	. . .
Coarse sand (1–0.5 mm)	55.2	33.7	. . .
Medium sand (0.5–0.25 mm)	19.9	4.6	. . .
Fine sand (0.25–0.1 mm)	8.4	1.7	. . .
Very fine sand (0.1–0.05 mm)	0.3	0.4	. . .
Total sand	99.5	95.5	. . .
Silt (0.05–0.002 mm)	0.2	3.0	. . .
Clay (<0.002 mm)	0.3	1.5	. . .
Fine clay (<0.0002 mm)	T	0.3	. . .
pH	4.8	4.6	4.2
Organic matter‡	0.6	3.1	5.3
Nitrogen	0.07	0.28	0.46
Exchangeable cations§		me/100 g	
Hydrogen	3.4	10.1	18.3
Calcium	<0.5	2.1	1.2
Magnesium	0.7	0.5	0.7
Potassium	1.2	1.9	1.0
Sodium	1.1	1.2	1.0
Total	<6.9	15.8	22.2
Water-extractable elements			
Calcium	T	T	0.3
Magnesium	T	0.2	0.4
Potassium	0.2	0.1	0.1
Sodium	0.3	0.5	0.5

* All analysis done at Ohio Agricultural Research and Development Center, Wooster, Ohio. All samples had approximately 400 ppm P and less than 4 ppm NO_2^- measured by the author using a Hellige-Truog Soil Testing Kit.

† Using pipette method.

‡ Wet combustion.

§ Using emission spectrograph, except for hydrogen.

Simultaneously, a second experiment was being carried out inside the Hallett Biology Laboratory near a window that faced south. The same kind of seeds and soil from the same area were used in both experiments. In the laboratory the seeds were planted in trays of soil and watered daily with distilled water.

Under field conditions none of the *Diapensia* seeds germinated; in the laboratory only one seed germinated and at the end of 10 days the seedling died.

Both strains of bluegrass germinated in the field on 1 January 1964, fifty days after the seeds were planted. For the remaining 23 days, the seedlings continued to grow but very slowly. Very few of these seedlings grew more than one leaf and none grew to a height of over 2.5 cm (Figures 13 and 14). In the meantime the bluegrass seeds in the laboratory germinated after 7 days and the seedlings continued to grow for the remaining 66 days, to reach, finally, a height of over 35 cm (Figures 12 and 13).

Judging from the ample growth of the plants under laboratory condition, the supply of nutrients in which the plants grew was apparently adequate for growth.

The microclimate around the seeds is of special interest. A previous attempt to grow seeds in this locality had failed [*Rudolph*, 1966]. In the two experiments just described, since moisture and light were not lacking, temperature seems to have been a critical factor. The period during which the seeds germinated in the plots was also the period (25 December through 7 January) during which the upper 0.5 cm of soil did not at any time freeze. In laboratory experiments to germinate these strains of bluegrass seeds at the Ohio State University, the strains were wetted and placed in alternating 6½-hour 18°C and 17½-hour 1°C daily temperatures, of which the warmer temperature occurred during hours of artificial light. Under these conditions germination was accomplished in 15 days. In experiments carried out by a lawn seed company (personal communication), light had a slightly stimulatory effect upon germination at temperatures in the 10°–20°C range.

An interesting comparison can be made between minimum temperatures of soil and temperatures for a moss patch and for a lichen rock surface, and at distances of 2 feet and 5 feet in the air above the soil. Figure 15 shows that wet moss appears to be better insulated from low temperatures than does soil and that mid-afternoon soil temperatures from 5 December 1963 to 23 January 1964 ranged from 4.7°C to 22.2°C. This portion of the 1963–1964 summer season was particularly mild, with quite a long warm period, overcast skies, and little wind. Given a mild season, if certain flowering plant seeds were present, they could apparently germinate and continue to grow in such an antarctic locality as Cape Hallett.

Fig. 12.   Bluegrass grown in Antarctic soil in the laboratory 73 days after planting:
left, 'Park' strain; *right,* 'Delta' strain.

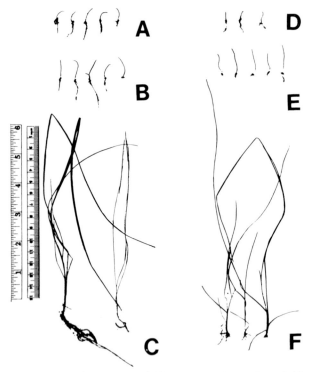

Fig. 13.   Voucher of pressed bluegrass specimens from field
and laboratory locations. 'Park' strain: (A) 7 days after
germination in field, (B) 14 days after germination in
field, and (C) 56 days after germination in laboratory;
'Delta' strain: (D) 7 days after germination in field, (E)
14 days after germination in field, and (F) 56 days after
germination in laboratory.

Corte [1961a] noted that the introduced grass near Cierva Cove did not form fertile seeds, and this may be an important influence on the establishment of another flowering plant species in Antarctica. The survival of such flowering plants in nature is questionable. *Taylor* [1913, pp. 173 and 182] reports that sea-kale seedlings at Granite Harbor (latitude 77°S) did not last more than 10 days. Falkland Islands plants introduced with their soil to the Antarctic Peninsula at latitude 64°10′S did not survive for more than a few seasons, even in a protected spot [*Holdgate*, 1964b]. Using a minimum-temperature thermometer, during the 1963 winter a temperature as low as —45.6°C was recorded on the soil surface at Cape Hallett. It is doubtful that under such temperature conditions vegetative parts of flowering plants could survive.

Lange [1962] reports, for example, the survival of hydrated lichens at a temperature of —75°C. The survival of these cryptogamic plants at very low temperatures is extremely pertinent to their presence in Antarctica. One can say that the first successful growth for any length of time of an alien plant from seeds within the antarctic circle, as reported above, does show that climatic conditions would allow for the introduction of plants should the propagules be present.

BIOLOGICAL IMPLICATIONS

The vegetation of an area is usually a good indication of many aspects of its physical environment. By its composition, ecology, and physiology, the terrestrial plant life in Antarctica indicates a rigorous climate and a short growing season. In other parts of the world this pioneer type of vegetation, composed of small-sized cryptogams, is most characteristic of recently exposed glacial moraines, high arctic deserts, or tops of high mountains. The antarctic vegetation is indicative of an 'open habitat,' where survival is determined by small differences in microclimate and microhabitat. In a place where vegetation develops very slowly, its effect upon change of environment is very slight indeed. Extremes and limitations in the environment make the Antarctic a place where vegetation studies can

Fig. 14. 'Park' bluegrass 7 days after germination *in situ* in field with scale (in millimeters) on ruler.

help us to understand better natural selection in action.

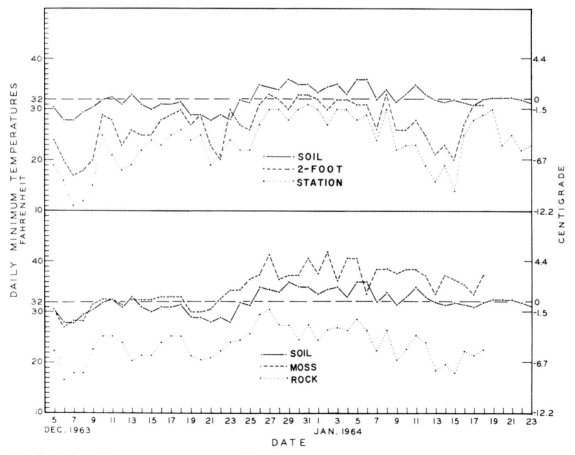

Fig. 15. Daily minimum temperatures: mean of two bluegrass plots at 0.5 cm below surface; absolutes of four weather boxes for 2 feet, Hallett Station weather box for 5 feet, surface of moss, and surface of lichen rock.

The microclimate in which plants grow in Antarctica has been found to be much different from the macroclimate generally recognized. Temperatures at the vegetation level are periodically high in summer, but over short periods of time they tend to vary widely. In terms of vegetation, this favors the plants that are able to withstand sudden changes as well as those that are capable of growing at any time when environmental conditions are favorable, which may be short, fragmented periods. The vegetation must also be able to grow in extreme desert conditions where moisture in the form of water is very scarce.

The accumulation of organic matter is very slow and very local. Mosses that grow in the wet, protected spots seem to rate best in the accomplishment of organic accumulation by building up under their clumps fair amounts of peat. In some areas there are large accumulations of dead blue-green and green algae, especially where small melt pools have become dried up. In areas where flying birds nest, particularly the south polar skua, large amounts of organic debris do accumulate. Penguin rookeries have organic matter, but owing to the high salt accumulations, the probable presence of antibiotics in the penguin guano [*Sieburth*, 1959], and the general activity of the penguins, plant development is prevented. The major vegetation component, the lichens, are very slow formers of organic matter, owing to their slow growth rates and the fact that, where small fragments of dead lichens are present, continuously strong winds tend to blow them away.

The establishment and growth of new plants in antarctic localities, even of such flowering plants as bluegrass, seem from experimental results to be a possibility. The introduction and continued survival of such invaders is, however, a problem for further investigation. One can readily say that the problems related to antarctic plant life are unlimited, and that they are well worth the concern of scientists.

Acknowledgments. The research part of this paper was supported by the U. S. Antarctic Research Program of the National Science Foundation under grant NSF G-19586 (The Ohio State University Research Foundation Project 1361). Appreciation is expressed to Scotts, Marysville, Ohio, for the bluegrass seeds, and to Lawrence C. Bliss, University of Illinois, for the *Diapensia* seeds.

REFERENCES

Benes, N. S., Inside Antarctica, No. 4: The Hallett story, *Weatherwise, 12,* 200–205, 1959.

Boyd, W. L., and J. W. Boyd, Soil microorganisms of the McMurdo Sound area, Antarctica, *Appl. Microbiol., 11,* 116–121, 1963.

Boyd, William L., James T. Staley, and Josephine W. Boyd, Ecology of soil microorganisms of Antarctica, *this volume,* 1966.

Brown, R. N. R., *The Polar Regions,* 245 pp., E. P. Dutton, New York, 1927.

Brown, R. N. R., Antarctic plant geography, in *Problems of Polar Research,* edited by W. L. G. Joerg, pp. 343–352, American Geographical Society, New York, 1928.

Bull, H. J., *The Cruise of the 'Antarctic' to the South Polar Regions,* 243, pp., Edward Arnold, London and New York, 1896.

Cailleux, A., Endémicité actuelle et passée de l'Antarctique, *Compt. Rend. Soc. Biogeograph., 334,* 65–71, 1961.

Corte, A., La primera fanerógama adventicia hallada en el continente antártico, *Instituto Antártico Argentino Contr. No. 62,* 14 pp., 1961a.

Corte, A., Fertilidad de las semillas en fanerógamas que crecen en Cabo Primavera (Costa de Danco), Peninsula Antártica, *Instituto Antártico Argentino Contr. No. 65,* 16 pp., 1961b.

Corte, A., Primera cita de la familia de Hepaticas 'Marchantiaceae' para la Anártida, *Instituto Antártico Argentino Contr. No. 68,* 12 pp., 1962.

Corte, A., and C. A. N. Daglio, Micromicetes aislados en el Antártico, *Instituto Antártico Argentino Contr. No. 74,* 27 pp., 1963.

Corte, A., and C. A. N. Daglio, A mycological study of the antarctic air, in *Biologie Antarctique* (SCAR Symposium, Paris, 1962), pp. 115–120, Hermann, Paris, 1964.

Cranwell, L. M., Nothofagus: living and fossil, in *Pacific Basin Biogeography, 10th Pacific Science Congress,* edited by J. L. Gressitt, pp. 387–400, Bishop Museum Press, Honolulu, 1963.

Di Menna, M. E., Yeasts from Antarctica, *J. Gen. Microbiol., 23,* 293–500, 1960.

Dodge, C. W., Ecology and geographical distribution of antarctic lichens, in *Biologie Antarctique* (SCAR Symposium, Paris, 1962), pp. 165–171, Hermann, Paris, 1964.

Dodge, C. W., Lichens, in *Biogeography and Ecology in Antarctica,* edited by J. van Miegham, P. van Oye, and J. Schell, pp. 194–200, W. Junk, The Hague, 1965.

Drouet, F., A brief review of the fresh-water algae of Antarctica, in *Science in Antarctica, 1: The Life Sciences in Antarctica, Natl. Acad. Sci., Natl. Res. Council Publ. 839,* pp. 10–12, Washington, D. C., 1961.

Eights, J., Descriptions of a new crustaceous animal found on the South Shetland Islands, with remarks on their natural history, *Trans. Albany Inst., 2,* 53–69, 1833.

Flint, E. A., and J. D. Stout, Microbiology of some soils from Antarctica, *Nature, 188,* 767–768, 1960.

Follmann, G., Das Pflanzenleben des Antarktis: Botanische Ergebnisse der 17. Chilenischen Antarktis-Expedition, *Umschau, 64*(4), 100–103, 1964.

Fritsch, F. E., Freshwater algae of the South Orkneys, *Scottish National Antarctic Expedition, Scientific Results of the Voyage of S. Y. 'Scotia,' 3*, 95–134, 1912.

Goldman, C. R., D. T. Mason, and B. J. B. Wood, Light injury and inhibition in antarctic freshwater phytoplankton, *Limnology Oceanography, 8,* 313–322, 1963.

Greene, S. W., Problems and progress in antarctic bryology, in *Biologie Antarctique* (SCAR Symposium, Paris, 1962), pp. 173–179, Hermann, Paris, 1964a.

Greene, S. W., Plants of the land, in *Antarctic Research, A Review of British Scientific Achievement in Antarctica,* edited by Sir Raymond Priestley, R. J. Adie, and G. deQ. Robin, pp. 240–253, Butterworths, London, 1964b.

Greene, S. W., and D. M. Greene, Check list of the subantarctic and antarctic vascular flora, *Polar Record, 11,* 411–418, 1963.

Gressitt, J. L., R. E. Leech, and C. W. O'Brien, Trapping of air-borne insects in the antarctic area, *Pacific Insects, 2,* 245–250, 1960.

Gressitt, J. L., et al., Trapping of air-borne insects in the antarctic area, 2, *Pacific Insects, 3,* 559–562, 1961.

Gressitt, J. L., R. E. Leech, and K. A. J. Wise, Entomological investigations in Antarctica, *Pacific Insects, 5,* 287–304, 1963.

Hamner, K. C., The biological clock at the south pole, *Nature, 195,* 467–480, 1962.

Harrington, H. J., et al., *Tucker Glacier; Geological Map of Ross Dependency, Antarctica* (folding map), D.S.I.R., Wellington, N. Z., 1963.

Harrington, H. J., et al., The geology of Cape Hallett-Tucker Glacier district, in *Antarctic Geology,* Proc. First Intern. Symposium on Antarctic Geology, edited by R. J. Adie, pp. 220–228, North-Holland Publishing Co., Amsterdam, 1964.

Holdgate, M. W., Terrestrial ecology in the maritime Antarctic, in *Biologie Antarctique* (SCAR Symposium, Paris, 1962), pp. 181–194, Hermann, Paris, 1964a.

Holdgate, M. W., An experimental introduction of plants to the Antarctic, *British Antarctic Survey Bull. No. 3,* pp. 13–16, 1964b.

Holm-Hansen, O., Algae: Nitrogen fixation by antarctic species, *Science, 139,* 1059–1061, 1963.

Hooker, W. J., Notes on the botany of the antarctic voyage conducted by Captain James Clark Ross, R. N., F. R. S. . . . in Her Majesty's Discovery ships Erebus and Terror; with observations on the Tussac Grass of the Falkland Islands, *London J. Botany, 2,* 246–329, 1843; also H. Bailliere, London, 83, pp., 1843.

Hoppe, G., Some comments on the 'ice-free' refugia' of northwestern Scandinavia, in *North American Biota and Their History,* edited by Á. and D. Löve, pp. 321–335, Pergamon, New York, 1963.

Janetschek, H., On the terrestrial fauna of the Ross-Sea area, Antarctica, *Pacific Insects, 5,* 305–311, 1963.

Lamb, I. M., Antarctic pyrenocarp lichens, *Discovery Rept., 25,* 1–30, 1948.

Lange, O. L., Die Photosynthese der Flechten bei tiefen Temperaturen und nach Frostperioden, *Ber. Deut. Botan. Ges., 75,* 351–352, 1962.

Llano, G. A., Botanical research essential to a knowledge of Antarctica, *Antarctica in the International Geophysical Year, Geophysical Monograph 1,* pp., 124–133, American Geophysical Union, Washington, D. C., 1956.

Llano, G. A., Status of lichenology in Antarctica, in *Science in Antarctica, 1: The Life Sciences in Antarctica,* Natl. Acad. Sci., Natl. Res. Council Publ. 839, pp. 13–19, Washington, D. C., 1961.

Llano, G. A., The flora of Antarctica, in *Antarctica, A New Zealand Antarctic Society Survey,* edited by T. Hatherton, pp. 331–350, Methuen, London, 1965.

Matsuda, T., Microclimate in the community of mosses near Syowa Base at East Ongul Island, Antarctica, *Antarctic Record (Tokyo), 21,* 12–24, 1964a.

Matsuda, T., Ecological studies on the community of mosses at Langhovde region, Antarctica, *Antarctica Record (Tokyo), 21,* 25–38, 1964b.

Meyer, G. H., et al., Antarctica: The microbiology of an unfrozen saline pond, *Science, 138,* 1103–1104, 1962.

New Zealand Antarctic Society, Work of New Zealand field parties enters new phase, *News Bull., N. Z. Antarctic Soc., 3,* 374–377, 1964.

Phillpot, H. R., The climate of the Antarctic, in *Biologie Antarctique* (SCAR Symposium, Paris, 1962), pp. 73–80, Hermann, Paris, 1964.

Plumstead, E. P., Fossil floras of Antarctica, *Sci. Rept. of Trans-Antarctic Expedition 1955–1958, 9(2),* 1–153, 1962.

Plumstead, E. P., Paleobotany of Antarctica, in *Antarctic Geology,* Proc. First Intern. Symposium on Antarctic Geology, edited by R. J. Adie, pp. 637–654, North-Holland Publishing Co., Amsterdam, 1964.

Pryor, M., Some environmental features of Hallett Station, Antarctica, with special reference to soil arthropods, *Pacific Insects, 4,* 681–728, 1962.

Reed, B., *Map of the Adélie Penguin Rookery, Seabee Spit, Cape Hallett, Antarctica,* with a summary of breeding populations (folding map and tables), D.S.I.R., Wellington, N. Z., 1963.

Rudolph, E. D., Vegetation of Hallett Station area, Victoria Land, Antarctica, *Ecology, 44,* 585–586, 1963.

Rudolph, E. D., Lichen ecology and microclimate studies at Cape Hallett, Antarctica, in *Proc. Third Intern. Biometeorol. Congr. Pau, France, 1963,* Pergamon, Oxford, 1966.

Sabbagh, M. E., A preliminary regional dynamic climatology of the Antarctic continent, *Erdkunde, 16,* 94–111, 1962.

Savicz-Ljubitzkaja, L. I., and Z. N. Smirnova, On the modes of reproduction of *Sarconeurum glaciale* (Hook, fil. et Wils.) Card. et Bryhn, and endemic moss of the Antarctica, *Rev. Bryol. Lichenol., 30,* 216–222, 1961.

Sieburth, J. McN., Gastrointestinal microflora of Antarctic birds, *J. Bacteriol., 77,* 521–531, 1959.

Singer, R., and A. Corte, A study of Antarctic basidiomycetes, in *Biol. Antarctique* (SCAR Symposium, Paris, 1962), pp. 161–163, Hermann, Paris, 1964.

Siple, P. A., The Second Byrd Antarctic Expedition, Botany I: Ecology and geographical distribution, *Ann. Missouri Botan. Garden, 25,* 467–514, 1938.

Skottsberg, C., Einige Bemerkungen über die Vegetation-sverhältnisse des Graham-Landes, *Wiss. Ergebn. Schwedischen Südpolar-Expedition 1901–1903, 4*(13), 1-16, 1912.

Skottsberg, C., Antarctic flowering plants, *Bot. Tidsskr., 51,* 330–338, 1954.

Soneda, M., On some yeasts from the antarctic region, *Biol. Results of the Japanese Antarctic Res. Exped., 15,* 1–10, 1961.

Steere, W. C., Preliminary review of the bryophytes of Antarctica, in *Science in Antarctica, 1: The Life Sciences in Antarctica, Natl. Acad. Sci., Natl. Res. Council Publ. 839,* pp. 20–30, Washington, D. C., 1961.

Steere, W. C., Antarctic bryophyta, *BioScience, 15*(4), 283–285, 1965.

Taylor, B. W., An example of long distance dispersal, *Ecology, 35,* 569–572, 1954.

Taylor, T. G., The western journeys, in *Scott's Last Expedition,* compiled by L. Huxley, vol. 2, pp. 124–198, McClelland and Goodchild, Toronto, 1913.

Tubaki, K., On some fungi isolated from the Antarctic materials, *Biol. Results of the Japanese Antarctic Res. Exped., 14,* 1–9, 1961.

Turrell, W. B., *Pioneer Plant Geography: the Phytogeographical Research of Sir Joseph Dalton Hooker,* 267 pp., M. Nijhoff, The Hague, 1953.

U. S. Department Commerce, Weather Bureau, *Climatological Data for Antarctic Stations, July 1957–December 1962,* 5 vols., Washington, D. C., 1962–1964.

Willie, N., Süsswasseralgen von der deutschen Südpolar-Expedition auf den Schiff 'Gauss,' *Deutsche Südpolar-Expedition 1901–1903, 8,* 383–445, 1924.

Wise, K. A. J., and J. L. Gressitt, Far southern animals and plants, *Nature, 207*(4992), 101–102, 1965.

ECOLOGY OF SOIL MICROORGANISMS OF ANTARCTICA

WILLIAM L. BOYD

Department of Pathology and Microbiology, Colorado State University
Fort Collins, Colorado

JAMES T. STALEY

Department of Bacteriology, University of California, Davis

JOSEPHINE W. BOYD

Fort Collins, Colorado

Abstract. Continental Antarctica possesses a characteristic flora and fauna, which varies both qualitatively and quantitatively among the different habitats. Bacteria and other micro-organisms are usually present in numbers far lower than those encountered in temperature regions. In a few areas of the Taylor and Wright dry valleys, no microbes could be detected, either microscopically or culturally. However, in the rookeries of Adélie penguins where organic matter is high and in areas either directly or indirectly contaminated by man, the numbers of bacteria found were within the range of temperate soils. There are a number of aspects of the physical and chemical environment which have a profound effect on growth and metabolism of the soil microflora. These same factors play an important role in limiting the flora to lichens and mosses as the highest type of plants and the growth of animals to no forms higher than insects and related arthropods. Metabolic activity can be demonstrated during the short growing season, although the rate is insignificant when equated to soil fertility and potential plant nitrogen. This activity cannot be ignored, how-ever, for its products are possible food for other members of the food chain of this region.

With activity increasing progressively among the scientific parties since the beginning of the International Geophysical Year of 1957, more and more microbes are being introduced on the continent. Some of these forms die at a rather rapid rate, but other species have been shown to survive over an extended period of time. Therefore, succession among indigenous and exogenous species may take place, resulting in a flora and perhaps even a fauna which may be entirely different from what is now present

INTRODUCTION

The waters around the antarctic continent repre-sent one of the most productive oceanic areas of the Earth. The key organisms in the food chain are various species of phytoplankton, which provide nutrients for the krill *Euphausia superba,* the pri-mary food for seals, whales, migratory birds, and penguins [*Murphy,* 1962]. Despite the large number of macroscopic and microscopic plants and animals in this region, however, the number of bacteria ap-pears to be low [*Lebedeva,* 1958]. That the number actually is low may not be certain; the low count

may, instead, reflect a selective action of method-ology and certain regulatory mechanisms on the growth of these forms [*Sieburth,* 1963]. Among the marine animals of these waters are a number of birds that derive their food entirely from the sea but nest on land. Through their metabolism, these birds are instrumental in converting marine eupha-sid protoplasm to animal protoplasm, and products of their decomposition may find their way into the rudimentary 'soil.' In Antarctica these birds, mostly species of penguins with some winged birds, are the most important systems on land for the pro-duction of organic matter. There are neither trees

125

nor higher forms of vegetation on the antarctic continent; only two species of flowering plants have been observed and these only in regions of the Palmer Archipelago [*Llano,* 1961]. Lichens and mosses represent the highest forms of plant life in Antarctica. By the same token, there are no higher animals systems that are true terrestrial forms, and only 50 species of insects and mites are present as terrestrial representatives of the animal kingdom [*Gressitt and Leech,* 1961].

The antarctic continent represents, therefore, an environment in which a more extensive flora and fauna could develop, if the pattern of organic matter deposition could be changed, at least along the coastal areas. The rich biosphere of the ocean is composed of living systems of a high order. These systems represent a potential source of humus, which, through microbial action, could result in food for plant growth, the most important selective factor in regulating the micro- and macrofauna as well as the growth of heterotrophic microorganisms. Succession may possibly take place in the dry valleys, because of the increased activity there of certain species of *Nostoc.* These species are photosynthetic autotrophs and can fix atmospheric nitrogen

[*Holm-Hansen,* 1963]. Needless to say there are other factors—particularly temperature, climate, precipitation, and the presence of permanently frozen ground (permafrost)—that effect growth. The ocean, however, still represents a source of nutrients for terrestrial forms, but it is a source that remains untapped because only a few biological systems can bridge the two habitats in significant numbers. Together, the various species of penguin represent the largest group of marine animals to nest on land. The south polar skua, which parasitizes the penguin, also nests on land near the rookeries, and on the ice near Weddell seal holes, near dumps at the various scientific bases, and, periodically, inland in the dry valleys of the Ross Sea area. Bodies of dead seals can also be found inland in limited numbers. In all areas other than the rookeries, which are located in the selected regions along the coast of the continent, the amount of organic matter deposited by penguins and skuas is, however, insignificant. Because of the high concentration of organic matter in the regions of the rookeries, no growth of lichens or mosses is observed, and in some cases the growth of certain members of the microflora is also affected. Thus, in Antarctica

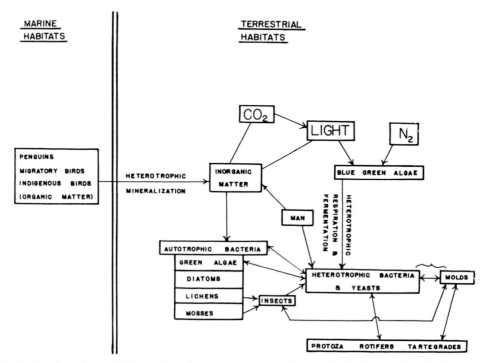

Fig. 1. Food chains and interactions between marine and terrestrial plants and animals of Antarctica.

the 'soil' is not, in the classical sense, a true soil, since an organic including a living phase may not be present; the penguin is the primary transporter of organic matter from the sea; and food chains are relatively simple (Figure 1).

During the last decade, as a result and outgrowth of the investigations during the International Geophysical Year, interest in all phases of the physical and biological sciences in antarctic regions has been renewed. From significant studies of the soil micropopulation it is now possible to evaluate the importance of some of the microbiological population and to speculate on its effect on the over-all ecology of this region. Also during the last ten years it has become necessary to consider another biological system, namely man, and to equate his role in the food cycles of these regions, since it is highly probable that he will be a year-round resident on the antarctic continent for many years to come.

This report reviews in some detail the investigations by various workers during the last three decades in a number of widely separated geographical areas; it also reports results of studies by the writers during the United States Antarctic Research Programs of 1961–1962 and 1962–1963 in the Ross Sea area, where the USARP biological laboratory at the McMurdo Station was used as a base of operations, and at Cape Hallett, where the facilities of the joint United States–New Zealand bases were used to process samples.

ANTARCTIC ARCHIPELAGO

Earlier workers reported that birds of the antarctic area has a sterile intestinal tract [Pirie, 1912; Gazert, 1912; Ekelöf, 1908; McLean, 1919], but in certain cases the methodologies of these studies was questionable. More recent work has shown conclusively that these earlier reports are erroneous [Bunt, 1955; Sieburth, 1959]. From the point of view of the 'soil' microflora, the conclusions of these earlier workers do, however, offer some interesting speculations. If there were no intestinal organisms present, the number of bacteria being introduced to selected land areas by penguins and winged birds would be of little significance and would be restricted to contaminants on the skin or in body fluids or tissues other than the intestines, or would be a result of microorganisms present as airborne forms. Sieburth [1959] has shown that a well-de-fined intestinal flora does exist among indigenous birds as well as some of the migratory and winged forms. Since, however, there are environmental mechanisms that affect the intestinal flora qualitatively as well as quantitatively, they might also affect the soil microflora in areas where there is a high density of these birds. During and after the International Geophysical Year, Sieburth made two cruises into the Palmer Archipelago area on the Argentine icebreaker A.R.A. General San Martín. He examined the intestinal flora of several species of penguins and other birds and also studied the flora of several rookeries. His earlier work during the first voyage [Sieburth, 1959] revealed that skua and sheathbill had demonstrable intestinal flora made up of aerobic and anaerobic bacteria. The number of coliform bacteria and enterococci varied, and in some cases these forms were not present in the same bird species. The Adélie penguin, gentoo penguin, and ringed penguin were devoid of typical strains of Escherichia coli, whereas the emperor penguin had significant coliform bacteria in all segments of its intestine. The gastrointestinal material and blood serum of some of these birds both showed some antibacterial activity. The food of these birds, the euphasid shrimp (Euphausia superba), was found to contain an antibiotic substance, which was localized in its stomach. Further investigation [Sieburth, 1960, 1961] revealed that algae (Phaeocystis pouchetii) eaten by the shrimp were the source of the inhibitory substance, which upon isolation and characterization proved to be acrylic acid, a three-carbon unsaturated aliphatic acid (CH_2=CH—COOH). The sodium salt of this acid has shown, by use of a filter paper–disc assay on heart infusion agar at a pH of 6.5, inhibitory action against 39 microbial species. Included among the spectrum were Pasteurella multocida, Staphylococcus aureus, and Corynebacterium pseudodiphtheriticum, which were inhibited to the greatest extent; Torula lactosa and Aspergillus fumigatus, which showed the least inhibition; and a number of different gram-positive and gram-negative forms, including Escherichia coli, Proteus vulgaris, and Aerobacter aerogenes. These results suggest that antibacterial activity may occur in nature, and this may be one reason why the numbers of bacteria in marine habitats are low while in other forms of life they are high.

TABLE 1. The pH, Antibacterial Activity, Bacterial Content, Biochemical Activity, and
Dominant Microflora of Fecal Material [after *Sieburth*, 1963]

Sample	Material	pH	Antibacterial Activity (mm) S. aureus	S. lutea	No. Organisms per Gram (wet weight) Total Aerobic	Coliforms	Cocci	Bacilli (apparent)	Biochemical Activity of Dominant Microflora Saccharolytic CHO's	Milk	Proteolytic Gelatin	Milk	Number of Isolates
					Ringed Penguin Rookery on Half Moon Island, South Shetland Islands								
A	Adult feces	5.7	1.0	3.0	8.0×10^5	3.6×10^5	5×10^2	$<10^2$	6	1	1	0	7
B	Chick feces	6.0	1.0	5.0	6.8×10^4	$<10^2$	$<10^2$	$<10^2$	2	5	0	0	7
C	Nest guano	9.1	9.0	6.5	1.2×10^5	1.8×10^3	3.5×10^4	$<10^2$	0	5	0	0	6
D	Nest runoff	9.2	17.0	8.0	1.1×10^5	3.5×10^4	9.0×10^4	$<10^2$	0	6	0	0	6
E	Guano pool	8.8	8.0	5.0	1.0×10^5	1.0×10^2	2.0×10^3	1.3×10^4	2	4	1	2	6
F	Guano 'Humus'	5.8	0	0	6.2×10^4	1.5×10^4	1.3×10^4	7.0×10^3	5	5	5	5	5
					Gentoo Penguin Rookery on King George Island, South Shetland Islands								
G	Chick feces	7.1	0	0	2.1×10^6	1.8×10^6	2.1×10^6	$<10^2$	3	5	1	1	6
H	Vacant nest	8.6	8.0	6.0	2.5×10^4	$<10^2$	$<10^2$	$<10^2$	7	7	7	7	7
J	Guano pool	8.1	7.0	5.0	4.3×10^4	9.5×10^3	1.5×10^3	$<10^2$	8	5	2	0	8
L	Dry feces	6.3	0	0	1.3×10^4	$<10^2$	$<10^2$	$<10^2$	0	0	0	0	8
I	Old nest guano	4.1	0	0	1.0×10^4	$<10^2$	1.8×10^3	6.0×10^2	3	3	3	3	3
K	Guano 'Humus'	6.6	0	0	1.3×10^6	4.8×10^5	1.4×10^4	1.0×10^3	—	—	—	—	—
					Ringed Penguin Rookery on Deception Island, South Shetland Islands								
M	Fresh feces	6.5	0	0	4.0×10^7	3.9×10^7	$<10^2$	$<10^2$	9	9	0	0	9
N	Vacant nest	8.4	0	0	1.5×10^5	$<10^2$	$<10^2$	3.0×10^4	6	2	2	2	9
O	'Soil' above rookery	7.1	0	0	9.6×10^4	6.0×10^2	3.0×10^4	$<10^2$	5	5	0	0	5
P	'Soil' between nests	5.6	0	0	3.0×10^2	$<10^2$	3.0×10^2	$<10^2$	—	—	—	—	—
Q	'Soil' between nesting areas	8.5	0	0	9.9×10^4	1.3×10^3	1.6×10^3	$<10^2$	7	7	0	0	7
R	Pond between rookeries	7.1	0	0	$<10^2$	$<10^2$	$<10^2$	$<10^2$	—	—	—	—	—

Acrylic acid may also play a role in regulating certain members of the soil population. Further studies carried out by *Sieburth* [1963] at Half Moon Island, King George Island, and Deception Island of the South Shetland Islands indicate that, although the sea contains few microorganisms, penguin rookeries are made up of guano in various stages of decomposition along with contaminated 'soil' which has significant microorganism counts (Table 1). The antibiotic substance was found to be present in all samples collected from the rookery on Half Moon Island and in two samples (samples *H* and *J*, Table 1) from King George Island; it was not, however, present in any sample from Deception Island. In some instances there was little variation in the counts, while in others, particularly among the coliform bacteria, the variation was wide. Although *Sieburth* [1963] presented numerous other data, it is difficult to evaluate the results of this study, since all counts were presented on a wet-weight basis, and no moisture values for the various samples were given. If, however, an equivalent mass of dry material per unit weight were arbitrarily assigned to each sample, the following con-

clusions could be drawn. Succession, due, apparently, to the metabolic breakdown of the acidic fecal material to basic products, altering the predominant type of fecal flora to one more characteristic of typical soil microflora, does take place. According to *Sieburth* [1963] the antimicrobial activity of the fecal material was more active in the material of higher pH.

Other factors concerned in regulating certain members of the soil population are drainage, such as that at the rookery on Deception Island, resulting in the accumulation of various soluble salts from guano and, of course, increased osmotic pressure brought about by increased salt concentration. When coliform counts in fresh feces are compared with counts from other sources, in most instances a significant decrease is noted, the exception being guano humus, which was, in all instances, within one to two logs of the original material. Several acknowledged species of bacteria have been identified in Table 2.

ROSS SEA AREA

The soil studies carried out by *Sieburth* [1963]

TABLE 2. Bacteria from Penguin Rookeries,
South Shetland Islands [after *Sieburth*, 1963]

Bacterial Species	Half Moon Island	King George Island	Deception Island
Achromobacter guttatus (Zimmermann) Bergey *et al.*	0*	+†	0
Bacillus pumilus Gottheil	0	+	0
B. sphaericus Neide	0	+	0
B. tinakiensis‡	+	+	+
Escherichia coli (Migula) Castellani and Chambers	+	0	+
Micrococcus conglomeratus Migula	0	0	+
Mycococcus albus Krassilnikov	0	+	0
Sarcina aurantiaca Flügge	+	0	0
S. ureae (Beijerinck) Löhnis	+	0	+
Streptococcus faecalis Andrews and Horder	0	0	+

* Not isolated.

† Present in material at this geographic location.

‡ Not listed in the 7th Edition of *Bergey's Manual* [*Breed, Murray, and Smith*, 1957]. Further studies have shown that *Bacillus tinakiensis* (Kurochin) listed above are actually typical strains of *Bacillus licheniformis* (Weigmann) Chester emend. Gibson.

were ancillary to the main scope of his work, which was concerned with the intestinal flora of birds. A more complete study devoted to the soil microflora was initiated by us on Ross Island during 1961–1962 and in the Taylor and Wright valleys and at Cape Hallett during 1962–1963.

In shape, Ross Island, in the Ross Sea close to the mainland, is almost a perfect equilateral triangle with sides approximately 50 miles in length; one leg of the triangle goes from Cape Bird to Cape Crozier, another from Cape Crozier to Cape Armitage, and a third from Cape Armitage to Cape Bird. The Ross Ice Shelf borders one leg of this triangular island, and for most of the year the coastlines of the other legs are bordered by fast ice. From Cape Royds to areas north of this point, open water may be present during the early spring (late October to early November). The Ross Ice Shelf, therefore, plays an extremely important role in the ecology of the Ross Sea area, since this large ice mass has a profound effect on the over-all temperature of the various habitats on the island. Another important ecological factor is the presence of an active volcano on the island. Mount Erebus, along with the extinct volcanoes Mount Terror and Mount Terra Nova, has played an important role in determining the

Fig. 2. Volcanic soil at Cape Royds near the sampling sites.

geological properties of this region. The predominant type of rock is volcanic ash—Ross Island differs from some areas on the mainland, such as the Wright and Taylor valleys, which are made up primarily of granites, gneisses, and dolomite.

Ross Island has three rather large Adélie penguin rookeries at Cape Royds, Cape Bird, and Cape Crozier. Although Cape Crozier also has an emperor penguin rookery, the birds have little or no effect, at least directly, on soil microorganisms, for emperor penguins nest on fast ice.

Prior to 1963, there were few publications dealing with indigenous flora and fauna of the region. Blue-green and green algae had been studied by *Fritsch* [1912] and *Flint and Stout* [1960], rotifers and tartegrades by *Murray* [1909], and mosses and lichens by *Cardot* [1907] and *Darbishire* [1910], respectively. Surveys of bacteria by *Darling* and *Siple* [1941] had been carried out at and near Little America, well up on the Ross Ice Shelf, but the studies of *Flint and Stout* [1960] represent the only studies made on Ross Island and the nearby mainland. A motile bacillus in snow was observed by Atkinson, the surgeon of the Scott Expedition of 1911–1913 [*Scott*, 1913]. These studies were all qualitative in nature.

To investigate possible seasonal changes, three soil plots were studied thoroughly during the 1961–1962 season. Samples in triplicate were taken on a weekly basis and analyzed within 3 hours after collection at the USARP biological laboratory at McMurdo Station. The methods of enumeration were those of *Boyd* [1958]. Soil 1 was a volcanic soil located outside of the rookery at Cape Royds, which had blown free of snow when the project was initiated and remained in that condition throughout the study (Figure 2); no vegetation was visible. Soil 2 was well within the Adélie rookery at Cape Royds (Figure 3). The site consisted of volcanic ash covered with ½ to 1 inch of brown guano, below which was a dark organic-gravel mixture. The samples were taken 6 inches below ground level. Soil 3 was also of volcanic origin but it supported the growth of lichens (Figure 4). In Figure 5, which gives the results of our work, soil 1 at Cape Royds is shown to be free of all the common microorganisms normally grown on the popular media used for these tests. Either this soil was sterile or it contained microbes that could not initiate growth on these media. In the case of either of the other two soils sampled, a significant increase over the short growing season was ob-

Fig. 3.   Adélie penguin rookery at Cape Royds.

Fig. 4. Hills above the base at McMurdo Sound where lichens are found growing in some areas. To the left on Hut Point Peninsula can be seen a storage hut erected by Scott's 1901–1904 British Antarctic Expedition.

served. Both soils showed maximum counts for both mesophilic and psychrophilic forms in the range of 10^5 to 10^6 bacteria per gram of dry soil. These counts approach those normally encountered in temperate regions in uncultivated soils [*Waksman,* 1952]. The only soil of this group which showed any mold was soil 3 above the base at McMurdo Sound where lichens were found growing.

A general survey of soils of the Ross Island area (Table 3) reveals that counts were extremely low in all instances except those in areas that had been inhabited in the past or that were presently occupied. In these latter areas human and animal contaminants undoubtedly were responsible directly or indirectly for the high counts. The increase in organic matter would probably have a profound effect on the heterotrophic microflora; in addition, new microbes that might be able to initiate growth would be introduced. No coliform bacteria could be detected in any of the samples.

Thermophilic Bacteria

During this investigation, all samples were tested routinely for the presence of thermophilic bacteria. In most instances the soils were free of this group of bacteria. On 16 November soils 1 and 2 from Cape Royds did, however, contain, respectively, 300 and 320 thermophilic bacteria per gram of dry soil, although for the remainder of the study the count for these soils was negative. Thermophilic bacteria were found in greatest numbers in areas where contamination from man and other animals had occurred. Volcanic soil from Shackleton's dump at Cape Royds, containing rusted cans, bottles, pony manure, and other debris left over from the British Antarctic Expedition of 1907 [*Shackleton,* 1909], had the highest counts and also a significantly high amount of ammonia derived from the organic matter present (Table 4). Hut Point, near the present McMurdo base, which had been used as a storehouse for Scott's 1901–1904 Expedition [*Scott,* 1905] and the later expedition of 1911–1912 [*Scott,* 1913], had fewer bacteria present in the surrounding soil, although the area around the Scott hut at Cape Evans was relatively high in numbers of bacteria. Soil that had recently been contaminated with sewage at the McMurdo base also contained significant numbers of thermophilic bacteria. It would appear that man and other animals are a source of many of the thermophilic bacteria found in soils of the Ross Sea area.

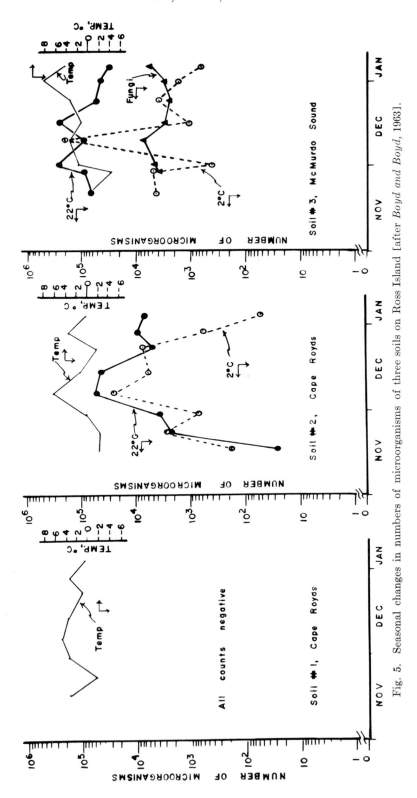

Fig. 5. Seasonal changes in numbers of microorganisms of three soils on Ross Island [after *Boyd and Boyd*, 1963].

TABLE 3. Counts of Microbes in Soils from Different Areas on Ross Island
and on the Mainland [after *Boyd and Boyd*, 1963]

Date (1961)	Location	Soil Temperatures (C)	Moisture (%)	Nutrient Agar* 55C 1 day†	Nutrient Agar* 22C 5 days†	Nutrient Agar* 2C 14 days†	Sabouraud's Dextrose Agar	Thornton's Standardized Agar 22C, 5 days†	Desoxycholate Agar 37C, 1 day†	Ferric Ammonium Citrate-Nitrate Agar, 22C, 5 days†
					Cape Royds					
29 Nov.	Shackleton's dump‡	0	3.6	2,700	300,000	280,000	64,000	10,000	0	0
13 Dec.	Soil #1, outside rookery	+3.7	4.3	0	0	0	0	0	0	0
13 Dec.	Soil #2, rookery	+1.3	6.8	0	45,000	5,200	0	73	0	0
					McMurdo Sound					
9 Dec.	Hut Point††	+3.6	8.2	4	98,000,000	63,000,000	0	65,000,000	0	0
9 Dec.	Street contaminated with sewage‡	+3.8	7.3	390	84,000,000	49,000,000	1,100	25,000,000	0	0
15 Dec.	Soil #3	+1.2	6.6	0	270,000	1,100	3,100	34,000	0	0
15 Dec.	Street contaminated with sewage‡	+6.3	5.9	0	250,000	180,000	5	770,000	0	0
16 Dec.	Soil #4, Crater Hill	+3.1	7.4	0	42,000	73,000	0	37,000	0	0
16 Dec.	Soil #5, Crater Hill	+3.1	4.5	0	3,500	38	0	730	0	0
23 Dec.	Observation Hill	+7.1	2.0	0	2,300	77	0	54	0	0
					Cape Evans					
22 Dec.‡		−1.8	6.4	160	870,000	680,000	1,300	390,000	0	13

* Per g of dry soil.

† Temperature and time of incubation.

‡ Areas inhabited by man during the past or at present.

TABLE 4. Chemical Composition (in ppm) of the Soils Sampled [after *Boyd and Boyd*, 1963]

Date (1961)	Location	pH	P	K	Ca	Mg	Nitrate	Ammonia	Sulfate	Chloride
					Cape Royds					
29 Nov.	Shackleton's dump	8.3	100	130	6,000	2,800	0	100	2,800	1,600
13 Dec.	Soil #1	8.3	180	1,300	3,800	600	0	0	11,000	22,000
13 Dec.	Soil #2	7.0	2,400	280	200	80	0	6,000	5,600	1,800
					McMurdo Sound					
9 Dec.	Hut Point	8.3	140	320	1,600	200	0	40	0	1,600
9 Dec.	Street contaminated with sewage	8.1	300	320	2,400	280	0	160	20	800
15 Dec.	Soil #3	8.0	100	320	3,200	1,800	0	60	0	20
15 Dec.	Street contaminated with sewage	7.0	1,000	320	2,400	80	0	600	1,000	1,200
16 Dec.	Soil #4, Crater Hill	8.2	260	320	4,000	1,000	0	14	0	40
16 Dec.	Soil #5, Crater Hill	8.0	200	320	4,000	180	0	14	0	40
23 Dec.	Observation Hill	8.0	120	320	40	80	0	10	0	120
					Cape Evans					
22 Dec.		8.1	300	320	2,800	120	0	30	0	800

Molds

The number of molds in all the samples was determined by use of Sabouraud's Dextrose Agar. In general, except where known contamination from exogenous sources had occurred, most of the soils were devoid of molds, which suggests that animals contributed to the mycotic flora of some of these soils. In soil 3 at McMurdo Sound, which supported the growth of mosses and lichens, mold counts were high, but in soils 4 and 5, where these plants also grew, the counts were not high. Molds were also found growing on leather and other objects in Ponting's darkroom in the hut at Cape Evans that had been occupied by members of past British expeditions. *Darling and Siple* [1941] also mention mold spoilage of food and fur clothing left over at Rockefeller Mountains from the first Byrd Antarctic Expedition.

Psychrophilic Microorganisms

All samples having a measurable mesophilic count also possessed some psychrophilic microorganisms. The ratios varied from Crater Hill soil, where more psychrophiles than mesophiles were present (the mesophilic count represented 57.5 per cent of the psychrophilic count), to soil 3, where the psychrophiles were only 0.14 per cent of the mesophilic population. These results are within the range observed by *Straka and Stokes* [1960], who sampled a variety of frozen material collected in Antarctica during 1958 by Captain C. E. Meyers. These workers found the psychrophile–mesophile ratio to be 1:1 for pony debris and less than 100 to 202,000 for one sample of soil. The other counts varied between these two extremes. The only difference between their work and our work was minor; we used 2°C for culturing psychrophilic forms and 22°C for growing mesophiles, whereas they used 0°C and 30°C, respectively, for culture growth. They also isolated various bacteria that would grow at a minimum temperature of −7°C.

One area at Cape Royds was consistently free of any demonstrable microorganisms (Table 4). The soil (soil 1) was extremely high in soluble chlorides and sulfate; the concentration was one that in temperate regions will inhibit plant growth. Since some of the soils of the Taylor Valley were also shown to be free of cultivatable bacteria, extensive studies were carried out in these areas during the 1962–1963 field season.

Dry-Valley Systems

In the Ross Sea region, continental Antarctica is made up of numerous glaciers and other areas covered with snow, but there are several dry valleys where, at least on the floor of the valley, no glaciers are present. The types of rock are predominantly granites, gneisses, and dolomite; since very little organic matter is present, soil in the classical sense does not exist. In some instances where weathering has taken place without the presence of a humus layer, a type of rudimentary soil may be present (F. C. Ugolini, personal communication). Precipitation is slight, being somewhere near or below the continental average of 10 cm in

Fig. 6.   Taylor Valley showing Lake Bonney partially thawed.

Fig. 7. Field laboratory at Lake Bonney, Taylor Valley.

terms of water equivalent [*Wexler and Rubin*, 1961]. For the most part, no higher forms of life are found at the lower levels; in a few areas, however, blue-green algae are present [*Holm-Hansen*, 1963], and, at higher levels, lichens have been reported growing on rock outcroppings (E. D. Rudolph, personal communication). Carcasses of fossil seals were found in many areas throughout some of these valleys [*Péwé, Rivard, and Llano*, 1959], but no reasons for their presence so far from water has yet been determined. From studies carried out during the United States Antarctic Research Program of the National Science Foundation (USARP) during 1961–1962 [*Boyd and Boyd*, 1963], a few areas exist, especially around Lake Bonney in the Taylor Valley, where neither viable bacteria

Fig. 8. Taylor and Wright valleys showing areas that were sampled.

nor molds could be demonstrated. These results at that time appeared, however, to be the exception rather than the rule, since *Holm-Hansen* [1963] reported that nitrogen-fixing blue-green algae of the *Nostoc* genus are present in both valleys and *Dougherty and Harris* [1963] isolated and identified several species of rotifers and tartegrades. Some forms of life can, therefore, grow and reproduce in certain habitats under these rigorous environmental conditions.

During the 1962–1963 USARP, a comprehensive survey of the Taylor and Wright valleys was carried out to enumerate the microbial population in random areas throughout these regions, to determine qualitatively if other forms of life were present, to study the factors that either limit or permit growth, and to reconstruct the food chains of the various indigenous biological forms. The general physiography of these regions can be observed in Figures 6 and 7.

All samples were collected on the mainland and analyzed within 5 hours after collection at the USARP biological laboratory at McMurdo Station on Ross Island. Although, in general, these studies

TABLE 5. Areas in Dry Valleys with Few or No Microorganisms

Area No.	No. Samples	No. Sterile	Conditions*	% Moisture	Nutrient agar			Sabouraud's Dextrose Agar	Thornton's Standardized Agar
					55C	22C	2C		
Taylor Valley									
4	20	15	L	0.3	0	0	0	0	0
			A	1.0	0	0	0	0	0
			H	3.8	0	1	0	0	1
17	10	6	L	0.1	0	0	0	0	0
			A	0.8	0	1	0	0	0
			H	3.0	1	3	0	1	0
18	10	9	L	0.0	0	0	0	0	0
			A	0.2	0	0	0	0	0
			H	0.6	0	1	0	4	0
19	10	6	L	0.0	0	0	0	0	0
			A	0.4	0	20	0	0	2
			H	0.7	0	84	0	0	19
Totals	50	36	L	0.0	0	0	0	0	0
			A	0.7	0	4	0	0	0
			H	3.8	1	84	0	4	19
Wright Valley									
9	10	6	L	0.0	0	0	0	0	0
			A	0.1	0	0	0	0	26
			H	0.2	0	3	0	0	213
10	10	5	L	1.2	0	0	0	0	0
			A	1.7	0	0	0	0	4
			H	2.2	0	1	0	1	28
11	10	5	L	0.1	0	0	0	0	0
			A	0.4	0	10	0	0	0
			H	3.1	0	49	0	1	2
8	10	6	L	0.3	0	0	0	0	0
			A	0.9	0	3	0	0	0
			H	1.3	0	4	1	1	0
Totals	40	22	L	0.0	0	0	0	0	0
			A	0.8	0	3	0	0	8
			H	3.1	0	49	1	1	213

* L = lowest count; A = average of samples; H = highest count

TABLE 6.   Areas in Dry Valleys and Adjacent Regions with Relatively High Counts of Bacteria and Molds

Area No.	No. Samples	No. Sterile	Conditions*	% Moisture	Nutrient agar			Sabouraud's Dextrose Agar	Thornton's Standardized Agar
					55C	22C	2C		
			Taylor Valley						
1	10	0	L	10.1	0	1100	290	0	93
			A	15.1	0	5000	630	1	190
			H	17.8	0	9600	1160	4	290
3	15	0	L	0.4	0	5	0	1	0
			A	1.0	0	320	0	0	74
			H	1.6	0	780	0	3	221
1	20	0	L	3.9	0	260	0	0	480
			A	9.8	0	7300	86	7	1400
			H	17.3	0	20,000	490	27	4000
3	10	1	L	1.6	0	0	0	0	0
			A	5.9	0	650	0	1	15
			H	9.3	0	1700	0	3	82
21	10	0	L	1.9	0	1400	0	0	110
			A	3.8	0	4400	430	0	2100
			H	7.0	0	11,000	2600	1	6800
5	5	0	L	1.4	0	17		5	0
			A	2.1	0	530		8	170
			H	2.5	0	970		11	320
24	10	0	L	1.4	0	19	0	0	0
			A	4.1	0	37	26	3	14
			H	7.5	0	73	160	8	49
23	10	0	L	0.4	0	23	0	5	0
			A	1.7	0	210	3	9	3
			H	2.3	0	1100	23	26	13
22	5	0	L	6.7	0	310	85	0	8
			A	10.4	0	840	170	1	70
			H	13.8	0	1000	240	10	140
Totals	95	1	L	0.4	0	0	0	0	0
			A	6.5	0	2600	150	3	580
			H	17.8	0	20,000	2600	27	6800
			Wright Valley						
13	10	0	L	0.4	0	15	0	0	1
			A	0.7	0	93	2	0	38
			H	1.0	0	230	15	1	97
16	10	0	L	5.7	0	260	2300	0	0
			A	10.9	0	1500	490	24	210
			H	14.2	0	3500	16	240	500
14	10	0	L	0.2	0	98	0	0	0
			A	10.8	0	1300	460	0	110
			H	16.4	0	2300	1800	0	300
15	10	0	L	0.1	0	480	0	0	1
			A	6.5	0	1500	540	0	170
			H	17.0	0	2700	1600	0	370
6	10	0	L	1.3	0	170	0	0	19
			A	8.9	0	610	1200	1	82
			H	13.7	0	1600	3900	2	570
Totals	50	0	L	0.1	0	15	0	0	0
			A	7.6	0	1000	530	5	120
			H	17.0	0	3500	3900	240	570
			Strand Moraines						
2	30	0	L	0.6	0	280	53	0	95
			A	14.7	0	170	900	0	530
			H	30.8	0	5700	2700	4	2200
			Marble Point						
5	30	0	L	4.6	0	1600	46	0	1000
			A	9.2	0	23,000	3600	550	7200
			H	19.2	1	79,000	25,000	4300	32,000

* See Table 5 for explanation of conditions.

were concentrated on the Taylor and Wright valleys, other regions were included for purposes of comparison.

The methods of enumeration were described earlier [*Boyd, 1958; Boyd and Boyd, 1963*]. Chemical analyses were carried out on pooled samples with a Hellige-Troug soil-testing kit.

Two different habitats were selected; one was characterized by the visible growth of blue-green algae and moisture, whereas the other type was generally in areas far from glacier melt water. Since studies from the previous year showed at least one area of the Taylor Valley to be sterile [*Boyd and Boyd*, 1963], a series of stations throughout the Taylor and Wright valleys and in two adjacent regions were established. In the valleys 21 different sites were studied (Figure 8); 315 samples were collected and subjected to microbiological and chemical analyses and at each site at least five samples were collected at random.

Throughout both valleys there were many areas which either were sterile or contained very low numbers of microorganisms (Table 5). In the Taylor Valley, out of a total of 50 samples from four different areas, 36 were completely sterile (72 per cent); in the 14 other areas counts were low. The picture for the Wright Valley was similar: 22 of 40 samples (55 per cent) were devoid of forms that could initiate growth on culture media. All these

areas were further characterized by a lack of visible growth of blue-green algae and other plant and animal microbes, although in many of the samples fragments of diatoms were present. Gram stains, however, failed to reveal the presence of bacteria or other microorganisms. In all instances, moisture was low; this could have been a very important factor, along with other factors of the physical and chemical environment, in limiting growth.

Conversely, there were many regions in both valleys that supported the growth of significant numbers of bacteria and molds (Table 6), as well as other macroscopic and microscopic forms. In all instances, a relatively high moisture content was present despite the fact that nearly all the samples consisted of sandy material which would allow downward percolation of water from the shallow active layer to the permafrost. Most of these samples were obtained from areas that were saturated with melt water from the many glaciers flowing into the valley bottom. With few exceptions, all these areas were characterized by the presence of large masses of blue-green algae (*Nostoc commune*). *Holm-Hansen* [1963] has shown that strains of blue-green algae from various regions in the Ross Sea area are capable of fixing N^{15} under laboratory conditions, including some from the Victoria Valley; but, nitrogen-fixation by indigenous strains

TABLE 7. Areas in the Wright Valley Where Mummified Seal Carcasses Were Present

No. Samples	No. Sterile	Conditions*	% Moisture	Nutrient agar			Sabouraud's Dextrose Agar	Thronton's Standardized Agar
				55C	22C	2C		
Area No. 12								
2†	0	L	0.5	0	1800	970	0	0
		A	0.7	0	1800	1000	1	0
		H	0.8	0	1800	1100	1	0
8	6	L	0.3	0	0	0	0	0
		A	0.7	0	0	0	0	0
		H	1.1	0	2	1	1	0
Area No. 7								
4†	0	L	0.7	0	460	9	4	0
		A	1.0	0	3000	370	180	4
		H	1.2	0	8300	860	460	11
6	1	L	0.8	0	0	0	0	0
		A	1.1	0	23	0	0	6
		H	1.5	0	60	2	1	17

* See Table 5 for explanation of conditions.
† With seals.

Fig. 9. Seal carcass found in the Wright Valley.

has not been demonstrated *in situ*. Microscopic green algae and diatoms were also present under these conditions as well as various species of protozoa, chief among which were ciliates of the genus *Colpoda*.

The highest form of life observed consisted of micrometazoa composed of rotifers and tartegrades; *Dougherty and Harris* [1963] recently characterized the species of these forms that are indigenous to the dry valleys.

In both valleys, except for two areas, thermophiles were almost entirely absent from the bacterial population. In the exceptions, Marble Point and area 17 in the Taylor Valley, two colonies were present on a single plant from each area. On Ross Island and some of the areas sampled the previous year, thermophiles were found in significant numbers only where contamination from man or animals had occurred. Although there are no higher terrestrial animals indigenous to this area, skua have been observed as far inland from the coast as Lake Bonney; their quantitative effect on the soil microflora, however, is probably insignificant.

Mold counts were generally low with the exception of samples from area 16 in the Wright Valley and in some of the samples from Marble Point. Counts were high in most samples from the areas in the Wright Valley next to mummified seals (Table 7). The low number of molds in those two valley systems is probably a very important factor in limiting the mesafauna, which might have become established. *Janetschek* [1963] suggested that *Collembola*, one of the most widely distributed in-

sect forms in Antarctica, subsist on soil fungi and are usually found only in their presence. According to *Gressitt, Leech, and Wise* [1963], the Victoria Valley is completely devoid of insects, while in the Taylor Valley (77°40'S) only one area below the terminus of one of the several small glaciers coming down the valley walls, was found to possess mites and springtails. If the food of *Collembola* or springtails consists of molds or hyphae or their spores, then insects in these regions could be lacking because molds are not found there. Or it might be a question of moisture; where moisture is available other forms of life are present (Table 6). Since, with the exception of molds, all forms from bacteria on up to tartegrades and rotifers are found in these valleys, the limiting factor for the growth of mites and insects in these regions is probably lack of food.

Because of recent activities by both research and support personnel in these dry valleys, microorganisms might be introduced into Victoria Land. Under present conditions reproduction may not be possible, but if the environment should change, for example if water should be introduced from melting glaciers, growth of certain species is conceivable. These conclusions are based on the results obtained from samples collected around seal carcasses found in the Taylor Valley.

For some unknown reason, over the years several species of seals left the surrounding waters of Antarctica and migrated into some of the valley systems on the continent; desiccation through wind action followed, leaving dry carcasses, in some instances in a good state of preservation (Figures 9 and 10). *Péwé, Rivard, and Llano* [1959] have

Fig. 10. Seal carcass found in the Wright Valley.

TABLE 8. Summary of Chemical Composition of Soils in the Dry Valleys

Area No.	pH	Parts per Million (ppm)							
		P	K	Ca	Mg	NO$_3$–N	NH$_3$–N	SO$_4$	Cl
Areas of little or no growth									
Taylor Valley									
4	8.1	120	100	2400	1200	6	10	0	4200
4	8.2	120	280	4000	2000	6	10	0	4800
17	8.1	100	130	800	1000	2	10	40	4200
18	8.0	90	840	2400	320	1	10	0	40
19	8.0	100	160	2400	400	0	20	0	40
Wright Valley									
8	8.0	90	320	400	200	100	10	40	800
9	8.0	80	120	1200	600	80	10	600	1600
10	8.0	70	64	120	200	120	12	1200	1200
11	8.0	80	320	560	40	10	6	280	33,000
12	8.0	56	120	400	240	80	6	400	1200
Areas of slight growth									
Taylor Valley									
3	8.0	120	80	1600	200	0	40	20	800
24	8.0	140	1700	1600	240	2	20	0	2800
Wright Valley									
7	7.6	80	190	400	40	2	20	40	600
*Areas of significant growth**									
Taylor Valley									
1, 21, 22, 23, 25	8.0	90	660	2200	120	1	12	10	400
Wright Valley									
6, 13, 14, 15, 16	7.7	90	150	230	130	9	10	17	400
Marble Point									
5	8.2	45	110	4400	540	20	20	20	900
Strand Moraines									
2	8.0	9	120	5600	220	1	15	0	20

*These values represent the average of all the samples from each area.

dated some of these remains and have come up with an age of 1700 ($\pm$100 years) with an upper age limit of 2500 ($\pm$100 years). Like other mammals, seals have a characteristic microflora. Although little work on seals has been done, *McBee* [1960] isolated *Clostridium perfringens, Cl. sordellii, Cl. difficile,* and a strain similar to *Cl. setiense* from the contents of the large intestine of a Weddell seal. This inland migration of seals might, therefore, represent a method of limited introduction of microorganisms into the valleys.

Results indicate (Table 7) that, in areas of the Wright Valley whose properties are similar to those of the areas described in Table 5, counts of microorganisms are either negative or extremely low, except in samples taken adjacent to or under a seal carcass. The mold count adjacent to a seal carcass in area 7 was the highest encountered except for area 16 in this valley and Marble Point. The data indicate that the microorganisms found in the soil must have originated from seals. Although the exact age of the seals was not determined, those forms capable of initiating growth must have been able to adjust to this new environment and to remain viable for a relatively long period of time. It will be interesting to see if the increased activities of USARP personnel result in the establishment of species indigenous to man or his materials in areas which were previously sterile.

POSSIBLE FACTORS THAT MIGHT LIMIT MICROBIAL GROWTH

The results of chemical studies on soils of the

mainland, determined with a Hellige-Troug Soil-Testing Kit, are given in Table 8. Those areas where little or no growth was found were areas in which moisture was extremely low and chloride and/or sulfate concentrations high. In two instances, areas 8 and 18 in the dry valleys, the chemical composition was low, but since moisture content was also low, it could have been the sole limiting factor.

Water is probably the most critical factor for growth in the dry valleys and on Ross Island. Although all areas, with the exception of the Strand Moraines, listed (Table 6) as high in counts of bacteria and molds, show maximum moisture contents of less than 20 per cent, these concentrations are high in comparison to those of areas that could support little or no growth (Table 5). In the dry valleys the average moisture was 0.7 to 0.8 per cent. In all the regions where growth was found, it was found in areas on the floor of the valleys where water was available from the melting of glaciers running down from above. Areas at Marble Point where samples were collected received run-off from the Wilson Piedmont Glacier and those from the Strand Moraines from the Blue Glacier. This moisture fulfilled a necessary function in growth and metabolism. Water also resulted in solubilizing both the sulfate and chloride that might have collected in these areas over a period of years and their concentrations to the point where salt susceptible–biological systems could initiate growth. It becomes possible, therefore, to predict that viable blue-green algae accumulations will be found at the front of glaciers, where there is melt water, or on the shores of certain lakes, such as Lake Vanda in the Wright Valley, Lake Fryxell, and the lower end of Lake Bonney in the Taylor Valley. Although the investigation did not cover the Victoria Valley, *Holm-Hansen* [1963] has found *N. commune* there as well as in the Wright and Taylor valleys. Low precipitation along with high winds account for lack of moisture. Lyophilization, or freeze-drying, of exposed materials such as algal masses and mummified seals (Figures 9 and 10) occurs in these valleys. As a method of preserving bacterial cultures, this process is not new to microbiologists; it has often been used for the preservation of convenience foods for present-day hunters and campers. Since the antarctic climate insures lyophilization, the stability of certain organic systems is enhanced.

Along with a high degree of evaporation there is an increase in osmotic pressure due to the concentration of various salts. This is especially common in the penguin rookery at Cape Royds, where the osmotic pressure is extremely high due to the presence of phosphate, chloride, ammonia, and other salts derived from penguin guano. Despite this high osmotic pressure, however, there were viable organisms present in these plots, and the counts increased during the short summer. Some degree of ammonification was also observed. The rookery soils were interesting in that no coliform bacteria were detected in them throughout the course of this study. Whether toxic salts constituted the limiting factor or whether the lack of coliform bacteria was due to the presence of acrylic acid in guano was not determined. Coliform bacteria do die at an extremely fast rate when seeded into soils of Ross Island [*Boyd and Boyd*, 1963a], but if they had been present their detection by means of appropriate enrichment and selective media would have been easy. These data differ from those of *Sieburth* [1963], who was able to detect coliform bacteria in a number of different materials in rookeries from the South Shetland Islands. He used Tergitol 7 Agar, which is supposed to yield counts of coliform bacteria that are about 30 per cent higher than counts on other selective media. This increased sensitivity does not, however, account for the difference in findings. Acrylic acid determinations were not run on these rookery soils, so whether this substance was present in higher concentrations or whether inhibitory substances unique to this environment were present, is not known.

The soil temperatures in Table 3 are deceiving, in that they represent values at 2 to 3 inches below the surface of ground. In Antarctica, during the summer, when the Sun shines continuously around the clock, a great deal of solar radiation is absorbed by the rocks and smaller particles; at the soil-air interface, temperatures may get above 20°C (68°F) [*Janetschek*, 1963] or above 32°C (90°F) to the north of Ross Island [*Rudolph*, 1963]. Since, for most microorganisms, temperatures are well within the range for optimum mesophilic physiological activity, mesophilic bacteria may very well play some role, however small, in the economy of antarctic soils.

From studies in the dry valleys and on Ross

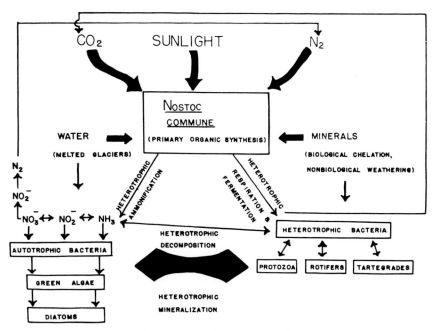

Fig. 11.   Food chains in the dry valleys.

TABLE 9.   Distribution of Bacteria in Antarctica [after *Darling and Siple,* 1941]

Bacterial Species	Scott Glacier, Queen Maud Mountains 86°58'S 152°36'W Elevation 9000 ft	Byrd Land, Ford Ranges 77°48'S 145°W	Little America 78°34'S 163°56'W
Bacillus mesentericus De Bary	+	+	+
B. subtilis Cohn	+	+	+
B. cereus Frankland & Frankland	0	+	+
B. fusiformis Gottheil	0	+	0
B. tumescens Zopf	+	+	+
B. malabarensis Lohnis & Pillai	0	+	+
B. megatherium De Bary	0	+	+
B. consolidus Bredemann & Stuhrk	0	0	+
B. albolactus Migula	0	+	0
Achromobacter liquidum (Frankland & Frankland) Bergey *et al.*	+	+	0
A. delicatulum (Jordan) Bergey *et al.*	+	+	0
Flavobacterium devorans (Zimmermann) Bergey *et al.*	+	+	+
F. flavescens (Pohl) Bergey *et al.*	0	+	0
F. solare (Lehmann & Neumann)	0	+	0
F. sulfureum Bergey *et al.*	0	+	0
F. turcosum (Zimmermann) Bergey *et al.*	0	0	+
Protoactinomyces agrestis Jensen	0	+	+
Micrococcus caseolyticus Evans	0	+	0
M. flavus Lehmann & Neumann	0	(+)?*	(+)?*
M. freudenreichii Guillebeau	+	+	+
M. halophilus Bergey *et al.*	0	+	+

* Listed in text as *M. flavescens.*

TABLE 10.   Bacterial Species* of the Ross Sea Area

Chromatium minutissimum Winogradsky
Chromobacterium violaceum (Schroeter) Bergonzini
Bacillus coagulans Hammer
B. licheniformis (Weigmann) Chester *emend.* Gibson
B. sphaericus Neide
Micrococcus cryophilis McLean *et al.*
Flavobacterium peregrinum Stapp and Spicher
F. diffusum (Frankland and Frankland) Bergey *et al.*
F. solare (Lehmann and Neumann) Bergey *et al.*
Achromobacter cycloclastes (Gray and Thornton)
    Bergey *et al.*
A. liquefaciens (Eisenberg) Bergey *et al.*
Pseudomonas fluorescens Migula
P. aeruginosa (Schroeter) Migula
P. striata Chester
Azotobacter chroococcum Beijerinck

---

* *Breed, Murray, and Smith* [1957].

Island, some of the factors which limit growth are now known. The most simple food chains (summarized in Figure 11) are found in the dry valleys. The key organisms are the autotrophic, photosynthetic, blue-green algae. Where these forms can initiate growth, a supply of organic matter is synthesized and can be used directly or indirectly by other heterotrophic and autotrophic plants and animals. Despite the growth of these forms, the rate of metabolism as evidenced by the accumulation of algal mats from year to year around the margins of small ponds is slow.

Bacterial Species of the Ross Sea Area

Until 1962, the only comprehensive study on species of bacteria indigenous to Antarctica was that of *Darling and Siple* [1941], who investigated a variety of materials from the area around Little America. One hundred seventy-eight cultures were isolated from air, soil, melted snow, ice, and plant debris and studied. The species, identified by Darling and Siple according to the criteria of *Bergen, Breed, Murray, and Hitchins* [1939], are shown in Table 9. These indigenous species represent forms commonly found in the soil and other natural materials of temperate regions.

In 1963 a number of species in the Ross Sea area were also observed and identified (Table 10). The dry valleys appear to have flora that differs markedly from that of nearby Ross Island. Ross Island

represents a habitat that has been influenced by the volcanic action of two extinct volcanoes, Mount Terror and Mount Terra Nova, and the still active Mount Erebus; few pigmented species were present in this volcanic soil except in areas contaminated in the past and/or present by man or other animals. Quite a few pigmented forms appeared on the Petri plates prepared from soil samples from many areas of the valleys. *Chromobacterium violaceum* was particularly abundant in Wright Valley and to some extent in Taylor Valley.

In all the samples collected in the valleys only one thermophilic bacterium was isolated; all samples other than this were negative. In a comparison of these studies with those made on Ross Island the previous year, thermophiles were found only in areas which had experienced contamination by human and/or animal feces, the probable source of these organisms. *Bacillus stearothermophilus* was not isolated, but *B. coagulans* was found in soil at Cape Evans, Cape Royds, and McMurdo Sound. In these areas also *B. licheniformis* was the most widely distributed thermophilic species. The only other spore-former was the mesophilic, biochemically inert *B. sphaericus,* which was found in soil from the Adélie penguin rookery at Cape Crozier. Other gram-positive and gram-negative forms are shown in Table 10. Molds and actinomycetes were, upon occasion, also isolated. *Streptomyces* was present in some of the samples from Ross Island and was also observed at Cape Hallett. In both these regions *Penicillium* and *Mucor* were also observed. At least three different species of yeast, each with different morphological and colonial characteristics, were observed at Cape Hallett. All the habitats studied lacked coliform bacteria.

Physiological Groups

Since in areas where contamination had not taken place the counts were low, it was assumed that physiological activity would be low. Because a humus layer was almost uniformly absent, the presence of highly active forms would probably be minimized.

In an attempt to learn more about the physiological potentiality of the soil microflora and microfauna, the following enrichment series was inoculated with samples of representative soil from a

TABLE 11. Physiological Groups of Microorganisms in Soil of Ross Island*

Physiological Group	Soil #1 Cape Royds	Soil #2 Cape Royds	Soil #3 McMurdo Sound	Soil Hut Point	'Skua Pond' Water
Iron oxidizers	0†	0	0	0	Bacteria
Acidophilic sulfur oxidizers	0	0	0	0	0
Photosynthetic nitrogen-fixers	0	0	0	0	Blue-green algae
Heterotrophic nitrogen-fixers	0	Bacteria	Bacteria	Bacteria	Bacteria
Ammonia oxidizers	0	0	Bacteria	Bacteria	0
Photosynthetic autotrophs	0	0	0	0	Green algae
Photosynthetic sulfur bacteria	0	0	0	0	Bacteria
Photosynthetic non-sulfur bacteria	0	0	0	0	Bacteria
Methane producers	0	0	0	0	0
Sulfate reducers	0	0	Bacteria	Bacteria	Bacteria
Lactate fermenters	0	Bacteria	Bacteria	Bacteria	Bacteria

* Incubated at 22°C for 6 weeks.

† Denotes no growth.

number of different habitats. A basal medium was made and varied in order to select out various physiological groups according to the protocol given below:

Basal medium

KH_2PO_4	1.6 grams
$MgSO_4 \cdot 7H_2O$	0.16 grams
$FeSO_4 \cdot 7H_2O$	0.16 grams
H_2O	8 liters

final pH, 4–4.5

A   200 ml of basal medium + 0.2 g NH_4Cl

A$_1$ 100 ml of medium A + 1 ml 5% Fe SO$_4 \cdot$7H$_2$O solution   *Iron oxidizers*

A$_2$ 25 ml of medium A + 0.1 g powdered sulfur   *Acidophilic sulfur oxidizers*

B   To remaining 7.8 liters of medium A was added 6.4 g K_2HPO_4 to give a near-neutral medium.

B$_1$ 1 liter medium B + 5.0 g NaHCO$_3$ *Photosynthetic nitrogen-fixers*

B$_2$ 1 liter medium B + 5.0 ml sodium lactate   *Heterotrophic nitrogen-fixers*

C   To remaining 5.8 liters of medium B add 6 g NH_4Cl

C$_1$ No further treatment   *Ammonia oxidizing autotrophs*

C$_2$ 2 liters of medium C + 10 g NaHCO$_3$ *Photosynthetic algae*

C$_3$ 1 liter of medium C$_2$ + 1 g Na$_2$S$\cdot$9H$_2$O   *Photosynthetic sulfur bacteria*

D   To the remaining 3.7 liters of

medium C was added 20 ml of sodium lactate.

D$_1$ 1 liter of medium D + 5.0 g NaHCO$_3$ + 0.5 g yeast extract   *Photosynthetic non-sulfur bacteria*

D$_2$ 1 liter of medium D + 10 ml Na$_2$S$\cdot$9 H$_2$O solution (0.1 g per 100 ml) + 5 g NaHCO$_3$ *Methane producers*

D$_3$ 1 liter of medium D + 2.5 g Na$_2$SO$_4$, 0.5 g yeast extract, and 10 ml Na$_2$S$\cdot$9H$_2$O solution (0.1 g per 100 ml)   *Sulfate reducers*

D$_4$ 0.7 liters of medium D + 7 ml Na$_2$S$\cdot$9H$_2$O solution (0.1 g per 100 ml)   *Lactate fermenters*

The results in Table 11 show that a number of different physiological groups are present in some of the soil habitats on Ross Island. Iron-oxidizing bacteria capable of converting ferrous iron to colloidal iron in the form of ferric hydroxide were observed in this area. These bacteria were also present in sea water and in soil from Cape Royds, Cape Evans, Butter Point, and White Island; on Ross Island, however, there are very few forms that can precipitate organic iron to the elemental form (Table 3). No sulfur oxidizers were present. Where Starkey's medium [*Allen*, 1951] was inoculated with soil and titrated, again no sulfur oxidation was observed. Mixed populations of bacteria were observed by Robert Starkey of Rutgers University in material collected by *Janetschek* [1963] at an altitude of 3600 meters on the western slope of Mount

Erebus. This material had a pH of 4.2 to 4.3, which is extremely low for the soils of the region. Perhaps one can speculate that some oxidation of volcanic sulfur occurred in the past, possibly by autotrophic sulfur oxidizers, and that the H_2SO_4 formed was responsible for the drop of pH to this low level. Blue-green algae and green algae were present in the pond water of 'Skua Pond' at Cape Evans, but were not present in any of the soils. Sulfate reducers were found in two of the soil samples and the pond water from 'Skua Pond.' *Barghoorn and Nichols* [1961] isolated sulfate reducers from kettle holes in the south side of Wright Valley in an area extending westward from the western terminus of the lower Wright Valley for about two miles. Chemical analyses of one of the Wright Valley ponds is given in a paper by *Meyer, Morrow, Wyss, Berg, and Littlepage* [1962]. Evidently some of the indigenous algae serve as sources of food for the growth of *Desulfovibrio*. Pyritic sediments occurred in the kettle holes of the Wright Valley, on the south side of New Harbor McMurdo Sound, in 'Green Lake' at Cape Royds, and in a small pond on Marble Point.

In our work, heterotrophic bacteria of the genus *Azotobacter* were found in many samples of water and soil. Other bacteria were also present, but they were not identified. *Boyd and Boyd* [1962] were able to isolate these heterotrophic bacteria from material containing organic matter which was collected from Wilkes Station. *Azotobacter*, which has also been reported in other antarctic locations, appears to be widely distributed in areas where some organic matter is present. This might be expected, since these bacteria are heterotrophs and require organic carbon for growth. What the exact role of *Azotobacter* is in the economy of the soil cannot be assayed at the present time.

Some photosynthetic sulfur bacteria along with green algae were observed in pond water but not in soil. The waters of 'Skua Pond' contained one group of photosynthetics that was capable of oxidizing H_2S to elemental sulfur. The original source of the organic matter was present in skua feces, which are deposited at a fast rate during the summer. Some heterotrophic source of desulfhydrase converts the organic sulfur to H_2S, which, in turn, is converted to elemental sulfur by *Chromatium minutissimum*, and a periodic bloom results, coloring the pond a dark purple.

Nitrogen Metabolism of the Soil Microflora

At Cape Royds, members of the *Azotobacter* genus were found in the rookery; they were also found

TABLE 12. Reactions of the Nitrogen Cycle Occurring in Antarctic Soils [after *Boyd and Boyd*, 1963]

Conditions* of Incubation	$N_2 \rightarrow$ Bacterial nitrogen	Organic N $\rightarrow$ NH$_3$ (μg NH$_3$/100 ml)	NH$_3 \rightarrow$ NO$_2 \rightarrow$ NO$_3$		NO$_3 \rightarrow$ NO$_2 \rightarrow$ N$_2$	
			μg NO$_2$/100 ml	μg NO$_3$/100 ml	μg NO$_2$/100 ml	μg N$_2$/100 ml
			Soil No. 1			
22°C	No species present	0	0	0	0	0
2°C		0	0	0	0	0
Outside		0	0	0	0	0
			Soil No. 2†‡			
22°C	*Azotobacter chroococcum*	2800	0	0	190	0
2°C		1600	0	0	3.7	0
Outside		120	0	0	0	0
			Soil No. 3†			
22°C	No species present	250,000	0	0.3	27	0
2°C		1300	0	1.4	5.1	0
Outside		0	0	1.7	5.1	0

* Covered with soil to a depth of 6 cm and incubated for 5 weeks.
† Control values have been subtracted from all experimental values.
‡ Soil control bottle contained 3100 μg NH$_3$–N/100 ml.

in an old rookery in the vicinity of Cape Royds, as described by *Shackleton* [1909], and in small ponds at McMurdo Sound and at Cape Evans. Blue-green algae, which are capable of growth in a carbon- and nitrogen-free medium, were also found in the ponds mentioned, and in areas near the shoreline they could have contributed to the nitrogen food chain of the aquatic as well as the terrestrial flora. No blue-green algae were found in any of the soils. Despite the fact that nitrogen-fixing microorganisms are present, no actual fixation was demonstrated.

The results of studies of some of the other reactions of the nitrogen cycle for these soils are given in Table 12. Soil samples were divided into three sets; two sets were taken into the laboratory and incubated at 2°C and 22°C, whereas the third set was tested outdoors. Soil 1 from Cape Royds was negative for all of the reactions tested; these results could be expected, since this soil was sterile most of the time as defined in the conditions imposed by this study. Ammonification occurred in soils 2 and 3. Temperature played a very important role, since more ammonia was produced at 22°C than at 2°C or out-of-doors. Very little nitrification occurred in soil 3, and for soils 1 and 2 the reactions were negative. Nitrate reduction was observed in soils 2 and 3, and the amount found was greatest in those samples incubated at 22°C. No denitrification was observed. When these values are translated into terms of plant nitrogen, soil metabolic activity will be seen to have little influence on plant growth.

Identification of Organic Matter in Soils of the Ross Sea Area

In regard to the microbial flora of antarctic soils, the heterotrophic bacteria are, to date, the forms most extensively studied, and the microbiological properties of antarctic soils have been defined in terms of this group of bacteria. It is well recognized, however, that autotrophic species of bacteria are the primary producers of the organic matter upon which heterotrophic organisms directly or indirectly depend for their nutrition. Carbon dioxide and inorganic nutrients supplied to plants result in protoplasm; this protoplasm becomes potential food for other species if there are enzymes present to break it down into units that can be metabolized

by other flora and fauna. Heterotrophic forms also produce usable nutrients.

In soil, there are found complex plant fibers and small carbohydrate degradation products, or carbohydrates of animal origin [*Alexander*, 1961]. The nitrogen content is made up of amino acid, nitrate, nitrite, or ammonia derived from the breakdown of plant or animal tissue or from the metabolism of microbial cells. The presence of one or more of these products, or their complete absence, will have a profound effect on the microflora. Their presence may also indicate indirectly that some metabolic activity has taken place.

There are bacterial species that can secrete amino acids in the free state. *Becker and Schmidt* [1960] have shown that isolates from the rhizosphere and non-rhizosphere of plants, and to a lesser extent from the root surface, produce extra-cellular free amino acids when cultured in a minimal glucose–nitrate–soil extract medium. The most prevalent of these amino acids were alanine, serine, and valine, while glutamic acid, leucine, and proline were detected to a lesser extent. That soil bacteria and other members of the microflora have the enzymatic potentiality to produce free amino acids becomes obvious from these studies; whether this occurs *in situ* was not determined by Becker and Schmidt.

To learn more about the state of nutrition of antarctic soils, partciularly as potential food for heterotrophic forms, microbiological assays were performed on soils, using standard techniques. The media were purchased from Difco Laboratories, Detroit, Michigan, and the microorganisms were purchased from the American Type Culture Collection, Washington, D. C. (ATCC). Folic acid was assayed with *Streptococcus faecalis* ATCC 8043; niacin with *Lactobacillus plantarum* ATCC 8014; vitamin B_{12} with *Lactobacillus leichmannii* ATCC 7830; L-tryptophane with *Lactobacillus arabinosus* 17-5 ATCC 8014; and L-arginine, L-lysine, L-glutamic acid, L-cystine, and L-histidine with *Leuconostoc mesenteroides* ATCC 8042.

Detectable amounts of amino acids and vitamins were found (Table 13) to be present in a number of areas in the Taylor Valley and Wright Valley. The amounts were greatest in area 1 (Table 13), above Lake Bonney, where well-developed fields of *Nostoc commune* were present. The presence or absence of these acids and vitamins could

TABLE 13. Amino Acids and Vitamins in Antarctic Soils

Area	Folic acid	Niacin	B$_{12}$*	L-tryptophane	L-lysine	L-argine	L-glutamic acid	L-histidine	L-cystine
				Microgr...					

Area	Folic acid	Niacin	B$_{12}$*	L-tryptophane	L-lysine	L-argine	L-glutamic acid	L-histidine	L-cystine
Taylor Valley									
1	0.003	0.2	0.034	6	0	0	10	0	0
3	0	0	0	7	0	5	0	0	0
4, 17	0	0	0	0	0	0	0	0	0
18	0.005	0	0	0	0	5	20	0	0
19	0	0	0	6	0	0	0	0	0
21	0.004	0	0	5	0	0	0	0	0
22	0	0	0	0	110	0	0	0	0
23	0	0	0	0	90	6	0	0	0
24	0	0	0	0	90	0	50	0	0
25	0.003	0	0	0	140	0	0	0	0
Wright Valley									
6	0.002	0.2	0	0	0	0	0	0	0
9	0	0	0	6	0	0	25	0	0
10	0	0	0	6	0	0	0	0	0
11	0.006	0	0	0	0	0	0	0	0
12	0	0.3	0	0	0	0	0	0	0
7, 8, 13, 14, 15, 16	0	0	0	0	0	0	0	0	0
Strand Moraines									
—	0	0	0.014	0	0	0	20	0	0
Marble Point									
—	0	0	0	8	0	0	30	0	0
Ross Island									
Cape Royds									
Soil #1	0	0	0	0	0	0	0	0	0
Soil #2	0.108	60	0.290	80	0	10	350	0	0
Shackleton's dump	0	0	0.135	0	0	0	125	0	0
McMurdo Sound									
Soil #3	0	0	0	45	0	6	0	0	0

The header above the data columns reads: "Micrograms per Gram of Dry Soil"

* Vitamin B$_{12}$ reported in millimicrograms per gram of dry soil.

not necessarily be correlated with the presence or absence of bacteria. Microscopic examination was routine. Gram stains failed to reveal the presence of organisms. Wet mounts did show that the broken shells of diatoms were present in the samples. Perhaps these amino acids and vitamins arrived by direct contamination from skua and other birds, or occurred through synthesis by some no longer living bacteria.

Samples from the Adélie penguin rookery contained high concentrations of vitamins and amino acids, which might be expected. That cystine was not detected is interesting. The presence of this amino acid might be expected, since feathers, which are composed of the protein keratin, represent a substantial part of the guano that was found in abundance in the rookery. Either keratinolytic microorganisms are completely absent or environmental conditions are such that enzymatic breakdown of keratin does not take place.

From a nutritional point of view it may be possible to have these amino acids and vitamins diffusing out from rookeries and providing a nutrient for peripheral forms as well.

TRANSMISSION AND VIABILITY OF MICROORGANISMS

Until recent times the antarctic continent was an isolated land mass with only very limited contact with outside biological systems. Even today there are areas of the continent that have never been visited by man and that remain isolated from the influences of other animals and from migratory birds. Since, however, some species of penguins build nests around the coast of the continent and on some of the islands, there may be some transfer of microorganisms from these birds to the soil. Some organic matter is also deposited, so that large numbers can and do exist in these regions.

Although early in the nineteenth century the continent was observed (at least three different nations claim its initial discovery), it was not until late in that century that man began to go ashore from ships, establish bases, and make scientific observations for periods that included changes in season. The first party to establish a base for one such period was made up of members of the Swedish Antarctic Expedition which set up headquarters on Snow Hill Island from 1901–1903. On the other side of the continent, in the Ross Sea area, various British parties under Scott and Shackleton occupied bases for much of the period between 1901 and 1913. With the exception of 8 years of U. S. occupation (1929–1947) of bases at Little America or some other area on the Ross Ice Shelf, the Ross Sea area has been free of human habitation from the time of Scott and Shackleton until early 1956, when construction teams first came into McMurdo Sound in preparation of the forthcoming International Geophysical Year. Since 1958 the base at McMurdo Sound has been occupied on a year-round basis and is now a permanent base operated by the U. S. Antarctic Research Program of the National Science Foundation.

That bacterial species are present in regions that support little or no growth of higher plants and animals is paradoxical. The presence of coal and petrified wood is conclusive evidence of a warmer era in the Antarctic [Doumani and Long, 1962] in which trees and other forms of higher vegetation were able to grow. Perhaps many of the indigenous forms represent forms left over from this era. Some of the bacteria, especially in areas where the temperature is extremely low, could represent forms that are at least two thousand years old.

How long the antarctic continent has remained covered with ice is uncertain, but there is no doubt that as late at least as the Tertiary Age, tempera-

tures were much higher. From the evolutionary viewpoint it would be interesting, indeed, to know whether the change from this more temperate environment to that of the extremely low-temperature climate of today occurred over many thousands of years or suddenly. If the process had been gradual, then mutation and selection of indigenous flora and fauna might have occurred, and species found in the Antarctic today might, in large part, be descendants of these previous inhabitants. If, on the other hand, the change had occurred suddenly, the role of natural selection probably would not have been very significant, since the earlier forms could not have survived the magnitude of the change; in this event, almost all life-forms (except any that may be in the permafrost) now present in Antarctica could be thought to have been introduced from other areas of the world after the beginning of the ice era(s). There is also the possibility that indigenous species are a result of transfer from an outside area by wind, as suggested by *McLean* [1919], or as contaminants in or on migratory as well as indigenous birds (the theory supported somewhat by the recent work of *Sieburth* [1963]).

With the present increased activity in Antarctica, bacteria and other microorganisms are being introduced in considerable numbers in many different areas. From the ecological point of view, the present flora may undergo alteration because of such activities as the disposal of sewage and other wastes, disturbances of the soil from construction work, and the introduction of microorganisms that can survive for long periods of time and even grow and reproduce in this new environment. A logical follow-up to studies that have shown that foreign organisms can survive in this area for long periods of time would be studies to determine if the microflora and fauna are changing and if foreign microbes will become established.

When bases are established in any region of the Earth, materials are brought in and the debris from construction or living collected, segregated, and disposed of by burying it, dumping it into the sea, or leaving it untreated, but seldom if ever is this debris brought out of the area. The presence in Antarctica of a substantial amount of debris and supplies evidences past or present human occupancy and includes the refuse of dogs and ponies that have been used to haul sledges. This debris, though of dubious aesthetic value, does represent a biological marker of known age and has been used in the area by at least two different groups in studies on viability.

Among the foods and sewage left over from early British expeditions that were examined by members of the University of Texas party [*Meyer, Morrow, and Wyss*, 1962, 1963] was a bottle of yeast from Scott's 1911 expedition which left Antarctica in 1913. Meyer found the bottle, labeled 'Rising-up Yeast,' 'Dauerhefe,' and 'Levure Inalterable' in a food cache partially covered by snow; it was still corked and covered with a wax seal. Samples, which were collected aseptically, revealed yeasts of the genera *Saccharomyces cerevisiae* Hansen and *Rhodotorula pallida* Lodder, two molds of the genus *Absidia corymbifera* Lichtheim and *Rhizopus arrhizus* Fisher, and bacteria of the *Bacillus* and *Pseudomonas* genera, as well as various cocci and spherical tetrads of the *Micrococcaceae* family. Other foodstuffs obtained from the Cape Evans area and from some food left over from Shackleton's expedition also possessed viable microorganisms. At Cape Royds, sample from a 'Hunter's Famed Oatmeal of Edinburgh' tin, which had been relabeled 'pearl barley,' contained barley which had a count on nutrient agar of 40 organisms per gram, including members of the genera *Pseudomonas* and *Bacillus*, a species of *Streptomyces*, and a single mold of the genus *Mucor*. A bottle of 'Heinz Tomato Catsup' from Cape Evans was found to possess a mold species with a dark mycellium that produced chlamydospores and a dark yeast-form which resembled a smutt. At Cape Evans also leftover hay was examined and found to have a count of nutrient agar of 30×10^6 bacteria per gram of material. Among the microbes observed were members of the genus *Pseudomonas*, the yeasts *Cryptococcus* and *Rhodotorula*, and molds of the *Mucor* and *Penicillium* genera.

These studies also included sampling of fecal material from these areas at Cape Royds and Cape Evans. When incubated aerobically at 20°C the sample from Cape Evans had a count of 17×10^6 organisms, or about 0.1 per cent of the number normally found in fresh feces, and the sample from Cape Royds a count of 20×10^6. Among the bacteria observed were members of the genera of *Staphylococcus, Mycobacterium, Alcaligenes, Bacil-*

lus, Pseudomonas, anaerobes of the *Clostridium, Bacteroides,* and *Lactobacillus* genera, yeast of the genera *Rhodotorula, Candida, Phoma,* and *Botrytis,* and other molds.

Boyd and Boyd [1963a] also studied viability of organisms at Cape Royds and Cape Evans. These studies were initiated when routine plating of soil samples from penguin rookeries and areas contaminated with human sewage on desoxycholate agar failed to reveal the presence of gram-negative bacteria capable of fermenting lactose. The explanation for the absence of coliform bacteria in penguins might be the possible presence of the antibiotic, acrylic acid, although no attempt was made to assay the guano for this material. The absence of coliform bacteria in recently contaminated soil was confirmed by inoculating 1-gram quantities in lactose broth. In all instances the enrichment cultures failed to produce gas in 48 hours. The data [*Boyd and Boyd*, 1963a] suggest that coliform bacteria remain viable only for short time periods and therefore are absent in all but freshly contaminated soil. From samplings of pony manure from Cape Royds, left over from Shackleton's expedition, and from Hut Point, left over from ponies introduced in 1911 by Scott, only one of the 315 1-gram samples assayed contained *Escherichia coli* and that sample was from Cape Royds.

To determine the relative viability of strains of *E. coli*, three different strains were tested. Soil was inoculated and tested, quantitatively, over a period of 6 weeks [*Boyd and Boyd*, 1963a]. In testing for two human strains, counts on desoxycholate agar dropped from an initial count of between 10^6 and 10^8 coliform bacteria to a level which could not be detected after 10 days for one strain and after 20 days for the other. The strain derived from old pony manure was more resistant to the soil environment, which would be expected. Apparently there were no toxic ions in the soil having an over-all disinfectant action, since the uninoculated soil had a bacterial flora which, though low, could be detected by conventional plating techniques.

During the following research season, it was planned to repeat and extend these studies at Cape Hallett by augmenting the three strains of *Escherichia coli* with other species of heterotrophic bacteria that could be enumerated by use of selective and differential media, or by culturing in a selective en-

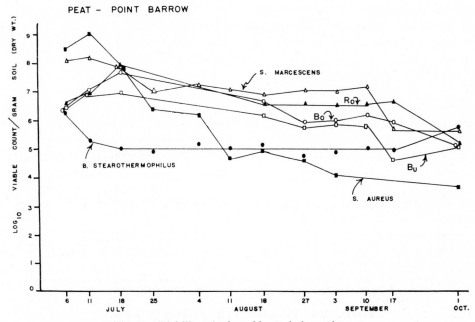

Fig. 12.   Viability of selected bacteria in arctic peat.

vironment so that each species could be easily and accurately recognized in mixed populations. Stocks of *Serratia marcescens,* producing red colonies, *Staphylococcus aureus,* producing yellow colonies, and *Bacillus stearothermophilus,* capable of growth on media incubated at 55°C, were also used to seed-selected samples of soil. Although *Chromatium violatium,* a purple pigment producer, was also

used for a short time, lack of success prompted the abandonment of further study.

During the summer of 1962 a comparative study in arctic North America was initiated prior to the antarctic study to be carried out during the austral summer of 1962. The location of Cape Hallett in the southern hemisphere (72°18′S, 170°18′E) is latitudinally equivalent to the location of Point

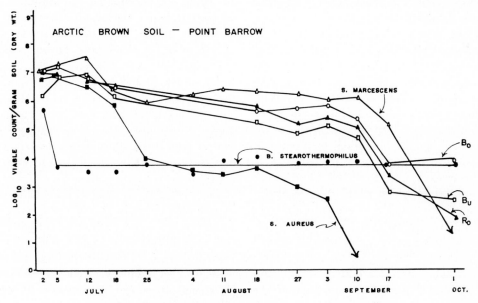

Fig. 13.   Viability of selected bacteria in arctic brown soil.

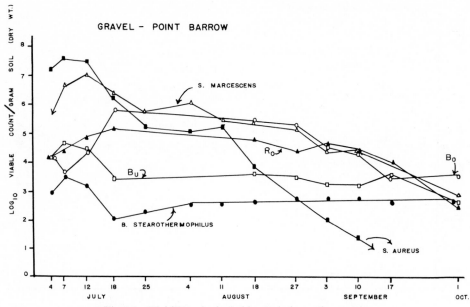

Fig. 14. Viability of selected bacteria in arctic gravel.

Barrow, Alaska (71°20′N, 156°40′W), in the northern hemisphere. Each of three soils typical of the Point Barrow area—a peat, arctic brown soil from a beach ridge, and one that originated from the gravel beach at Point Barrow—was inoculated with strains mentioned in the preceding paragraph.

Except for the beach gravel, massive soil samples in each instance were seeded with the spectrum of organism mentioned above and replaced in the point of origin; although the beach gravel had been collected near the geographical Point Barrow, its replacement was in a gravel area within a half mile of the other sites. Coliform bacteria were cultured in desoxycholate agar; all the other bacteria were cultured on nutrient agar plus 0.1 per cent mannitol. Soil temperature varied little among the various sites. Soil moisture was a significant variable, although throughout the study period little variation was observed in each individual habitat: peat varied from 76% to 82%, arctic brown from 7% to 26%, and the beach gravel from 0% to 6%. The chemical composition, which showed no measurable change during the study, was radically different in each individual soil; the peat showed the greatest amount of organic matter and the gravel showed the least. The organic content of the arctic brown soil, the most highly developed kind of soil, was somewhere between that of peat and that of the gravel.

Selected strains of bacteria sometimes showed marked variation in survival ability (Figures 12, 13, and 14). Among the three types of samples the counts observed in peat were the most stable. The three strains of *E. coli* showed the lowest incidence of death throughout the period. Although, for a significant time period, the counts were constant, approximately 10 per cent of the population died late in September; as a result, by 1 October, when the study was terminated, the counts had decreased by more than one logarithm. These *E. coli* organisms showed a greater drop of one to two logs on the gravel, with the B_0 strain showing more stability than the other two strains. The B_0 strain was also more stable on the beach ridge soil, although the drop in total numbers observed on the beach ridge soil was always greater than in the other two soils. These results are similar to those obtained earlier [*Boyd and Boyd*, 1962a], when a single strain of a coliform bacteria isolated from lemming feces was seeded in two of these same soils.

The thermophilic spore-former, although seeded at different levels in the different soils, showed essentially the same pattern of stability in all the soils; an initial drop, which might have resulted from the death of vegetative cells, was followed by a longer period during which there was no further significant decrease in numbers. This strain exhibited the same stability as that shown by a

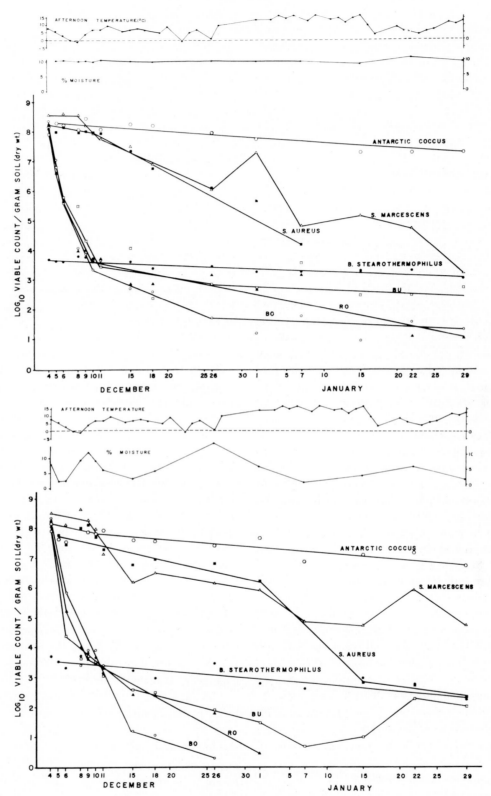

Fig. 15. Viability of selected bacteria in antarctic soil.

strain of *B. stearothermophilus* isolated from arctic soil and tested along with the strain of coliform bacteria described above [*Boyd and Boyd*, 1962a].

The two pigmented species showed the greatest degree of variation. Red-pigmented *S. marcescens* showed a gradual decrease in peat but only by three logs; a high count of 4.4×10^5 bacteria per gram of dry soil was still present on October 1. The drops in number in the other two soils were more marked; the greatest reduction was observed during September when the soil began to freeze.

The most sensitive species studied was *S. aureus*, the yellow-pigmented strain that produced typical yellow colonies on the mannitol-nutrient agar. In the peat, where the coliform bacteria and the thermophile showed a one-log decrease and *S. marcescens* a three-log decrease in population, this *S. aureus* dropped five logs, whereas in the arctic brown soil and the beach gravel, on 1 October, counts were at or near the point when enumeration was no longer possible.

These studies emphasize the fact that viability will vary among habitats and that there are factors in each case which must be defined before the stability of organisms being introduced from an exogenous source can be determined.

The studies were repeated at Cape Hallett. Again, an indigenous species was used. This culture produced a yellow pigment, was a coccus, and grew readily on nutrient agar. Evidently this coccus is widely distributed in the Cape Hallett area (E. D. Rudolph, personal communication).

Prior to inoculation of the soil, which was obtained from the skuary area at Cape Hallett, all organisms were grown on nutrient agar with 0.1 per cent mannitol for 48 hours. The amount of soil used for each species filled a gallon-size container. After mixing a culture thoroughly with the soil, half the mixture was put into a canning jar and sealed with an air-tight lid, and the other half in a small burrow on the slope of an abandoned penguin mound. After 3 hours of equilibration, during which the exposed soil lost about 3 per cent of its moisture, samples were taken for the initial count. For the first week, counts were made daily when possible; thereafter counts were made on a weekly basis.

The results are shown in Figure 15. The spore-forming thermophilic bacteria exhibited a con-

siderable resistance to the effects of the environment in both the sealed jars and the exposed plots, the number of organisms dropping off slightly during the season. This is in agreement with previous studies conducted in both arctic and antarctic regions by *Boyd and Boyd* [1962a, 1963a]. The only organism other than the thermophilic bacteria with this characteristic was the indigenous strain. Again, in both the sealed and exposed experiments there is no significant difference, the lines being parallel to those of *Bacillus stearothermophilus*.

The initial death rates for the coliform bacteria are dramatically different from these results and, since both the sealed and exposed curves are similar, there seems to be little relation of microbial activity to moisture content of the soil. These data (Figure 15) might explain why in polar areas previously contaminated by sewage it is difficult to detect the presence of coliform organisms, whereas thermophile counts are quite high. The factor(s) responsible for the death of the coliform strains are inherent in this particular environment. Compared to the results of a parallel study with these same strains at Point Barrow in the Arctic, our results in the Antarctic are significantly different; the rate of death in the Arctic is lower, although death in each case does result. Other species seem to have an intermediate resistance to the adverse effects of environment. Although both *Staphylococcus aureus* and *Serratia marcescens* eventually drop to low levels, the initial death rate is not as abrupt as with *E. coli*. It is interesting to compare the point by point data of both these organisms in the exposed plots with the average per cent of soil moisture. Generally, any increase in per cent moisture was accompanied by a decrease in death rate; in one instance there was an actual increase in cell numbers (*S. marcescens,* January 22). Since, however, even in the sealed vessels, where moisture content was uniformly high, the numbers drop to low levels, soil moisture does not seem to be the only factor that limits survival.

The data (Figure 15) for the coliform organisms indicate that moisture is important in the second stage of the survival of the organisms, that is after the initial death rate has changed. The numbers of organisms in sealed vessels show a fairly uniform leveling off when the counts reach around 100 per gram of soil. In the exposed plots this occurs with only the B_u strain, whereas the levels to which the B_0 and R_0 strains drop are so low it is difficult to make an accurate count. Following the initial death rate there was a period of fairly high uniform counts (over a thousand per gram of soil).

Although moisture is certainly an important factor in determining the survival of newly introduced bacteria to these regions, it obviously is not the sole factor. Other environmental characteristics, such as pH, ionic concentration, and temperature, must also be considered. Chemical studies of the soil at Cape Hallett indicate that salt concentrations are high; this, coupled with normally low moisture, suggests that the microenvironment in many areas is saturated with ions in solution. The concentrations of the ammonium ion in guano are extremely high (about 24,000 ppm) as compared with typical temperate soil (about 20 ppm). This may explain the absence of lichens in rookery areas. The pH of antarctic soils is also high (although at Hallett the skuary soil was about 6.0 in midsummer) in comparison to the very low pH in the Arctic. Normally day-to-day variation in antarctic temperature is not as great as the 24-hour maximum and minimum. Every night during the austral midsummer the soil temperatures were below freezing, a condition different from that found in midsummer in the Arctic.

Although no pathogenic species could be employed in a study of this type, the results of the study might be useful in predicting the survival time of pathogenic bacteria that might be present in sewage and other waste; such bacteria could produce a soil so contaminated that it becomes a reservoir for infection, a contamination that would be of particular significance as far as such enteric diseases as typhoid and dysentery were concerned. It would also be of some importance to determine if agents such as foot-and-mouth virus and *Bacillus anthracis*, which might be introduced with meat and dairy foodstuffs, could survive in the soil for any significant time, or if the pony manure left from past expeditions contains viable spores of *Clostridium tetani*, or if *Clostridium welchii* is present in soil contaminated with sewage. As Antarctica becomes more populated interest in these questions will increase.

In conclusion then, it seems that at Cape Hallett the primary limiting growth factors—temperature, moisture, humidity, and such—are physical in nature. That certain species of bacteria from temperate regions can survive in the soil for at least two months with no significant loss in viable cells can

TABLE 14. Bacterial Counts* of Fertilized Soil in the Point Barrow, Alaska, Area

Date	None	Bacterial Counts for Various Additives*				
		NH_4NO_3 60 g/yd²	KCl 60 g/yd²	$Na_2HPO_4 \cdot 2H_2O$ 60 g/yd²	CaOH 1000 g/yd²	Peptone 60 g/yd²
Arctic brown soil: pH = 4.5–5.1; moisture = 11–21%						
1962						
10 July	1.7×10^5	2.1×10^5	2.9×10^4	2.9×10^4	5.1×10^4	9.9×10^4
11 Sept.	1.1×10^5	9.3×10^4	1.6×10^5	1.4×10^5	1.8×10^5	4.7×10^5
1963						
11 July	9.2×10^4	1.2×10^5	1.6×10^5	1.0×10^5	3.5×10^6	9.6×10^6
27 Aug.	1.2×10^5	1.7×10^5	1.3×10^5	2.4×10^5	6.3×10^5	1.0×10^6
Peat: pH = 5.2–5.7; moisture = 65–86%						
1962						
10 July	4.9×10^4	1.7×10^5	5.0×10^4	1.5×10^5	8.2×10^4	9.0×10^4
11 Sept.	1.1×10^6	5.6×10^5	5.2×10^5	1.6×10^6	1.5×10^6	2.8×10^6
1963						
11 July	1.4×10^6	5.3×10^5	8.0×10^5	8.2×10^5	2.0×10^5	1.2×10^7
27 Aug.	3.0×10^5	1.2×10^6	2.2×10^5	1.1×10^6	2.1×10^5	4.6×10^6

* Samples incubated at 22°C; counts reported as number of bacteria per gram dry soil.

† The same amounts used in antarctic experiments. Also: 20 grams lecithin (animal, 90% pure) and 60 grams yeast extract per square yard of soil.

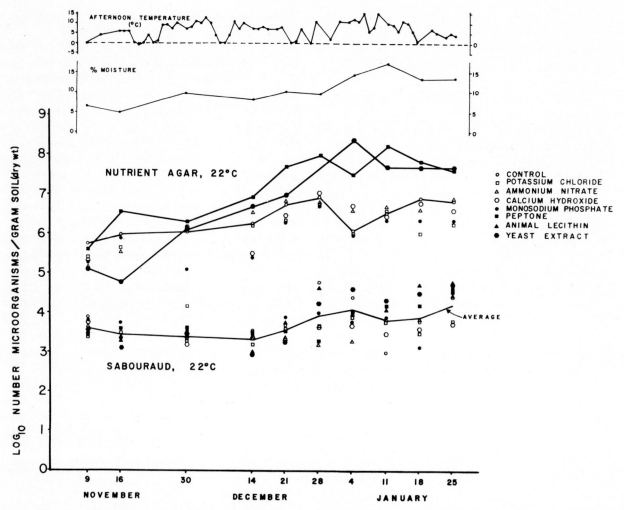

Fig. 16. Effect of organic and inorganic additives on the mesophilic bacterial population of antarctic soils.

be established experimentally. There is also some evidence that succession of species, especially among the blue-green algae *Nostoc,* is taking place in some of the dry valleys [*Holm-Hansen,* 1963].

Effect of Fertilization on Soil Microflora

Along with viability studies in arctic and antarctic areas, selected plots were fertilized with different organic and inorganic additives. The concentrations of these additives used were those determined for arctic soils by Lowell Douglas of Rutgers University (personal communication), despite the fact that antarctic soils were very rudimentary and have neither the low *p*H nor the organic concentration of the arctic soils.

During 1962 the mesophilic counts of the treated arctic plots of peat and arctic brown soil showed little or no change when compared with control plots (Table 14). During the following year some increase in counts was observed for arctic brown soil treated with peptone; the peat also showed some increase in counts for various additives but in no case were they more than about tenfold.

The Cape Hallett area is a typical coastal region. Its Adélie rookery and a comparatively large population of skua represent a source of organic matter that could be used by heterotrophic bacteria. That large numbers of lichens are found in the area indicates that organic nitrogen is converted by microorganisms into either ammonia, nitrate, or substrates, which can be utilized as nitrogen sources.

The skuary of Cape Hallett was chosen at the location for the parallel antarctic experimental plots. Since penguins nested nearby and wandered through the area only occasionally, most of the excrement and litter came from the skuas, which did nest there or on the cliff above.

Seven experimental plots were treated with various chemical additives at the same concentrations per unit area as used at Point Barrow. These plots plus a control plot and a plot located in guano were sampled weekly for viable microorganisms, using the culture media and incubation described by *Boyd and Boyd* [1963]. In most instances, daily temperatures, taken at approximately 3 P.M. L.S.T., were above freezing (Figure 16). Mold counts were relatively high and resembled counts in temperate regions. These data also confirm the results obtained at McMurdo Sound during the past year that, other than areas contaminated by man and/or other animals, the mold counts in antarctic soils, except where lichens grow, appear to be low when compared to soils of warmer climates.

Bacterial counts were higher than those encountered in the rookery at Cape Royds during 1961–1962; only in areas contaminated by sewage did the counts at Ross Island approach those given in Figure 16. During the summer about a tenfold increase in numbers was observed in the control plot. During this same period counts of those quadrats treated with yeast extract and peptone showed better than a hundredfold increase in bacterial populations. Counts on Thornton's medium resembled the nutrient agar counts; normally, nutrient agar plates incubated for 2 weeks at 2°C had half the number found on the 22°C plates. Nutrient agar counts of guano showed between 10^6 and 10^7 colonies per gram throughout the season, while mold counts on Sabouraud's dextrose agar averaged about one per gram of guano.

In conjunction with this study, chemical analyses of the Cape Hallett soils showed (Table 15) normal optimum concentrations of nutrients for temperate-region soils. Guano concentrations are all very much higher than normal optimum levels of essential minerals. This suggests that the flora may include organisms capable of ammonification and nitrification. Phosphorus and potassium are both found in very high concentration in the skuary soil, and the calcium content is above normal. The nitrate and ammonium forms of nitrogen seem to be slightly deficient in these soils, as is magnesium. The results of the ammonium nitrate fertility plot indicate that the inorganic nitrogen deficiency is not limiting. This is supported by a plant-growth study at the Cape Hallett laboratory, in which the soil from the skuary was fertilized with Knop's solution, whereas another portion of the soil remained untreated. Several varieties of flowering plants were seeded into both soils, and although the plants with the Knop solution seemed to grow better, there were no differences between the control and the fertilized plants that would indicate either nitrate or magnesium deficiency.

TABLE 15. Chemical Composition of Soils in the Cape Hallett Area, Antarctica

Element	Temperate Region Optimum for Plant Growth* (pH 6.5)	Skuary Control Plot (pH 6.0)	Rookery Guano (pH 7.0)	Red Volcanic Ash† (pH 8.0)
Parts per million of element in soil				
Phosphorus	—	400‡	24,000	130
Potassium	—	265‡	76,000	210
Calcium	800	1060	38,000	520
Magnesium	—	<65	48,000	135
Nitrogen				
nitrate	10	4	18,000	<2
ammonium	10	7	24,000	4
Parts per million of ion in soil				
Sulfate	<400	<250	1200	—
Chloride	<400	<130	2400	—

* Values from Hellige-Truog Soil Testing Kit.
† Obtained from crease of ridge directly above Seabee Hook.
‡ Values from 16 November 1962; all others from 25 January 1963.

Acknowledgments. This work was carried out while the authors were on leaves of absence from the Department of Microbiology, The Ohio State University, by grants No. G-17789 and G-23308 from the U. S. Antarctic Research Program, National Science Foundation, to the Ohio State University Research Foundation, the Department of Microbiology, and the Institute of Polar Studies, and from grants from a contract between the Office of Naval Research, Department of the Navy, and the Arctic Institute of North America. Reproduction in whole or in part is permitted for any purpose of the United States government.

Grateful acknowledgment is made to Chester I. Randles, who helped with the enrichment procedure, and to David E. Pixley, who performed the vitamin and amino acid microbiological assays on the various soil samples. Thanks are also extended to the Charles Thomas Company, Springfield, Illinois, to the editors of *Applied Microbiology* and the Williams and Wilkins Company, Baltimore, Maryland, and to John McN. Sieburth, University of Rhode Island, for permission to reproduce certain copyrighted material.

REFERENCES

Alexander, M., *Introduction to Soil Microbiology*, 472 pp., John Wiley & Sons, New York, 1961.

Allen, O. N., *Experiments in Soil Bacteriology*, 117 pp., Burgess, Minneapolis, 1951.

Barghoorn, E. S., and R. L. Nichols, Sulfate-reducing bacteria and pyritic sediments in Antarctica, *Science, 134,* 190, 1961.

Becker, G. E., and E. L. Schmidt, Excretion of amino acids by soil and rhizosphere isolates, *Bacteriol. Proc. (Soc. Am. Bacteriologists)*, 29, 1960.

Bergey, D. H., R. S. Breed, E. G. D. Murray, and H. P. Hitchens. *Manual of Determinative Bacteriology*, 1032 pp., 5th ed., Williams and Wilkins, Baltimore, 1939.

Boyd, W. L., Microbiological studies of arctic soils, *Ecology, 39,* 332–336, 1958.

Boyd, W. L., and J. W. Boyd, Presence of *Azotobacter* species in polar regions, *J. Bacteriol., 83,* 429–430, 1962.

Boyd, W. L., and J. W. Boyd, Viability of thermophiles and coliform bacteria in arctic soils and water, *Can. J. Microbiol., 8,* 189–192, 1962a.

Boyd, W. L., and J. W. Boyd, Soil microorganisms of the McMurdo Sound area, Antarctica, *Applied Microbiol., 11,* 118–121, 1963.

Boyd, W. L., and J. W. Boyd, Viability of coliform bacteria in antarctic soils, *J. Bacteriol., 85,* 1121–1123, 1963a.

Breed, R. S., E. D. G. Murray, and N. R. Smith, *Bergey's Manual of Determinative Bacteriology*, 1094 pp., Williams and Wilkins, Baltimore, 1957.

Bunt, J. W., A note on the faecal flora of some antarctic birds and mammals at Macquarie Island, *Proc. Linnean Soc. N. S. Wales, 80,* 44–46, 1955.

Cardot, J., Musci, *National Antarctic Expedition 1901–1904. Natural History*, vol. 3, British Museum (Natural History), London, 1907.

Darbishire, O. V., Lichenes, *National Antarctic Expedition 1901–1904, Natural History*, vol. 5, British Museum (Natural History), London, 1910.

Darling, C. A., and P. A. Siple, Bacteria of Antarctica, *J. Bacteriol., 42,* 83–98, 1941.

Dougherty, E. C., and L. G. Harris, Antarctic micrometazoa: freshwater species in the McMurdo Sound area, *Science, 140,* 497–498, 1963.

Doumani, G. A., and W. E. Long, The ancient life of Antarctica, *Sci. American, 207* (3), 169–184, 1962.

Ekelöf, E., Bakteriologische Studien während der Schwedischen Süd-polar Expedition, *Wiss. Ergeb. Schwed. Südpolar Exped., 1901–1903, 4* (7), Stockholm, 1908.

Flint, E. A., and J. D. Stout, Microbiology of some soils from Antarctica, *Nature, 188,* 767–768, 1960.

Fritsch, F. E., Freshwater algae, *National Antarctic Expedition 1901–1904, Natural History*, vol. 6. British Museum (Natural History), London, 1912.

Gazert, H., Untersuchungen über Meeresbakterien und ihren Einfluss auf den Stoffwechsel in Meere, *Deutsche Sudpolar-Expedition 1901–1903*, George Reimer, Berlin, *1,* No. 3, 1–296, 1912.

Gressitt, J. L., and R. E. Leech, Insect habitats in Antarctica, *Polar Record, 10,* 501–504, 1961.

Gressitt, J. L., R. E. Leech, and K. A. J. Wise, Entomological investigations in Antarctica, *Pacific Ins., 5,* 287–304, 1963.

Holm-Hansen, O., Algae: nitrogen-fixation by antarctic species, *Science, 139,* 1059–1060, 1963.

Janetschek, H., On the terrestrial fauna of the Ross Sea area, Antarctica, *Pacific Ins., 5,* 305–311, 1963.

Lebedeva, M. N., Quantative distribution of heterotrophic microorganisms in the Indian Ocean and in adjoining antarctic seas, *Doklady Akad. Nauk USSR, 121,* 557–560 (AIBS trans. 650–653), 1958.

Llano, G. A., Status of lichenology and Antarctica, *Science in Antarctica, Natl. Acad. Sci. Publ. 839* (part 1, *The Life Sciences in Antarctica*), chapter 3, pp. 13–19, 1961.

McBee, R. H., Intestinal flora of some antarctic birds and mamals, *J. Bacteriol., 79,* 311–312, 1960.

McLean, A. L., Bacteriological and other researches, *Australasian Antarctic Expedition, 1911–1914, Scientific Reports, Series C, 7,* No. 4, 15–44, Sydney, 1919.

Meyer, G. H., M. B. Morrow, and O. Wyss, Viable microorganisms in a fifty-year old preparation in Antarctica, *Nature, 196,* 598, 1962.

Meyer, G. H., M. B. Morrow, and O. Wyss, Viable organisms from feces and foodstuffs from early antarctic expeditions, *Canadian J. Microbiol., 9,* 163–167, 1963.

Meyer, G. H., M. B. Morrow, O. Wyss, T. E. Berg, and J. L. Littlepage, Antarctica: The microbiology of an unfrozen saline pond, *Science, 138,* 1103–1104, 1962.

Murphy, R. C., The oceanic life of the Antarctic, *Sci. American, 207* (3), 186–210, 1962.

Murray, J., Biology, in Shackleton's *Heart of the Antarctic*, vol. 2, Appendix 1, pp. 233–268, W. Heinemann, London, 1909.

Péwé, T. L., N. R. Rivard, and G. A. Llano, Mummified seal carcasses in the McMurdo Sound regions, Antarctica, *Science, 130,* 716, 1959.

Pirie, J. E. H., Notes on antarctic bacteriology, *Scottish National Antarctic Expedition, Rept. of the Sci. Results of S. Y. Scotia, 3,* No. 10, 137–148, 1912.

Rudolph, E. D., Vegetation of Hallett Station area, Victoria Land, Antarctica, *Ecology, 44,* 585–586, 1963.

Scott, R. F., *The Voyage of the 'Discovery,'* 2 vols., Charles Scribner's Sons, New York, 1905.

Scott, R. F., *Scott's last expedition*, 2 vols., Smith, Elder and Co., London, 1913.

Shackleton, E. H., *Heart of the Antarctic; Being the story of the British Antarctic Expedition 1907–1909*, 2 vols., W. Heinemann, London, 1909.

Sieburth, J. M., Gastrointestinal microflora of antarctic birds, *J. Bacteriol.*, *77*, 521–531, 1959.

Sieburth, J. M., Acrylic acid, an 'antibiotic' principle in *Phaeocystis* blooms in antarctic waters, *Science, 132,* 676–677, 1960.

Sieburth, J. M., Antibiotic properties of acrylic acid, a factor in the gastrointestinal antibiosis of polar marine animals, *J. Bacteriol., 82,* 72–79, 1961.

Sieburth, J. M., Bacterial habitats in the antarctic environ-ment, *Symposium on Marine Microbiology,* 769 pages, Charles C. Thomas, Springfield, Illinois, 1963.

Straka, R. P., and J. L. Stokes, Psychrophilic bacteria from Antarctica, *J. Bacteriol., 80,* 622–625, 1960.

Waksman, S. A., *Soil Microbiology,* 356 pages, John Wiley & Sons, New York, 1952.

Wexler, H., and M. J. Rubin, Antarctic meteorology, in *Science in Antarctica, Natl. Acad. Sci. Publ. 839* (part 2, *The Physical Sciences in Antarctica*), chapter 2, pp. 6–24, 1961.

ANTARCTIC SOILS

J. C. F. Tedrow and F. C. Ugolini

Rutgers University, New Brunswick, New Jersey

Abstract. Much of the ice-free surficial mantle of Antarctica, particularly the older deposits, has been subjected to intensive weathering, and, with this weathering, the products in the soil become redistributed. When iron-bearing minerals weather, they become brown in color, and lime and gypsum layers may form and genetic horizonation may develop. Antarctic soils are alkaline and are usually well supplied with potentially available nutrients, particularly K, Na, Ca, and Mg. N and P occur in very low amounts. Soil-forming processes take place in a virtual ahumic system. Of the conventional soil-forming factors, the biotic element scarcely enters the system.

The following subdivisions of the soils of Antarctica, referred to collectively as *soils of the cold desert,* are tentatively proposed: (1) *ahumic soils;* (2) *evaporite soils;* (3) *protoranker soils;* (4) *ornithogenic soils;* (5) *regosols;* and (6) *lithosols (rockland).* Although the soils should be referred to as varieties of desert soils, the conditions in the deserts of Antarctica are quite different from those in the deserts of temperate and warm climates. Unless the term 'polar desert soil of the north' is redefined, its use should not be extended to include Antarctica.

Recent studies indicate that many of the ice-free areas of Antarctica have been subjected to intense physical and chemical weathering. These weathering processes have been or are now operating and at a magnitude far greater than was originally believed. In such a cold environment, one is perhaps inclined to postulate a static condition with little mineral alteration and no soil formation, but this is not, in fact, the case. Our observations in Victoria Land clearly show that soil-forming agencies have operated or are now operating not only in the comparatively warmer valleys but also on the frigid nunataks of the polar plateau. In nearly all instances, however, the geochemical processes that produce various horizons in the surficial material operate without effective biotic elements.

Although the exact size of the antarctic continent is not known, it is estimated to be about 5 million square miles, or about the size of continental United States plus Mexico. Only a small percentage of the continent is free of ice and snow. The ice-free areas of Antarctica are shown on a map (Figure 1) compiled from maps of the U. S. Geological Survey. Most of these ice-free areas are on the periphery of the continent. Victoria Land, where most of our studies were carried out, has a number of valleys

that are up to 30 to 40 miles in length, several miles wide, mantled with glacial drift, and free of snow during the summer months. These valleys and adjacent uplands are ideal for pedologic study.

Whether or not genetic soils are to be recognized in Antarctica will depend first upon the definition of the term soil. When Ramann, Hilgard, Glinka, Zakharov, Marbut, and, to an extent, Dokuchaev defined soil, the biotic element was emphasized. In terms of the definitions of these investigators the ice-free areas of Antarctica cannot be said to be mantled with soils. Their definitions required the surficial mantle to have a certain minimum organic content, which would, in turn, function as an integral part of the system, and in nearly all the ice-free regions of Antarctica the organic components are of an extremely low order, especially in comparison with soil systems of other climates. During the inception and development of the science of pedology, Antarctica was not taken into consideration. With the exception of the unique conditions of the penguin rookeries and a few scattered areas colonized by mosses and lichens, antarctic conditions are almost ahumic, and here the meaning of such processes as ion uptake or mineral ratios in a potential soluble state is not the same as in other

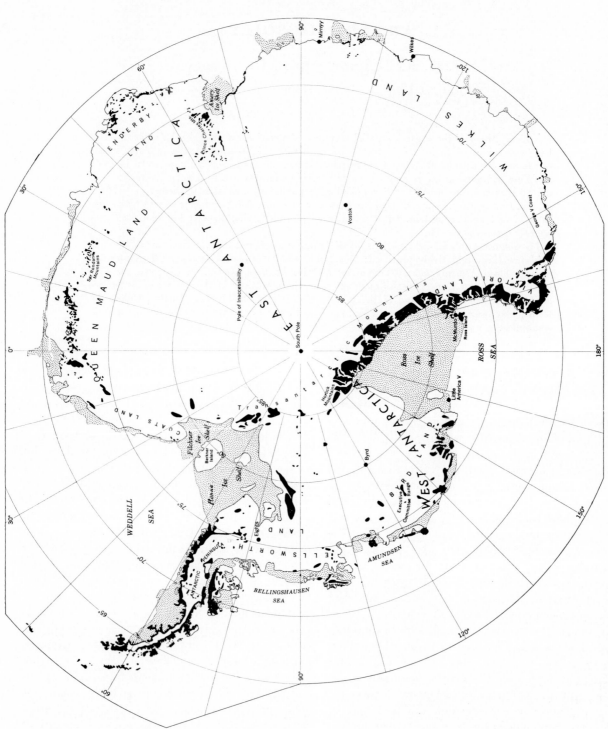

Fig. 1. Map of Antarctica. Regions of mountains or exposed rock (*dark areas*). The map is a modification of Plate 1 (C. R. Bentley *et al.*), Folio 2, Antarctic Map Folio Series, American Geographical Society.

Fig. 2. The eastern portion of the Taylor Valley showing the mantle of glacial drift. Extensive polygonization is shown in the central portion of the photograph.

climatic regions where vascular plants colonize the mineral substrate. In Antarctica, with a low-temperature–mineral system, genetic horizons develop as a result of the action of physico-chemical processes near the surface of the Earth. But with the system virtually void of humus, is horizon differentiation a pedologic process or is it entirely within the realm of geochemistry? This is a problem of semantics, but for the purposes of this discussion we shall refer to these altered surficial deposits as soil just as the terms podzol or chernozem are used by other investigators for soils in various other parts of the world. In nearly every instance, instead of the five classical soil-forming factors, in Antarctica we deal with only four: lithology, climate, topography, and time.

Neustruev [1927] preferred to define soil processes with wide latitude when he stated that the 'weathering processes in the abiotical layers of the Earth's crust may be scarcely separated from the soil-forming processes in that part of it where organisms chiefly live. At any rate, soil science has no right to decline studying such processes as occur in the "abiotical" layers without the risk of being converted into a purely biological discipline. In this case, as well as in the case of other sciences, no distinct line may be drawn for separating soil science from cognate disciplines.' This definition points out the broad aspects of weathering and horizon formation and does not exclude mineral systems from the field of soils.

THE AREA

Less than 5 per cent of the antarctic continent is free of ice and snow, but it is these ice-free areas that are of direct concern to the pedologist. Figure 1 indicates in a highly generalized manner the regions of the continent in which sizeable ice-free areas are found.

Victoria Land has many ice-free areas, especially in the coastal regions from Cape Adare southward to the Beardmore Glacier. The dry valley system, 50 to 100 miles west of the main United States base on Ross Island, offers excellent opportunity for pedologic study (Figure 2). This valley system has recently been receiving considerable attention from geologists, glaciologists, and limnologists. Although Queen Maud Land, the Antarctic Peninsula, and other peripheral areas have considerable ice-free land, these areas have not as yet been visited by pedologists. A small ice-free area at Mirnyy near the Shackleton Ice Shelf, has received considerable attention from Soviet pedologists. New Zealand investigators have been studying soils in Victoria Land. None of the ice-free areas scattered throughout other portions of the continent, particularly in the Horlick Mountains, Ellsworth Land, Byrd Land, Enderby Land, Queen Maud Land, and Coats Land (Figure 1), have been visited by pedologists.

CLIMATE

The climate of the Antarctic is by far the most rigorous of any found on Earth. Coastal areas have mean annual temperatures approximating $-10°F$, which, in the vicinity of the south geographic pole and the pole of inaccessibility [*Wexler and Rubin*, 1961; *Rubin*, 1962], decrease to an estimated $-55°F$. The record low of $-127°F$ was recorded at Vostok I (*circa* 72°S, 97°E). Approximate monthly mean temperatures from selected south polar locations are shown in Table 1. Mean annual temperatures of Antarctica are much lower, prob-

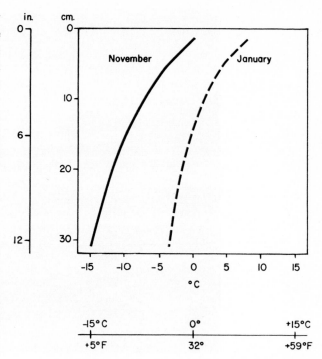

Fig. 3. Idealized summer soil temperatures in an antarctic soil from Wright Valley, Victoria Land.

TABLE 1. Approximate Mean Monthly Temperatures at Selected Antarctica Weather Stations

Month	Approximate Mean Monthly Temperatures*	
	McMurdo Sound (77°40'S, 166°30'E) °F (°C)	South Pole† (90°S) °F (°C)
January	25 (−4)	−20 (−29)
February	16 (−9)	−40 (−40)
March	−2 (−19)	−67 (−55)
April	−6 (−21)	−72 (−58)
May	−9 (−23)	−71 (−57)
June	−11 (−24)	−71 (−57)
July	−17 (−27)	−74 (−59)
August	−20 (−29)	−71 (−57)
September	−11 (−24)	−74 (−59)
October	−4 (−20)	−60 (−51)
November	16 (−9)	−36 (−38)
December	25 (−4)	−20 (−29)

* Based on six-year data (1956–1963) of the U. S. Weather Bureau.
† 2800 m.

ably some 30°F, than those of analogous northern latitudes. Altitudes of the polar plateau, which commonly exceed 10,000 feet, contribute to the low temperatures.

Air temperatures of the dry valleys of Victoria Land approximate 10° to 30°F in the summer months, but on sunny days during these months they may, for a few hours, go above the freezing point. Soil temperatures are well below the freezing point for about 9 months each year, but during midsummer they may go above the freezing point (Figure 3).

Relative humidity is very low throughout the continent and this has a pronounced effect on soil processes, because together with low temperatures, slight precipitation, and desiccating winds an extreme-cold desert condition is produced. *Avsiuk, Markov, and Shumskiy* [1956] report about 50 per cent relative humidity during the 'night' and 10 to 15 per cent during the 'day.'

During the austral summer of 1960, relative humidity at the South Pole Station averaged 40 to 45 per cent, and for the summer months (December, January, and February) at McMurdo Sound it

Fig. 4. Terminus of the Suess Glacier, Taylor Valley, showing the general nature of the glacial deposits.

approximated 70 per cent; in the dry valleys of Victoria Land, however, it is apparently lower.

Rubin [1962] estimates that the mean annual precipitation on the continent amounts to the equivalent of 5 to 6 inches of water. Annual precipitation in the coastal areas is as much as 16 inches, with the amount decreasing to less than 2 inches in the central portion of the continent. Rainfall as such is unknown on the continent, except in the Antarctic Peninsula. Field evidence indicates that in the dry valleys much of the snowfall sublimates into the atmosphere.

Despite the low temperatures during part of the summer season, small streams, usually alkaline in reaction, flow from many of the glaciers.

Wind velocity is of special interest because of its effect on soils. The katabatic winds pouring off the polar plateau into the dry valleys and other ice-free areas cause some blowing and drifting of sand, but just how much mineral material is transported by wind activity is not established.

Paleoclimate of Antarctica is of great concern in reconstructing possible past pedologic events. The Quaternary deposits do not appear to contain any terrestrial plant remains nor is there any evidence of buried soil profiles, but this subject requires much additional study. We examined the drift in a number of areas near glacial termini and also certain fluvial deposits but found no direct or indirect evidence of organic terrestrial remains in the Quaternary deposits (Figure 4). There is unquestionable evidence, however, that in earlier geologic time plants not only grew but flourished within a few degrees of South Pole [*Barghoorn*, 1961; *Schoph*, 1962; *Doumani and Long*, 1962]. Near the end of the Tertiary, climate apparently began to change and ice began to accumulate contemporaneously with the glacial build-up in the northern hemisphere [*Doumani and Long*, 1962]; thus our present-day conditions in Antarctica are somewhat analogous to those of the northern hemisphere during the Pleistocene epoch. *Zeller and Pearn* [1960] estimate, from thermoluminescence of rocks, that 170,-000 years might be considered a minimum value for the elapse of time since Antarctica became cold.

GEOLOGY

Geologists have played a major role in nearly every antarctic expedition since the turn of the century.

The expeditions of, among others, Scott, Shackleton, Byrd, and Mawson produced excellent information on the geology of selected areas. Fortunately, the geologists have renewed studies and have been attacking the problem on a broad front for the past ten years, and from this activity many valuable findings have been forthcoming [*Nichols*, 1953; *Crary*, 1959, 1962; *Davies*, 1961; *Craddock and Hubbard*, 1961; *Woollard*, 1962], but many complex geologic problems of the continent remain to be solved.

The characteristics and dynamics of the ice sheet and related problems of Antarctica are receiving major attention from the glaciologists [*Cameron and Goldthwait*, 1960; *Field*, 1961; *Różycki*, 1961; *Hollin*, 1962; *Loewe*, 1963]. Glaciology is of special concern to the pedologist because the areas peripheral to the glaciers are ideal for studying the time factor in soil development. *Gould* [1939] stated that the gross glacial picture indicated that the glaciers of Antarctica must be considered as remnants of a former, more intensive, and more extensive period of glaciation.

The investigations reported in this paper have centered around Victoria Land, where, fortunately, the geology has been worked out in considerable detail. The dry valley region of Victoria Land consists of a Precambrian, or a lower Paleozoic, complex. These rocks are overlain by the Beacon Hill group of sediments of Paleozoic or Mesozoic age, which consist mainly of sandstone and conglomerate [*Webb and McKelvey*, 1959; *McKelvey and Webb*, 1961, 1962; *Zeller, Angino, and Turner*, 1961]. Massive sills and dikes of dolerite intrude both the basement complex and the Beacon Hill sediments.

A network of east-west–trending valleys 2 to 5 miles wide and up to about 35 to 50 miles long cut through the sedimentary rocks and the dolerite intrusions and into the basement complex. The valley floors vary from near sea level to some 800 feet and are mantled almost continuously with glacial drift. Glacial debris in the valleys is loose, sandy, and stony; little clay or silt is present. Steep, rock walls rise boldly some 2000 to 3000 feet above the valley floors. Higher valley walls have many rock exposures, but the lower valley walls are mantled with talus aprons.

In Wright Valley, four glaciations have been recorded [*Bull, McKelvey, and Webb*, 1962], a con-dition somewhat analogous to that of Taylor Valley. It has been shown that the older drift has acquired some weathering characteristics. Ages of the deposits are unknown, but fragmentary evidence indicates the youngest drift in the Taylor Valley has a minimum age of 6000 years [*Péwé*, 1960]. *Bull* [1962] presented an excellent analysis of Quaternary glaciations in Victoria Land. The younger drift deposits in Victoria Land do not have the yellowish brown color in the surface horizon that the older ones do.

BIOTIC FACTORS

On the ice-free areas of the continent continuous expanses of the snow-free areas are encountered without any signs of terrestrial life [*Llano*, 1959, 1961]. *Llano* [1962] points out that the antarctic tree line approximates 54°S and the flowering plant line about 64°S. South of the flowering plant line clumps of lichens, mosses, and algae are occasionally found, but their presence is quite rare; one may travel the ice-free areas on foot for many miles without any sign of plants. On the dry valley floors, where most of our observations were made, no lichens or mosses were observed. At Gneiss Point, at Ross Island, and on some of the higher walls of the dry valleys of Victoria Land lichens are present. That lichens are present at higher altitudes and not on the valley floors is ascribed to higher humidity, melt from the lower névé, or age of landscape. Along the edges of some of the frozen lakes clumps of dead algae are present.

Flint and Stout [1960] examined the microflora and microfauna associated with antarctic soils and found protozoa, amoebae, rotifers, tardigrades, and nematodes present. The organic-inorganic cycle of the lower life forms may be somewhat similar, qualitatively, to that of the temperate regions, but the reaction rate is retarded by low temperatures. Algal growth was recorded [*Flint and Stout*, 1960] at temperatures as low as 32°F, and bacterial growth at about 39°F. *Boyd* [1962] found the soils in the McMurdo Sound area to be low in bacterial population. Thermophylic, mesophylic, and psychrophilic bacteria are present, and there are indications that some decomposition takes place during the summer months.

That a biotic spectrum is present in many antarctic soils has been well established, but as to how important a part this plays in weathering remains to be worked out. As a gross picture, there is little evidence to indicate that the biotic element is an important agent in the weathering and soil formation in Antarctica.

WEATHERING PROCESSES

The antarctic desert is the scene of intense chemical and physical weathering processes. Occasionally one encounters advance stages of physical weathering in the rocks. Pitted and fretted surfaces are quite common, but the exact mechanism responsible for producing this condition remains unknown [*Nichols*, 1953]. *Wade* [1945] suggested that the pitted rock surfaces in the Rockefeller Mountains may be due to wind-blown ice crystals and rock fragments. Boulders and rocks that have been exposed for a considerable time show effects of extensive weathering (Figure 5). Slabs and concentric shells of weathering are easily removed from parent boulders, and frequently rotten slabs can be easily crushed into gravel-size fragments. *Nichols* [1953] discussed many weathering conditions in the Antarctic Peninsula. *Markov* [1956] described the 'shells of exfoliation' in the antarctic desert and the splitting of boulders. *Shumskiy* [1957] mentioned the shells of exfoliation present in the antarctic desert. *Glazovskaia* [1958] described exfoliation crusts up to 20 inches thick. *Avsiuk,*

Fig. 5. Exfoliated boulders in Wright Valley.

Markov, and Shumskiy [1956] spoke of the desquamational forces acting upon rocks. Weathering is not confined to rocks that are easily weatherable, it appears to be equally intense in the crystalline rocks.

Few processes in Antarctica are as striking as those related to the chemical weathering of rocks. The processes of mineral alteration have been well established by *Glazovskaia* [1958], who reported feldspar being weathered into clay-like substances, hornblende and chlorite becoming discolored, and garnets being split and filled with a clay-like substance. Glazovskaia's work on thin sections clearly shows the high degree of mineral alteration, with secondary calcite and fine crystals of secondary epidote covering the surfaces of disintegrated feldspars, augite, and hornblende. In the boulders of Wright and Taylor valleys, we observed many feldspars weathered into clay substance and the results of attendant processes. Weathering is not confined to the periphery of the boulders but is, instead, deep-seated. Boulders on the surface and those a foot or two deep in the soil seem in many ways to be similarly affected by the deep-seated weathering processes. Working on a quartz diorite from Antarctica, *Kelly and Zumberge* [1961] selected specimens that had undergone various degrees of weathering. Field evidence indicated advance mineral alteration, but the bulk of the chemical and mineral composition remained quite constant, the major changes being those relating to iron conversion and limonite formation.

Examination of weathered boulders shows that there is, in conjunction with mineral alteration, an accumulation of salts in cracks and crevices. This salt accumulation is a widespread phenomenon and appears to take place on nearly all kinds of rocks. The matrix of the weathered boulders has the consistency of deteriorated concrete, with accumulated salts filling the voids. It is quite evident that there is a transfer of material from the crystalline portion of the matrix to the voids of the rocks [*Markov*, 1956, 1960; *Glazovskaia*, 1958]. Salt crusts from a variety of rocks in the Mirnyy area indicate that composition varies considerably from one rock to another. Figure 6 shows a salt-filled cavity in an exposed boulder in Taylor Valley. *Shumskiy* [1957] described salt efflorescence in Antarctica, and *Kelly and Zumberge* [1961] re-

Fig. 6.   Salt accumulation on the surface of the boulder,
Taylor Valley.

is present on the polar plateau and in the dry valleys of Victoria Land. *Glazovskaia* [1958] analyzed desert-varnish crusts from Antarctica and found that they had accumulated Fe and Mn. *Markov* [1956] related the development of desert crusts and soluble salts to temperature-moisture gradients established within the rock. Even though air temperatures in Antarctica may be well below freezing, on sunny days solar radiation causes the rocks to have high surface temperatures. *Rubin* [1962] reports that a theoretical value of 29,000 calories per square centimeter reaches the snow surface at the south pole during December. *Avsiuk, Markov, and Shumskiy* [1956] report radiation values up to 700 calories per square centimeter per 24 hours. *Avsiuk, Markov, and Shumskiy* [1956] and *Markov* [1956] report air temperatures near 0°C and rock surface temperatures of 25° to 30°C. *Kelly and Zumberge* [1961] report air temperatures of 38°F and rock temperatures of approximately 50° to 70°F. In the Taylor Valley, *Angino, Armitage, and Tash* [1962] have measured rock temperatures as high as 25°C, and in the Horlick Mountains, where air temperatures seldom exceed −12°C, rock temperatures of 27.8°C have been recorded [*Anonymous*, 1962]. These data strongly suggest that, with the establishment of large temperature differentials in the rocks and soil material of the desert environment during periods of sunshine, salts move to the periphery of the rocks, but this does not explain the salt in rocks equally decomposed but buried beneath the surface of the soil and beyond the reach of the Sun. *Glazovskaia* [1958] examined the rock peripheries which were previously thin-sectioned and found the crusts to be minerals of the goethite and psilomelanic groups. Apparently the Fe and Mn move across a large temperature (and moisture) gradient as Fe^{2+} and Mn^{2+} and, upon reaching the zone of the rock surfaces, oxidize to Fe^{3+} and Mn^{4+} with subsequent stabilization.

To return to the composition of the salts formed in the cold desert, great variation is found from one location to another [*Glazovskaia*, 1958; *Kelly and Zumberge*, 1961; *Gibson*, 1962; *Johannesson and Gibson*, 1962]. The most complete work on this to date is that of *Glazovskaia* [1958], who dissolved numerous salt crusts in acid and determined the constituents in solution. In some of the desert-varnish conditions the dissolved material

ported NaCl crystallized in rocks at Marble Point. *Avsiuk, Markov, and Shumskiy* [1956] reported salt crusts forming in the cold deserts of Antarctica. *Gibson* [1962] described many conditions of the cold desert involving salt formation. *Nichols* [1963] reported salt concentrations immediately below the surface of glacial deposits in Victoria Land. By subsequent redistribution these salts serve as a source for the salt that is found in the soil.

Crusts of desert varnish coat many exposed rocks of Antarctica. These desert varnish conditions have been reported by *Markov* [1956], *Avsiuk, Markov, and Shumskiy* [1956], *Taubert* [1956], and *Glazovskaia* [1958]. Crusts vary from brown to dark red, purplish, and nearly black colors, and may be as much as a half inch thick. Desert varnish, which tends to be more prevalent on older land surfaces,

TABLE 2. Partial Chemical Composition of the
Salt Crust From a Boulder at the Foot of
Canada Glacier, Taylor Valley

Element*	Amount (%)
Na	43.34
K	0.05
Ca	3.59
Mg	0.16
Cl	25.36
Residue	30.20

* Soluble in 10% HCl, except for the Cl value, which is
total amount present in sample.

consisted almost exclusively of either iron or man-
ganese or both, with small quantities of Ca and
Mg. We found that the composition of the salts
on boulders varies considerably, but Table 2 shows
the partial chemical composition of a salt crust
from one boulder in Taylor Valley.

Since we are concerned with the fate of soluble
salts from the rocks to the soil and bodies of water,
it is highly important to consider the mineral composition of drainage and lake water. Considerable
variation is found in antarctic waters in both total
solids and ratios of elements [*Markov*, 1956; *Glazovskaia*, 1958; *Ball and Nichols*, 1960; *McKelvey
and Webb*, 1961; *Barghoorn and Nichols*, 1961;
Gibson, 1962; *Hamilton, Frost, and Hayes*, 1962;
Nichols, 1962; *Angino and Armitage*, 1963; *Tedrow,
Ugolini, and Janetschek*, 1963]. In connection with
saline and alkali soil formation, the geochemical
system involving release of elements from their
original crystalline structures is also important,
because this is the major source of the salt that
later finds its way into the soil.

Returning to physical weathering processes in
Antarctica, there are periods of violent winds which
cause the shifting and blowing of sand. Ventifacts
are present. Desert pavement (Figure 7) naturally
retards wind erosion by maintaining a closely knit
pattern of gravel and cobbles at the surface, but
there are, nevertheless, instances where the action
of wind erosion cannot be questioned [*Wade*, 1945].
With the shifting of surface sands, a natural dis-
turbance of the surficial materials results. *Avsiuk,
Markov, and Shumskiy* [1956] report the dispersion
of dry dust; *McKelvey and Webb* [1961] and *Gibson* [1962] mention dunes in Antarctica. The magni-

tude of sand movement is somewhat uncertain, since
the late-snow patches and the cracks and joints
of the perennially frozen lakes are usually free of
sand. *Nichols* [1953] indicated a lack of evidence for
extensive aeolian activity in the Antarctic Peninsula
area.

SOIL FORMATION

Since the soils of the antarctic continent form under
conditions of extreme aridity, they have a number
of features in common with the soils of the temperate and warm deserts. With, however, the apparent
lifelessness and extremely low temperature of the
antarctic deserts, it is more appropriate to consider
soils of these areas as belonging to paradesert varieties. Soils of the dry valleys of Victoria Land and
the peripheral ice-free uplands, including nunataks,
are very sandy and stony; only small quantities
of silt and clay are present. Weakly indurated
or mechanically compacted layers are sometimes
observed within the soil profiles. Even though
much of the soil is below the freezing point during
most of the summer months, owing to the low
clay and silt contents together with low moisture, the
soil usually remains in a loose uncohesive state to
a depth of two or more feet. Since the soils are
very loose, dry, dusty, and uncohesive, they are
most difficult to examine for detailed morphology.

Particle size does not appear to change per-
ceptibly with depth as a result of pedogenic proc-

Fig. 7. Ahumic soil with desert pavement, Upper Wright
Valley. Scale 6 in.

esses, unless one takes into consideration the formation of salt layers through the movement and precipitation of the more soluble materials. Where these layers occur, the soil matrix is nearly as loose and uncohesive as that of a salt-free horizon. No compound structure was detected in the soils.

Clays of Antarctica have not been identified to any great extent, but such work is now under way in New Zealand and in our laboratories. *Glazovskaia* [1958] reported clay-like material in the Mirnyy area, probably nontronite or beidellite weathering from feldspar. *Blakemore and Swindale* [1958] reported the presence of hydrous mica from Ross Island. *Kelly and Zumberge* [1961], in their weathering sequence studies of quartz–diorite specimens, found no clay formed from weathering, despite the fact that the rocks had a highly weathered appearance. Examination of random antarctic samples has shown the presence of a mica approximating an illite; also present are vermiculite, chlorite, clay-size feldspar, and clay-size quartz.

Over a half a century ago *Jensen* [1916] recognized the high degree of alkalinity in antarctic soils. *Llano*'s [1962] work, as well as the work of the writers, has shown that nearly all these soils are alkaline. The high pH values also suggest considerable soluble or potentially soluble cations in the soil. Under certain circumstances Cl, SO_4, and related anions are present, in which instance the soils will be well below pH 7. Samples of lithosols on Mount Erebus, which were no more than disintegrated rock, had pH values as low as 4.5, a condition controlled by volcanic gases. By usual standards, antarctic soils can be considered well supplied with potentially available nutrients, particularly Ca, Mg, Na, and K. Except in the rookeries and in the spots colonized by lichens or mosses, organic matter is virtually nonexistent. Recently *Johannesson and Gibson* [1962] reported deposits of nitrate salts in Antarctica. *Gibson* [1962] reports the presence of Na_2SO_4, $MgSO_4 \cdot 7\ H_2O$, $CaSO_4 \cdot 2\ H_2O$, $NaNO_3$, and $NaIO_3$ in various locations of Victoria Land. *Jensen* [1916] described the presence of mirabilite in the soil and soil water being charged with salt. His work clearly demonstrates that there is a large quantity of soluble material in the soil, and the writers' data support his work. *Blakemore and Swindale* [1958] conducted analyses on a soil sample from Scott Base, Ross Island, and reported

the presence of large quantities of exchangeable bases, particularly K, Na, and Ca.

It is evident that at least a 3-stage evolution and transfer of the salts takes place. Salt (1) accumulates within rocks by natural desert processes, (2) transfers from rocks to the soil, and (3) by slow partial leaching from the soil subsequently accumulates in basins, lakes, and the sea. Geochemical systems related to sea salt, salt accumulation from volcanic activity, and salt in glacier ice do not come within the scope of this report.

MAJOR SOILS

There is an extreme break in the qualitative pedologic processes between the tundra regions of the southern hemisphere and those of the antarctic mainland. In depicting soils of the south polar regions one cannot follow a pedologic continuum from the southern tundra belt to the cold deserts of Antarctica, because conditions in the latter area are of an entirely different character than those of the land masses girdling the southern hemisphere at around 50° to 60°S, and between these two sets of diverse conditions are huge ocean expanses. Tundra-like soils are present on the southern tip of South America [*Molfino*, 1956], Macquarie Island [*Taylor*, 1955], the high country of South Island, New Zealand [*Billings and Mark*, 1961], and South Georgia [*Shackleton*, 1920], but these soils have received very little investigation.

In Antarctica, *McCraw* [1960] was the first to establish taxonomic soil units based on morphology. In field studies, mainly in the Taylor Dry Valley, McCraw developed a legend (personal communication) that took into account various genetic soils and the associated patterned ground features. *McCraw* [1960] presented field data that indicated that certain pedologic phenomena, such as the formation of desert varnish, rock weathering, and carbonate accumulation, were taking place. Certain features of the soils were correlated with Quaternary chronology.

Antarctic soils do not fit very well into any of the great soil groups of the present global classification schemes. From the standpoint of chemical and morphologic parameters, they would approximate soils of the desert regions, including many alkali soils. The soil-forming processes in the various deserts, including Antarctica, have many qualitative and quantitative features in common. It would, however, be somewhat unrealistic and premature to include the soils of the cold desert of Antarctica, where temperatures are usually below the freezing point of water, with those of the temperate and warm deserts.

In depicting antarctic soil conditions, the term *polar desert*, as used in the far north, is unsuitable. When *Gorodkov*'s [1939] term *polar desert* was adopted [*Tedrow and Brown*, 1962] it referred exclusively to the polar regions of the northern hemisphere. While it is evident that both north and south polar regions have a degree of barrenness about them, the soil-forming processes in the two regions do not appear to be entirely the same.

The high degree of weathering in Antarctica is viewed as a result of present climate and not as a relic condition of a warmer period. Ideas set forth by *Meinardus* [1930], *Polynov* [1945], and *Targul'yan* [1959] for weathering in the northern temperate and far-north areas cannot be applied to Antarctica. The only known cold regions of the northern hemisphere with certain qualitative processes similar to those of Antarctica appear to be those of the high mountain country of Tein Shan [*Glazovskaia*, 1952] and, possibly, northern Greenland. *Markov* [1956] used the term *cold desert* to typify the antarctic landscape. This seems to be an appropriate term to apply to soils; thus all soils of the antarctic continent will be referred to as *soils of the cold desert*.

Nikiforoff [1937] used the term abiotic to describe desert soil processes in the United States, but, in almost all antarctic soil samples, microbiologists have identified bacteria and other life forms. Antarctic soils cannot, therefore, be considered in *senso stricto* as being abiotic, although for all practical purposes they can be considered ahumic.

Evaporite soils are those which have a high salt content and which are usually found in dischargeless basins.

The term protoranker soil is adapted from *Kubiena* [1953]. Although this term is not entirely satisfactory for antarctic soils, where the organomineral conditions have not really advanced to a state similar to those of the ranker soils described by Kubiena, it is used provisionally for the mineral substrates colonized by lichens and mosses.

The term ornithogenic soil, taken from *Syroechov-*

sky [1959], is ideally suited for the organic soils of the rookeries.

Ahumic Soils

Ahumic soils are those soils that are most common to the dry valleys. They mantle the rolling valleys and talus slopes. Ahumic soils, some of the important features of which are shown in Figures 7, 8, and 9, are occasionally present on the nunataks of the polar plateau. Organic matter is almost nonexistent, and both soluble salt content and pH are rather high throughout. Soil-forming processes include the release of Ca, Mg, K, Na, Cl, and S from parent rocks and the redistribution of these elements throughout the profile. Lime and gypsum layers may or may not be present. Slight accumulations of lime and gypsum may cause the formation of chemically indurated pans (Figure 8); these zones of accumulation may build up to thicknesses of some 6 to 8 inches, and are usually present at a depth of about 1 foot. Ahumic soils include all of *McCraw*'s [1960] genetic soils; when more information is available on the ahumic soils, they will be subdivided along the general ideas outlined by him. Perhaps, with more extensive field work on the continent, the presence of lime and gypsum layers can be correlated with parent material, position, age (chronologic), and related factors, but to date the work of the writers has not shown any specific trend regarding the

Fig. 8. Ahumic soil in the Taylor Valley. The 6-inch scale rests on a zone having carbonate accumulation.

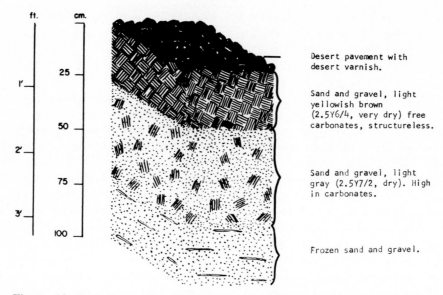

Desert pavement with desert varnish.

Sand and gravel, light yellowish brown (2.5Y6/4, very dry) free carbonates, structureless.

Sand and gravel, light gray (2.5Y7/2, dry). High in carbonates.

Frozen sand and gravel.

Fig. 9. Idealized ahumic soil of the cold desert. Older aged glacial drift tends to have soils of a brownish color, while the younger retains more of a light gray (2.5 Y 7/2) color throughout.

occurrence of these layers. *McCraw* [1960] postulated formation and subsequent destruction of lime-bearing horizons in the soil. The youngest materials have thus not yet acquired a lime pan; with increased time, however, a pan will form but only to be subsequently destroyed.

Glazovskaia [1958] and *Kelly and Zumberge* [1961] report the weathering of iron-bearing minerals, and *Bull, McKelvey, and Webb* [1962] describe the older drift sheets as having a weathered appearance. In the field it is quite apparent that the older (chronologic) soils have acquired a brownish color in the surface horizon. In our examinations of the soils of the McMurdo area [Taylor glaciation of *Péwé*, 1960; first and second glaciations of *Bull, McKelvey, and Webb*, 1962], we commonly found surface soil of a yellowish brown color, a condition not in evidence in the youngest glacial deposits. Soils of Koettlitz, and in part the Fryxell glaciations [*Péwé*, 1960; third and fourth glaciations of *Bull, McKelvey, and Webb*, 1962], retain their original pale gray color throughout the profile.

Desert pavement is commonly present on all soils, including the ahumic; it apparently follows no specific pattern with regard to age or composition of the deposit. Younger deposits tend to show little desert varnish. Many cobbles and boulders have a highly developed desert varnish; this de-

velopment appears to be largely confined to the residuum and older glacial deposits. Surfaces of the cobbles, having developed a desert varnish, are glossy and have acquired a colored rind as well.

Ahumic soils are not confined to the valleys; they are present also in the adjacent mountains. Well-developed soils may be found on the protected sites of the polar plateau. Rock weathering also is in evidence at the higher altitudes. *Glazovskaia* [1958] reported strongly weathered granite-gneiss with calcite crusts from a nunatak in the Endelholmen Mountains at an altitude of some 6300 feet.

Within the soil profile secondary salts occur as crusts on the upper and/or lower sides of cobbles and within the matrix of the rock itself.

During the course of rock weathering and mineral alteration in Antarctica, simple salts of Na, K, Ca, and Mg are released and thus become available for easy solubilization and movement (Table 2). Even though rainfall is non-existent, field evidence strongly supports the concept that salts move within the profile and eventually find their way into many low-lying areas, such as basins and swales, in a manner similar to that in the temperate and warm deserts [*McCraw*, 1960; *Tedrow, Ugolini, and Janetschek*, 1963].

Table 3 gives certain data of two selected ahumic soils of the cold deserts. Lack of organic carbon is the general rule for these soils. In the Cape Royds profile a trace of nitrogen is present, probably in a nonorganic form. That values for pH are high reflects the potentially soluble cations. Determination of the electrodialyzed constituents showed the presence of considerable quantities of various anions and cations, reflecting the aridity of the desert system.

Since Antarctica is a very arid region and underlain by permafrost, low positions are natural structures for the accumulation of salts. Antarctic soils are very sandy and void of humus, and naturally have extremely low cation-exchange capacities. With soluble Na and K commonly present in measurable quantities, most of these soils of the cold desert are saline. Insofar as salt content is concerned, we are provisionally allowing wide latitude in the definition of an ahumic soil.

Evaporite Soils

During the last decade there have been a number of saline lakes reported in Antarctica [*Markov*, 1956; *Glazovskaia*, 1958; *Ball and Nichols*, 1960; *Bull, McKelvey, and Webb*, 1962; *Gibson*, 1962; *Tedrow, Ugolini, and Janetschek*, 1963]. Similarly, a number of surficial salt deposits have been recorded [*Markov*, 1956; *Glazovskaia*, 1958; *Johannesson and Gibson*, 1962; *Gibson*, 1962]. Saline waters have been identified in a number of localities [*Hamilton, Frost, and Hayes*, 1962; *Ball and Nichols*, 1960; *Kelly and Zumberge*, 1961]. This combined evidence indicates that there are widespread potential sources of alkali materials that conceivably could find their way into certain soils and surficial deposits. Evaporite soils are very common in the dry valleys and occupy the depressions, basins, and low, flat drainage ways. These soils have no outstanding morphologic fea-

TABLE 3. Partial Data of Two Ahumic Soils from Antarctica

Factor Measured	Victoria Land, Beacon Heights, 161°21'E, 77°53'S Dolerite and Sandstone Drift; Altitude 5800 ft		Ross Island, Cape Royds, 166°15'E, 77°35'S Kenyte and related rocks [*Treves*, 1962]	
	10 YR 4/3* Brown Medium sandy loam	10 YR 4/3* Brown Medium sandy loam	N3/0* Very dark gray loamy sand	10 YR 2/1* Black loamy sand
	1/4–3 in.	5–9 in.	2–4 in.	6–10 in.
pH	7.6	8.0	7.8	7.8
EC (1:2)	28.5	12.5	40	101
Ca† (ppm)	—	—	315	450
Mg† (ppm)	240	270	72	135
Na† (ppm)	1910	1240	3260	6410
K† (ppm)	160	31	1350	3710
P† (ppm)	9	11	11	18
SO₄ (ppm)	12,000	24,000	1100	2000
Cl† (ppm)	1100	900	7000	10,400
Reducible Fe‡ (%)	0.51	0.61	0.10	0.41
Organic C§ (%)	ND	ND	ND	ND
N	Tr	Tr	ND	ND
CO₃ (%)	0.66	0.23	ND	ND

* Field estimation, Munsell soil color charts. ND = not detected, Tr = trace.
† Electrodialysis [*Hanna and Purvis*, 1955].
‡ *Kilmer* [1960] procedure.
§ Chromic acid oxidation.

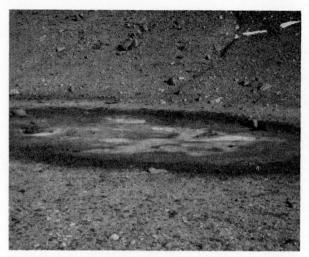

Fig. 10. View of an evaporite soil, 'South Fork,' Wright
Valley.

tures except for a concentration of salt; the salt
occurs at the surface and at times is an inch or
more thick. Evaporite soils tend to have a fluffy
appearance near the surface and, depending upon
the deliquescency of the salt, may have a 'moist'
appearance (Figure 10). A single sample of a
saline soil showed 3.5 per cent soluble salt, but
field conditions indicate that the range of salt in
the soils, both in quantity and composition, is
highly variable.

Saline soils that probably closely approximate
evaporite soils are also present in the mountains, but
they tend to occur only as small pockets. Future
work will also have to consider the possibility of
saline soils resulting from earlier marine transgression and the possibility of salt being added
as spray in the littoral areas.

Protoranker Soils

In the Antarctic, sites covered by lichens and
mosses are rare, but in certain locations plants
colonize the mineral substrate in irregular, scanty
patches, and it is on these sites that we see the first
sign of soil formation in the classical sense. *Llano*
[1962] reported flowering plants on the Antarctic
Peninsula to about 64°S. *Glazovskaia* [1958] reported up to nearly 10 per cent humus in some
earthy material under lichens of Haswell Island.
In most instances, the plants are closely knit to
the rock surfaces, with no fines being present. There

are, however, a very few isolated places, usually
in the general vicinity of melt water, where processes have progressed somewhat further; a thin
organic horizon underlain by a brown-colored mineral horizon is suggested. There are no well-suited
terms in which to describe this soil, but *Kubiena*'s
[1953] ranker soil is, qualitatively, the best approximation. We suggest protoranker as a tentative
term. Theoretically, the soil-forming potential for
protoranker soils should be a little greater in the
northern Antarctic Peninsula than in regions further
south, because in the north conditions of temperature and precipitation are more favorable.

Ornithogenic Soils

Syroechkovsky [1959] proposed the term ornithogenic for the organic soil of the rookeries of Antarctica. This term is ideally suited and we have
adopted it. Penguin rookeries of Antarctica are of
special importance because they are the only
known locations on the continent where organic
soils occur. The organic matter does not accumulate in the usual manner, that is by biosynthesis
in situ, but is, instead, brought to the rookery from
outside. During the summer penguins, whose food
source is exclusively from the sea, spend much of
their time ashore, and thus a considerable quantity
of organic matter is contributed to the rookery in
the form of droppings. Here the presence of organic
deposits is, therefore, entirely dependent upon penguin activities. In the rookeries, organic matter has
the characteristic of low-rank guano. The organic
deposits may be a foot or more thick, but usually
the depth is considerably less. The guano deposits
acquire a reddish brown color to a depth of 4 to 6
inches and then grade into darker-colored organic
horizons, until, finally, the underlying mineral deposit is encountered. *Glazovskaia* [1958] estimates
that the penguin rookeries of Haswell Island annually accumulate in the form of droppings 10 tons
of organic matter per square kilometer. *Syroechkovsky* [1959] estimates that penguins in the vicinity
of Haswell Island harvest 556,000 kg of organisms
from the ocean each year. Large quantities of N
and P are contributed to the rookeries and secondary calcium phosphates form [*Glazovskaia*, 1958].
At the Cape Royds rookery on Ross Island the
writers observed extensive secondary crusts on the
guano deposits.

Regosols

Regosols are present in a number of locations such as areas of fluvial, recent glacial (Figure 4), and other deposits. These deposits have no apparent genetic features but chemically would qualify as saline soil [*Richards,* 1954].

Lithosols

Within the ice-free areas of Antarctica, lithosols are very extensive. Most valley walls (Figure 4) and nunataks are comprised of bedrock with almost no loose surficial mantle. Of the six soils (ahumic, evaporite, protoranker, or ornithogenic, regosols, and lithosols), lithosols are perhaps the most extensive on the continent.

Patterned Ground

Patterned ground is rather extensive in the ice-free valleys of Victoria Land. The most common form is a complex system of polygons, which are some 20 to 50 feet across with channels up to 6 feet wide and 2 feet deep (Figure 2). Some sorting is usually present at the periphery of the polygon, with a concentration of coarse material at the edge of the channel. The channels vary in size, shape, and composition, and some are filled with sand [*Péwé,* 1959]. In northern areas polygon formation has considerable influence on edaphic factors and plant cover. In Antarctica, however, with its extremely

Fig. 11. Patterned ground on volcanic debris, Cape Armitage, Ross Island.

dry soil conditions plus the absence of plant cover, the microrelief, caused by polygon formation itself, appears to impart no particular soil features.

The preservation of certain types of patterned ground on the steep terrain of Antarctica is quite striking. In respect to northern polar areas, *Sharp* [1942] has shown a sequence (stone rings, stone garlands, stone stripes) with increasing slope. In Antarctica, as polygons form they appear to remain remarkably stable and do not move downslope at a rate comparable to arctic conditions. Just south of Suess Glacier well-developed polygons are present on slopes as steep as 40 per cent. Yet there is evidence that some solifluction processes are operating [*Nichols,* 1953].

An example of sorted circles was recorded at Cape Armitage (Figure 11). The material is mainly of volcanic origin with surficial sands and silts weathered to a strong brown color. Genetically the soils at this site can be considered ahumic.

Acknowledgments. Journal series paper of the New Jersey Agricultural Experiment Station, Rutgers—The State University of New Jersey, Department of Soils and Crops. This study was financed through grant G-17212 from the National Science Foundation. The authors express their appreciation: to the National Science Foundation, Antarctic Research Program, for their specially helpful assistance and cooperation; to U. S. Navy Squadron VX-6, for their excellent field support; to the U. S. Geologic Survey, for their special help in making available photographs and for information used in the compilation of Figure 1; to A. J. Owens, for certain chemical determinations; to the Polar Meteorology Research Project, U. S. Weather Bureau, for the data in Table 1 and certain other climatic information; and to J. D. McCraw of the New Zealand Soil Survey, for his specially helpful cooperation and for making available considerable valuable information, including his preliminary soils map of Taylor Valley.

REFERENCES

Angino, E. E., and K. B. Armitage, A geochemical study of Lakes Bonney and Vanda, Victoria Land, Antarctica, *J. Geol., 71,* 89–95, 1963.

Angino, E. E., K. B. Armitage, and J. C. Tash, Air temperatures from Taylor Glacier Dry Valley, Victoria Land, 1961, *Polar Record 11,* 283–284, 1962.

Anonymous, Geological work in eastern Horlicks, *Bull. U. S. Antarctica Project Officer, 3,* 21, 1962.

Avsiuk, G. A., K. K. Markov, and P. A. Shumskiy, Cold deserts in the Antarctic, *Izvest. Akad. Nauk S.S.S.R. Ser. Geograf., No. 4,* 16–25, 1956.

Ball, D. G., and R. L. Nichols, Saline lakes and drill-hole brines, McMurdo Sound, Antarctica, *Bull. Geol. Soc. Am., 71,* 1703–1708, 1960.

Barghoorn, E. S., A brief review of fossil plants of Antarctica and their geologic implications, *Natl. Acad. Sci., Natl. Res. Council Publ. 839,* 5–9, 1961.

Barghoorn, E. S., and R. L. Nichols, Sulfate-reducing bacteria and pyritic sediments in Antarctica, *Science, 134* (3473), 190, 1961.

Billings, W. D., and A. F. Mark, Interactions between alpine tundra vegetation and patterned ground in the mountains of southern New Zealand, *Ecology, 42,* 18–31, 1961.

Blakemore, L. C., and L. D. Swindale, Chemistry and clay mineralogy of a soil sample from Antarctica, *Nature, 182,* 47–48, 1958.

Boyd, W. L., Comparison of soil bacteria and their metabolic activities in arctic and antarctic regions, *Polar Record, 11,* 319, 1962.

Bull, C., Quarternary glaciations in southern Victoria Land, Antarctica, *J. Glaciol., 4,* 240–241, 1962.

Bull, C., B. C. McKelvey, and P. N. Webb, Quarternary glaciations in southern Victoria Land, Antarctica, *J. Glaciol., 4,* 63–78, 1962.

Cameron, R. L., and R. P. Goldthwait, The US-IGY contribution to antarctic glaciology, *Intern. Assoc. Sci. Hydrologists Symposium on Antarctic Glaciology, Helsinki, No. 55,* 7–13, 1960.

Craddock, C., and H. A. Hubbard, Preliminary geologic report on the 1960 U. S. Expedition to Bellingshausen Sea, Antarctica, *Science, 133,* 886–887, 1961.

Crary, A. P., Antarctica, *Trans. Am. Geophys. Union, 40,* 331–339, 1959.

Crary, A. P., The Antarctic, *Sci. American, 207,* 60–73, 1962.

Davies, W. E., Antarctic research in geology, in *Science in Antarctica, Natl. Acad. Sci., Natl. Res. Council Publ. 878,* 98–104, 1961.

Doumani, G. A., and W. E. Long, The ancient life of the Antarctic, *Sci. American, 207,* 169–184, 1962.

Field, W. O., Antarctic, in *Science in Antarctica, Natl. Acad. Sci., Natl. Res. Council Publ. 878,* 36–56, 1961.

Flint, E. A., and J. C. Stout, Microbiology of some soils from Antarctica, *Nature, 188,* 767–768, 1960.

Gibson, G. W., Geological investigations in southern Victoria Land, Antarctica, 8, Evaporate salts in the Victoria Valley Region, *New Zealand J. Geol. Geophys., 5,* 361–374, 1962.

Glazovskaia, M. A., Biological factors of weathering in high mountains, *Priroda, No. 12,* 106–110, 1952.

Glazovskaia, M. A., Weathering and primary soil formation in Antarctica, *Scientific Paper of the Inst., Moscow Univ., Faculty of Geography, No. 1,* 63–76, 1958 (in Russian).

Gorodkov, B. N., Peculiarities of the arctic top soil, *Izvest. Gosudarst. Geograf. Obshchestva, 71,* 1516–1532, 1939.

Gould, L. M., The glacial geology of the Pacific Antarctic, *Proc. 6th Pacific Sci. Congr.,* 732–740, 1939.

Hamilton, W., I. C. Frost, and P. T. Hayes, Saline features of a small ice platform in Taylor Valley, Antarctica, *U. S. Geol. Survey Prof. Paper 450-B,* article 28, 73–76, 1962.

Hanna, W. J., and E. R. Purvis, Techniques for determining the nutrient status of soils and crops, *N. J. Agr. Expt. Sta. Bull. No. 780,* 15 pp., 1955.

Hollin, J. T., On the glacial history of Antarctica, *J. Glaciol., 4,* 173–195, 1962.

Jensen, H. I., *Report on Antarctic Soils, British Antarctic Expedition 1907–1909, Part VI,* pp. 89–92, 1916.

Johannesson, J. K., and G. W. Gibson, Nitrate and iodate in antarctic salt deposits, *Nature, 194,* 567–568, 1962.

Kelly, W. C., and J. H. Zumberge, Weathering of a quartz diorite at Marble Point, McMurdo Sound, Antarctica, *J. Geol., 69,* 433–446, 1961.

Kilmer, V. J., The estimation of free iron oxides in soils, *Soil. Sci. Soc. Am. Proc., 24,* 420–421, 1960.

Kubiena, W., *The Soils of Europe,* 317 pp., T. Murby, London, 1953.

Llano, G. A., Antarctic plant life, *Trans. Am. Geophys. Union, 40,* 200–203, 1959.

Llano, G. A., Status of lichenology in Antarctica, in *Science in Antarctica, Natl. Acad. Sci., Natl. Res. Council Publ. 839,* 13–19, 1961.

Llano, G. A., The terrestrial life of the Antarctic, *Sci. American, 207,* 213–230, 1962.

Loewe, F., The scientific observations of the Ross Sea party of the Imperial Trans-Antarctic expedition of 1914–1917, *Institute of Polar Studies, Ohio State University, Rept. No. 5,* 43 pp., 1963.

Markov, K. K., Some facts concerning periglacial phenomena in Antarctica (preliminary report), *Herald of Moscow Univ. (Georg.), No. 1,* 139–148, 1956 (in Russian).

Markov, K. K., Zonalite des phenomenes periglaciares en Antarctide, *Biul. Peryglacjalny, No. 8,* 43–48, 1960.

McCraw, J. D., Soils of the Ross Dependency, Antarctica, *New Zealand Soc. Soil Sci. Proc., 4,* 30–35, 1960.

McKelvey, B. C., and P. N. Webb, Geological reconnaissance in Victoria Land, Antarctica, *Nature, 189,* 545–547, 1961.

McKelvey, B. C., and P. N. Webb, Geological investigations in southern Victoria Land, Antarctica, *New Zealand J. Geol. Geophys., 5,* 143–162, 1962.

Meinardus, W., Boden der Kalten Region, *Handbuch der Bodenlehre,* Bd. 3, edited by E. Blank, J. Springer, Berlin, 1930.

Molfino, R. H., Ensayo edafologico sobre la antartida Argentina, Republica Argentina, *Ministerio de agricultura y granaderia, Publ. No. 51,* 48 pp., 1956.

Neustruev, S. S., Genesis of soils, *Russian pedological investigations. Academy of Sciences U.S.S.R., Leningrad III,* 1–98, 1927.

Nichols, R. L., Geomorphology of Marguerite Bay, Palmer Peninsula, Antarctica, *Office of Naval Research, Tech. Rept. 12,* Washington, D. C., 151 pp., 1953.

Nichols, R. L., Geology of Lake Vanda, Wright Valley, South Victoria Land, Antarctica, *Antarctic Research, Geophysical Monograph No. 7,* pp. 47–52, American Geophysical Union, Washington, D. C., 1962.

Nichols, R. L., Geologic features demonstrating aridity of McMurdo Sound area, Antarctica, *Am. J. Sci., 261,* 20–31, 1963.

Nikiforoff, C. C., General trends of the desert type of soil formation, *Soil Sci., 43,* 105–132, 1937.

Péwé, T. L., Sand-wedge polygons (tesselations) in the McMurdo Sound region, Antarctica—A progress report, *Am. J. Sci., 257,* 545–552, 1959.

Péwé, T. L., Multiple glaciation in the McMurdo Sound region, Antarctica—A progress report, *J. Geol., 68,* 498–514, 1960.

Polynov, B. B., First stages of soil formation on massive crystalline rocks, *Pochvovedenie,* No. 7, 327–338, 1945 (in Russian).

Richards, L. A. (ed.), Diagnosis and improvement of saline and alkali soils, *Agricultural Handbook No. 60,* U. S. Dept. Agr., Washington, D. C., 1954.

Rózycki, S. Z., Changements Pleistocenes de l'extension de l'inlandis en Antarctide orientale d'après l'étude des anciennes plages élevées de l'oasis Bunger Queen's Mary Land, *Biul. Peryglacjalny No. 10,* 257–283, 1961.

Rubin, M. J., The Antarctic and the weather, *Sci. American, 207,* 84–94, 1962.

Schoph, J. M., A preliminary report on plant remains and coal of the sedimentary section in the central range of the Horlick Mountains, Antarctica, *Institute of Polar Studies, Ohio State Univ. Rept. 2,* 61 pp., 1962.

Shackleton, E., *South,* Macmillan, N. Y., 374 pp., 1920.

Sharp, R. P., Soil structures in the St. Elias Range, Yukon Territory, *J. Geomorph., 5,* 274–287, 1942.

Shumskiy, P. A., Glaciological and geomorphological reconnaissance in the Antarctic in 1956, *J. Glaciol., 3,* 56–61, 1957.

Syroechkovsky, E. E., The role of animals in primary soil formation under conditions of pre-polar region of the globe (exemplified by the Antarctic), *Zoologicheskyi J., 38,* 1770–1775, 1959 (in Russian).

Targul'yan, V. O., The first stages of weathering and soil formation on igneous rocks in the tundra and taiga zones. *Pochvovedenie, No. 11,* 37–48, 1959 (in Russian).

Taubert, H., Sowjetische Untersuchungen in der Bunger "Oase" (Antarktika), *Petermanns Geographische Mitt., 100,* 329–334, 1956.

Taylor, B. W., The flora, vegetation and soils of Macquarie Island, *Australia Natl. Antarctic Res. Expeditions, Series B, Vol. 11, Botany,* 192 pp., 1955.

Tedrow, J. C. F., and J. Brown, Soils of the Northern Brooks Range, Alaska; Weakening of the soil forming potential at high arctic altitudes, *Soil Sci., 93,* 254–261, 1962.

Tedrow, J. C. F., F. C. Ugolini, and H. Janetschek, An antarctic saline lake, *New Zealand J. Sci., 6,* 150–156, 1963.

Treves, S. B., The geology of Cape Evans and Cape Royds, Ross Island, Antarctica, in *Antarctic Research, Geophysical Monograph No. 7,* pp. 40–46, American Geophysical Union, Washington, D. C., 1962.

Wade, F. A., The geology of the Rockefeller Mountains, King Edward VII Land, Antarctica, U. S. Antarctic Service Expedition 1939–1941, *Am. Phil. Soc.,* Philadelphia, p. 67–77, 1945.

Webb, P. N., and B. C. McKelvey, Geological investigations of South Victoria Land, Antarctica, *New Zealand J. Geol. Geophys., 2,* 120–136, 1959.

Wexler, H., and M. J. Rubin, Antarctic meteorology, in *Science in Antarctica, Natl. Acad. Sci., Natl. Res. Council Publ. 878,* 6–24, 1961.

Woollard, G. P., The land of the Antarctic, *Sci. American, 207,* 151–166, 1962.

Zeller, E. J., E. E. Angino, and M. D. Turner, Basal sedimentary section at Windy Gully, Taylor Glacier, Victoria Land, Antarctica, *Bull. Geol. Soc. Am., 72,* 781–786, 1961.

Zeller, E. J., and W. C. Pearn, Determination of past antarctic climate by thermoluminescence of rocks, *Trans. Am. Geophys. Union, 41,* 118–121, 1960.

M.